Geography in Place 1

Second Edition

Michael Raw

Contents

- The more-difficult exercises are indicated by *.
- Glossary words are highlighted in bold letters in the text the first time they appear.

KEY SKILLS OPPORTUNITIES
Opportunities for producing evidence of Key Skills are identified in the chapter summaries. The bold reference relates to the QCA Key Skill (given below in full for level 2). The numbers that follow identify the exercises in the chapter that provide the relevant opportunities.

Communication
C2.1a Contribute to discussions
C2.1b Give a short talk
C2.2 Read and summarise information
C2.3 Write different types of documents

Application of Number
N2.1 Interpret information from different sources
N2.2 Carry out calculations
N2.3 Interpret results and present findings

Information Technology
IT2.1 Search for and select information
IT2.2 Explore and develop information and derive new information
IT2.3 Present combined information, including text, numbers and images

1 Tectonic activity

1.1 Introduction

Earthquakes and volcanic eruptions are forces that shape the Earth's surface. They have awesome power (Fig. 1.1). They not only shape the planet's surface but also affect the lives of millions of people. In this chapter we look at the causes of earthquakes and volcanoes, and their impact on the physical and human environment.

Fig. 1.1 Flyover destroyed by an earthquake in Japan.

Fig. 1.2 Cultivating rice on rich volcanic soil, Java.

Fig. 1.3 Geothermal power, Iceland.

Fig. 1.4 The structure of the Earth.

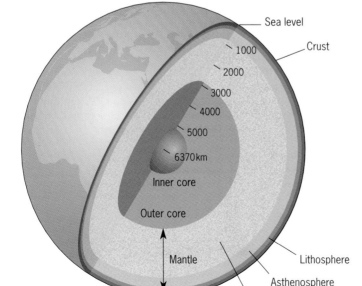

1.2 The interior of the Earth

We know very little about the Earth's interior. The world's deepest hole (in the Kola peninsula in Russia) reaches only 12 km below the surface. Most of what we know about the interior comes from studying earthquake waves. They show that the Earth is rather like an onion, made up of several concentric layers (Fig. 1.4). At the surface there is a thin rocky layer, or **crust**, which forms the continents and ocean basins (Fig. 1.6). Below the crust and attached to it is the **lithosphere**. Deeper still is the **mantle**, which occupies more than 80 per cent of the Earth's volume. Finally, near the centre of the Earth, there is the **core**. Each of these layers has a different density, rock type and temperature (Table 1.1).

4

Table 1.1 Composition of the Earth

Layer		Depth of layer (km)	Average density (g/cm³)	Rock type	Temperature (°C)
Crust	Continental	0–70	2.7	Granite	10
	Oceanic	0–5	3.0	Basalt	
Mantle		2900	5.5	Peridotite	375
Core	Outer	2000	10.0	Iron/nickel (liquid)	3000
	Inner	1450	13.3	Iron/nickel (solid)	

> **EXERCISES**
>
> **2a** Study Table 1.1 and describe how the density of the Earth's interior changes with depth. Suggest a possible reason for this.
>
> **b*** With reference to Figure 1.6, explain why the continental crust always rests above the oceanic crust.

1.3 Plate tectonics - the global conveyor

The Earth's crust and lithosphere do not make a solid shell. In the mid-1960s American geologists discovered that the crust was broken into a number of large pieces, or plates. They found seven major plates and lots of smaller ones (Fig. 1.7). This discovery led to an important new theory called **plate tectonics**, which helps to explain earthquakes, volcanoes, fold mountains, ocean trenches and many other landforms.

The central idea of plate tectonics is that the plates are moving all the time. However, this movement is important only along the plate edges, where two plates come together.

● **REMEMBER**

There are three types of plate margin:
- **constructive (tensional) margins**, where new oceanic crust is formed;
- **destructive (compressive) margins**, where old oceanic crust is destroyed;
- **conservative margins**, where oceanic crust is neither formed nor destroyed.

Fig. 1.5 The Strokkur geyser in south-west Iceland: a tourist attraction.

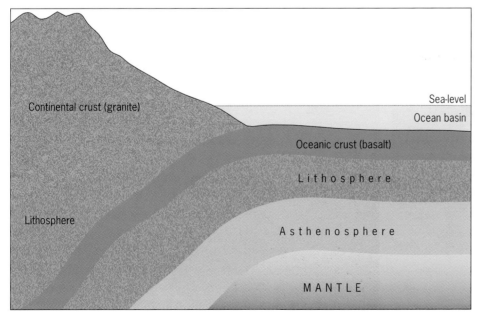

Continental crust (granite)

Sea-level

Ocean basin

Oceanic crust (basalt)

Lithosphere

Lithosphere

Asthenosphere

MANTLE

Fig. 1.6 The continental and oceanic crust.

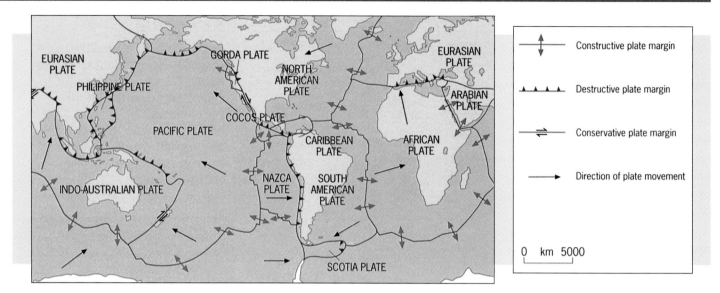

Fig. 1.7 The major lithospheric plates.

Fig. 1.8 (below left) Constructive plate margin (mid-ocean ridge).

Fig. 1.9 (below right) Constructive plate margin in Iceland. The North American plate is on the left and the Eurasian plate on the right.

Constructive plate margins

New crust forms in undersea valleys in mid-ocean. These valleys lie bounded by steep undersea mountain ranges called **mid-ocean ridges** (Fig. 1.8). Here, molten rock continually wells up from the mantle on to the ocean floor to create new crust. The new crust gradually pushes the older crust sideways and away from the ridge. This sideways movement, or sea-floor spreading, is like a slow conveyor belt. It is as slow as the rate at which your finger nails grow! None the less, this movement adds up to a large distance over long periods of time. Thus, in a million years, new crust moves about 10 kilometres, and in 100 million years, it moves about 1000 kilometres.

Early in the 20th century, many scientists suspected that the continents had not always been in the same position. However, they could not explain how areas as huge as continents could move across the globe. This was the puzzle of **continental drift**. Sea-floor spreading finally provided them with the answer. Because the continents are lighter than the oceanic crust, they ride on the conveyor of sea-floor spreading.

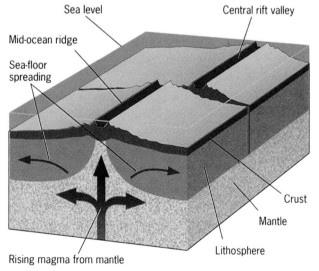

Destructive plate margins

We live on a planet whose size remains constant, and yet sea-floor spreading tells us that new crust is continually forming at the mid-ocean ridges. How is this possible? There is one simple answer: old crust must be destroyed at the same rate as new crust forms. To find out where this is happening, we once again have to look at the plate margins. Old crust is consumed at the destructive plate margins (Fig. 1.7).

Sea-floor spreading gradually shifts oceanic crust away from the mid-ocean ridges until it reaches a **subduction zone** (Fig. 1.11). This process typically takes about 200 million years. The subduction zone is where the crust (and lithosphere) plunge into the mantle. The zone is usually marked by a deep **ocean trench**. Subduction is accompanied by violent earthquakes and volcanic activity.

Conservative plate margins

At conservative margins, no crust is added or destroyed. Instead, the two plates that are in contact slide past each other with a shearing motion. This movement is not always smooth and easy. When there are sudden movements of the plates, earthquakes occur. These earthquakes are just as severe as those at destructive plate boundaries.

Fig. 1.10 The Atlantic Ocean.

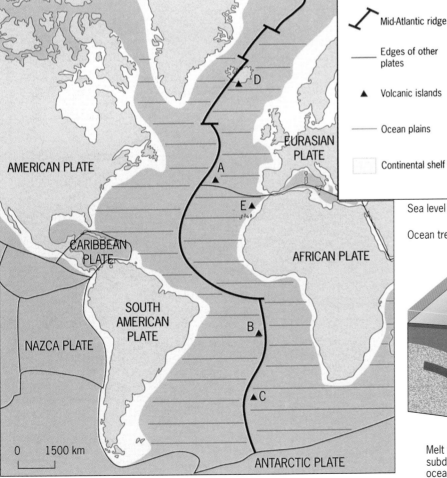

AMERICAN PLATE

EURASIAN PLATE

CARIBBEAN PLATE

AFRICAN PLATE

SOUTH AMERICAN PLATE

NAZCA PLATE

ANTARCTIC PLATE

0   1500 km

Mid-Atlantic ridge

Edges of other plates

▲ Volcanic islands

Ocean plains

Continental shelf

Fig. 1.11 Destructive plate margin (subduction zone).

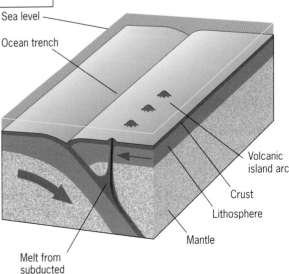

Sea level

Ocean trench

Volcanic island arc

Crust

Lithosphere

Mantle

Melt from subducted oceanic crust

Darkness at dawn in India

Fear turns to reality as the Big One hits California

Inside the ruin that was once a city

Thousands flee ruins of Japanese quake city

Fig. 1.12 Some newspaper headlines reporting recent earthquakes.

City consumed by flames

1.4 Earthquakes – living on the edge

'The rising sun created darkness for us this morning, swallowed up our villages, and made our houses into tombs.'
Survivor from the earthquake in central India in 1993.

To geologists, earthquakes are simply a natural event. However, for people like the Indian earthquake survivor, they are a human tragedy. They bring destruction, suffering and death, often without warning (Fig. 1.12).

How earthquakes happen

An earthquake is the result of a sudden release of energy within the Earth, which causes shocks, or seismic waves. These seismic waves spread out from the origin or focus of the quake. The **epicentre** is the point of the Earth's surface immediately above the focus, and it is here that the destructive effects of the quake are greatest (Fig. 1.13).

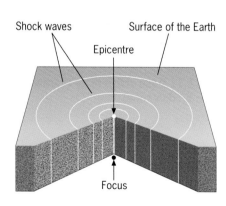

Seismic waves spread out from the focus of the earthquake and are recorded on seismometers, which produce a trace. The peaks in the graph show the time when the earthquake shocks were recorded.

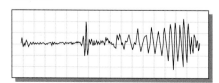

Fig. 1.13 Earthquake epicentre, focus and seismic trace.

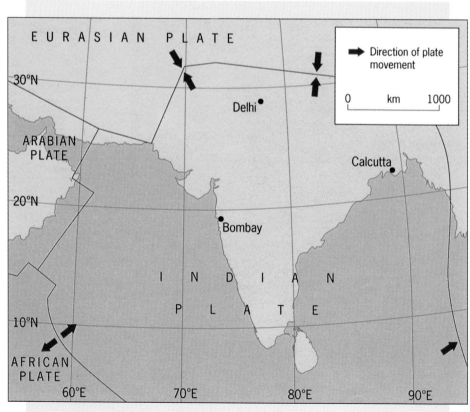

Fig. 1.14 Plate boundaries in South Asia.

Fig. 1.15 The San Andreas fault, California: a conservative plate margin.

REMEMBER
The impact of earthquakes depends on:
• their magnitude;
• their location (e.g. mid-ocean ridges, subduction zones);
• population density;
• levels of economic development.

Table 1.2 Indian earthquake, 30 September 1993

	Time of first shock waves	Time difference from epicentre	Distance from epicentre (time difference/60 x 1000)
Epicentre	03.56.00	0	0
Bombay	03.56.30	30 sec.	500 km
Delhi	03.57.15		
Calcutta	03.57.20		

Earthquakes occur when rocks that have been compressed or stretched snap along a fault in the crust. The best way to understand the origin of earthquakes is to plot quake epicentres on a world map showing the major plate boundaries (Fig. 1.16). Most epicentres lie on plate boundaries close to mid-ocean ridges and subduction zones.

◆ Earthquakes at mid-ocean ridges, where the crust is stretched and magma forces its way to the surface, occur at shallow depths.

◆ Earthquakes at subduction zones occur at great depths, where an oceanic plate is forced down into the mantle. Subduction is rarely a smooth process. Subducted plates often get stuck, causing enormous pressure to build up. If this pressure is released by a sudden movement (e.g. when a rock fractures) it creates powerful shock waves or earthquakes. This was the cause of several recent earthquakes, such as those in India (1993), Japan (1995) and Sumatra (2000).

Major earthquake zones

Probably the most celebrated earthquake zone in the world is in California. This region lies along a major fault line – the San Andreas – which marks the edge of the North American and Pacific plates (Fig. 1.15). Although California is on a conservative plate margin, it is a very active earthquake zone, and there were large earthquakes there in 1989 and 1993. In 1906, the most severe earthquake of the 20th century struck San Francisco, killing more than 700 people.

EXERCISES

7 A severe earthquake struck India on 30 September 1993. In the area around the epicentre 10 000 people died. Study Figure 1.14 and suggest the possible cause of the Indian earthquake.

8 Find the epicentre of the Indian earthquake and give its approximate latitude and longitude. To determine the epicentre you need the following information:
• earthquake waves travel at a speed of 1000 km/min.
• the time when the earthquake was recorded at its epicentre.
• the time when the shock waves were recorded at three other places (Table 1.2).
a Complete the calculations in Table 1.2.
b Make a copy of Figure 1.14 and draw three circles centred on Bombay, Delhi and Calcutta with radii proportional to their distance from the epicentre. The intersection of the circles gives the approximate epicentre.

9

9 With the help of an atlas, find the location of the earthquakes in Table 1.3. How many of these earthquakes are close to (a) destructive (b) constructive (c) conservative plate boundaries? (See Fig. 1.7)

10 Using the information on deaths in Table 1.3, describe and explain the different effect that earthquakes have on rich countries (i.e. Japan, USA and Italy) and poor countries.

11* Plot a scattergraph of the death toll for each earthquake (y axis) in Table 1.3 against its magnitude (x axis). Describe the relationship. Would you say that it was strong, moderate, weak or non-existent?

12 Log on to the US Geological Survey's website (www.usgs.gov.). Make a list of the earthquakes that have occurred in the past week. Note their location and magnitude.

Table 1.3 Major earthquakes 1976 – 2000

Date	Location	Richter scale magnitude	Deaths
05.06.00	Sumatra	7.9	58
20.09.99	Taiwan	7.7	4 000
07.09.99	Greece	5.9	122
17.08.99	Turkey	7.8	15 000
26.09.97	Italy	5.9	12
17.01.95	Japan	7.2	5000
15.02.94	Indonesia	6.5	37
17.01.94	Los Angeles, USA	6.6	57
30.09.93	India	6.4	22 000
12.07.93	Japan	7.8	26
12.12.92	Indonesia	6.8	1912
28.06.92	California, USA	7.4	1
25.04.92	California, USA	6.9	0
13.03.92	Turkey	6.8	1000
01.02.91	Afghanistan/Pakistan border	6.8	1200
16.07.90	Philippines	7.7	1621
21.06.90	Iran	7.3-7.7	50 000
07.12.88	Armenia	6.9	25 000
19.09.85	Mexico	8.1	9500
30.10.83	Turkey	7.1	1300
13.12.82	North Yemen	6.0	2000
23.11.80	Italy	7.2	4800
10.10.80	Algeria	7.3	4500
12.12.79	Colombia and Ecuador	7.9	800
16.09.78	Iran	7.7	25 000
04.03.77	Romania	7.5	1541
24.11.76	Turkey	7.9	4000
17.08.76	Philippines	7.8	8000
28.07.76	Tangshan, China	7.8-8.2	242 000*/800 000**
06.05.76	Italy	6.5	946
04.02.76	Guatemala	7.5	22 778

* official estimate **unofficial estimate

Fig. 1.16 The distribution of earthquakes around the world.

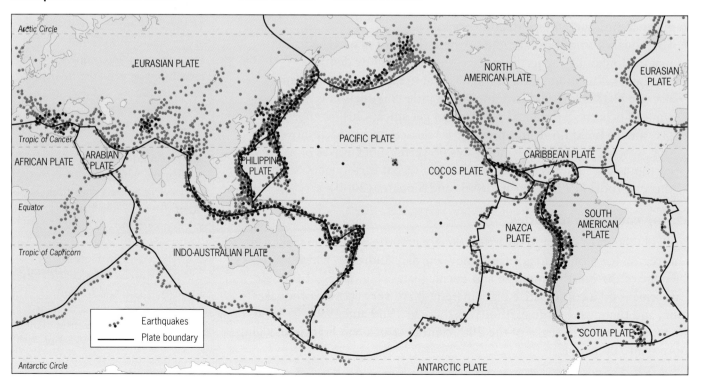

CASE STUDY

1.5 Kobe earthquake, Japan, 1995

By Japanese standards, the earthquake that struck Kobe in January 1995 was not large. It was, nonetheless, devastating (see Factfile). Three factors help to explain the devastation. First, the quake was shallow, with its focus near the surface. Second, the epicentre was close to Kobe. And third, the Kobe

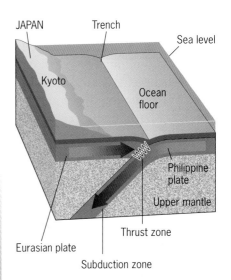

Fig. 1.17 Geology of the Kobe earthquake.

FACTFILE

- *The Kobe earthquake struck at 05.46 on 17 January 1995.*
- *It measured 7.2 on the Richter scale.*
- *It caused 5000 deaths and injured 25 000.*
- *It destroyed 56 200 buildings.*
- *It caused damage worth $200bn.*
- *It was caused by movement along the subduction zone off the south coast of Japan, where the Philippine plate underthrusts the Eurasian plate (Fig. 1.17).*

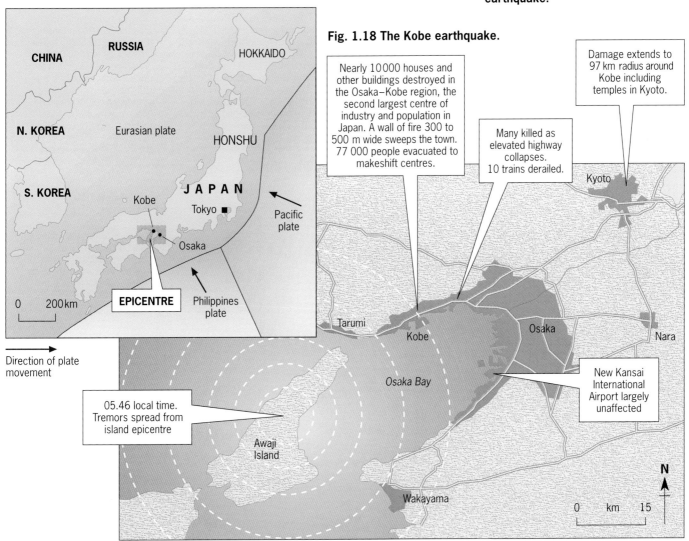

Fig. 1.18 The Kobe earthquake.

Nearly 10 000 houses and other buildings destroyed in the Osaka–Kobe region, the second largest centre of industry and population in Japan. A wall of fire 300 to 500 m wide sweeps the town. 77 000 people evacuated to makeshift centres.

Many killed as elevated highway collapses. 10 trains derailed.

Damage extends to 97 km radius around Kobe including temples in Kyoto.

New Kansai International Airport largely unaffected

05.46 local time. Tremors spread from island epicentre

area was not thought to be especially at risk from earthquakes, so the city was less well prepared than other more vulnerable regions, such as Tokyo.

Impact of the Kobe earthquake

Most casualties were caused by the collapse of traditional buildings designed before the development of modern earthquake engineering (Fig. 1.20). Most modern buildings withstood the earthquake without damage. Many deaths were caused by fires started by broken gas mains. In the days immediately after the quake there were shortages of water and food. Tens of thousands of people were left homeless in the Japanese winter. Disposal of dead bodies was delayed and, with no sewerage system, there was risk of disease. Like the Taiwan quake in 1999, the Kobe disaster showed that earthquakes can devastate even the richest countries.

Fig. 1.19 (right) Report by Mark Dowdney, *Scottish Daily Record*, 18.1.95.

Fig. 1.20 How to design buildings to resist earthquakes.

No escape in nightmare

A HUGE firestorm was last night threatening to turn quake-ravaged Kobe to ashes.

By MARK DOWDNEY

Hundreds of blazes swept through the Japanese city of 1.5 million people, after the tremor flattened 10,000 buildings in seconds.

More than 1700 people were confirmed dead. And with at least 1000 feared trapped in rubble, the toll was set to keep rising.

By last night, the growing inferno was threatening to rival the quake itself in savagery. Troops were called in to try to stem the destruction.

Survivors told how a 500 metre wide wall of flame swept through one area, fanned by strong winds.

Swathes of wooden houses were razed to the ground as gas mains ruptured and exploded.

With roads blocked by rubble, fire engines couldn't get to where they were most needed.

Crews who managed to reach fires quickly ran out of water, because the quake had destroyed main pipes. Many dazed and terrified residents had tried to save their homes with buckets of water, as aftershocks from the quake went on.

As night fell in Kobe, 12 hours had passed since the quake. More than 134 fires were still burning.

Crumbled

From the air, the busy port looked like it had been hit by a massive bombing raid. A deathly pall of smoke covered huge areas.

Kobe's hell began at dawn, when it was hit by Japan's worst earthquake in nearly 50 years.

The tremor, measured at 7.2 on the Richter scale, went on for 60 seconds of pure carnage.

A huge section of elevated motorway collapsed like a house of cards, hurling buses and cars to the ground. At least 14 people died.

Twenty trains were derailed. Bridges collapsed, and millions of people were left without water, gas, electricity or phone services.

Wharves at the harbour crumbled into the sea. A coach could be seen underwater.

One survivor, whose house collapsed around him, said: 'It felt like the end of the world.'

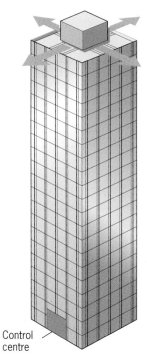

Concrete counter-weight

Control centre

A large concrete weight on top of the building, controlled by computer, moves in the opposite direction to the force of the earthquake.

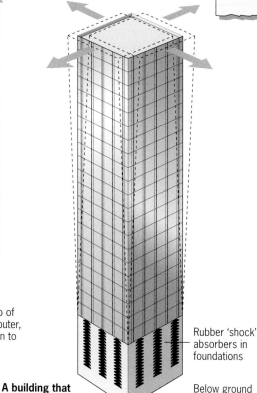

Large rubber shock absorbers in the foundations allow the building to rock back and forth and up and down without too much damage.

Rubber 'shock' absorbers in foundations

Below ground

A building that rocks back and forth

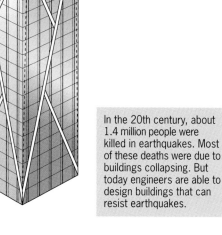

A twisting tower

Cross-bracings are added to the building which allow it to be more flexible and respond to the pressures caused by earthquakes.

In the 20th century, about 1.4 million people were killed in earthquakes. Most of these deaths were due to buildings collapsing. But today engineers are able to design buildings that can resist earthquakes.

Fig. 1.21 The collapsed Kobe-Osaka expressway in eastern Kobe.

EXERCISES

13 Estimate the magnitude of the Kobe earthquake on the Mercalli scale (Table 1.4).
14 Read Figure 1.19.
a Describe the impact of the Kobe quake on the city's infrastructure (roads, electricity system etc.).
b What problems did earthquake damage pose for Kobe's emergency services?
c The earthquake struck at 05.46. How might this timing have helped to reduce the number of deaths and injuries?
15 Study Figure 1.20 and explain how modern buildings can be constructed to be earthquake-proof.

Table 1.4 Mercalli scale of earthquake intensity

Seismologists use the Mercalli scale to measure the physical effects of earthquakes. The scale goes from 1 (least effect) to 12 (greatest effect).

1 Rarely felt.
2 Felt by people who are not moving, especially on the upper floors of buildings. Hanging objects may swing.
3 The effects are noticeable indoors. The vibration is like that experienced when a truck passes.
4 Many people feel it indoors, a few outside. Some are awakened at night. Crockery and doors are disturbed, and standing cars rock.
5 Felt by nearly everyone. Most people are awakened. Some windows are broken, plaster becomes cracked and unstable objects topple. Trees may sway and pendulum clocks stop.
6 Felt by everyone. Many are frightened. Some heavy furniture moves, plaster falls. Structural damage is usually quite slight.
7 Everyone runs outdoors. Noticed by people driving cars. Poorly designed buildings are appreciably damaged.
8 Considerable amount of damage to ordinary buildings. Many buildings collapse; well designed ones survive with slight damage. Heavy furniture is overturned and chimneys fall. Some sand is fluidised.
9 Considerable damage occurs, even to buildings that have been well designed. Many buildings are moved from their foundations. Ground cracks and pipes break.
10 Most masonry structures are destroyed, some wooden ones survive. Railway tracks bend and water slops over banks. Landslides and sand movements occur.
11 No masonry structure remains standing. Bridges are destroyed. Broad fissures occur in the ground.
12 Total damage. Waves are seen on the surface of the ground. Objects are thrown into the air.

Richter scale

The Richter scale is a precise measure of earthquake magnitude. However, unlike the Mercalli scale, it tells us nothing about an earthquake's destructive effects. Instruments called seismometers record earthquakes (a sensitive arm records the vibrations on a moving graph – see Fig. 1.13) and these are scaled logarithmically. This means that an earthquake of magnitude 7 on the Richter scale is ten times more powerful than a magnitude 6 event, and 100 times more powerful than one of magnitude 5. The most powerful earthquake of the 20th century was the San Francisco quake in 1906. It measured 8.6 on the Richter scale.

REMEMBER
Most earthquakes and volcanoes are concentrated along plate margins.

Fig. 1.22 Pompeii in the shadow of Mount Vesuvius, a cone-shaped strato-volcano.

Table 1.5 Catastrophic volcanic eruptions in the past

Year	Location	Effect
1500BC	Santorini, Greece	Island destroyed
AD 79	Vesuvius, Italy	Pompeii destroyed
1586	Kelud, Indonesia	10 000 dead
1669	Etna, Italy	20 000 dead
1815	Tambora, Indonesia	90 000 dead
1883	Krakatoa, Indonesia	36 000 dead
1902	Mont Pelee, Martinique	30 000 dead
1985	Nevado del Ruiz	25 000 dead

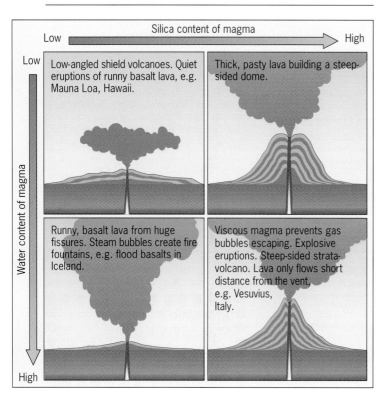

1.6 Volcanoes and volcanic eruptions

Volcanic eruptions are among the most spectacular and destructive events in nature. They change landscapes, the global weather and climate and affect the lives of millions of people (Table 1.5).

Types of volcano

Mount Vesuvius in southern Italy (Fig. 1.22) is an active volcano that has erupted more than 50 times in the last 2000 years. Active volcanoes erupt molten rock or lava, ash, steam and hot gases. Layers of ash and lava from old eruptions eventually build up to form the classic cone-shaped strato-volcano, but not all volcanoes are cone-shaped (Fig. 1.23).

◆ Thick, pasty lava, which doesn't flow very far, produces steep-sided volcanic domes.
◆ Thin, runny lava can flow for many kilometres, and builds low-angled shield volcanoes.

Eruptions from fissures rather than from volcanoes are common in Iceland and Hawaii. Here, molten rock quietly reaches the surface through great cracks in the Earth's crust. This type of eruption can form lava plateaus a kilometre or more thick, such as the Antrim plateau in Northern Ireland (Fig. 1.24).

Volcanic eruptions and climate

During eruptions, ash is pumped high into the air. The finest particles may remain suspended there for several years, blocking the sun's rays and disrupting the world's weather and climate. In 1815, Mount Tambora in Indonesia erupted, hurling several cubic kilometres of rock into the air. There was so much dust that it scattered and blocked the sun's rays. In Europe, in 1815, harvests failed, there were frosts in June and July, and widespread famine. The eruption of Mount Pinatubo in the Philippines in 1991 caused a significant cooling of the global climate the next year.

Unpredictable volcanoes

Sometimes volcanoes that have been inactive, or dormant, for hundreds of years suddenly burst into life. Some of the worst disasters have come from volcanoes thought to be extinct, such as Mount Vesuvius, which overwhelmed Pompeii in A.D. 79. Today, Mount Vesuvius is an ever-present threat to the nearby city of Naples and its one million inhabitants.

Fig. 1.23 Different types of volcanoes and eruptions.

Distribution of volcanoes

There are more than 600 active volcanoes in the world (Fig. 1.25). Indonesia alone has more than one hundred. The greatest concentration of volcanic activity is around the Pacific Ocean. In the western Pacific, the so-called 'ring of fire' extends from Kamchatka in Russia, through Japan, the Philippines and Indonesia. In the eastern Pacific it follows the Andean and Rocky Mountain ranges. Finally, in the north, the chain of volcanic islands known as the Aleutians completes the ring, by linking North America and Eurasia (Fig. 1.26).

Fig. 1.24 Columnar basalt: the Giant's Causeway in Antrim, Northern Ireland.

Fig. 1.25 The world distribution of active volcanoes.

Table 1.6 Volcanoes and plate margins

Volcano	Type of plate margin
Fuji	
St Helens	
Cotopaxi	
Etna	
Pinatubo	
Mauna Loa	
Hood	
Hekla	
Aconcagua	
Krakatoa	
Surtsey	
Tristan da Cunha	

EXERCISES

16a Use an atlas to find the location of the volcanoes listed in Table 1.6. Identify the type of margin on which they are located.
b* Log on to the website www.vulcan.wr.usgs.gov/volcanoes/framework.html. Select a volcano and produce a word-processed report of no more than 1000 words, with photos and charts, about it. Your report should cover • location •eruption history •types of eruption •impact on people.

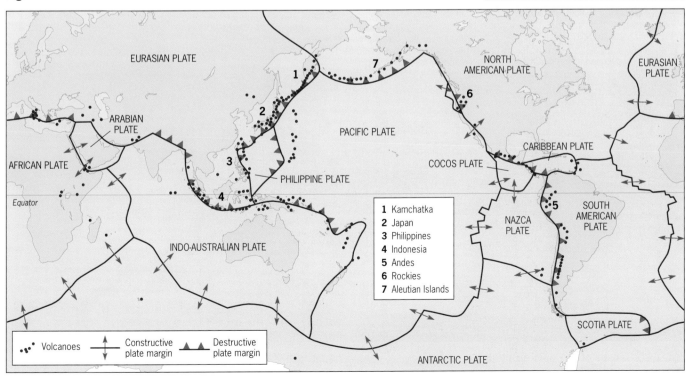

1 Kamchatka
2 Japan
3 Philippines
4 Indonesia
5 Andes
6 Rockies
7 Aleutian Islands

•••• Volcanoes   Constructive plate margin   ▲▲ Destructive plate margin

1.7 Causes of volcanic eruptions

Volcanic eruptions occur where molten rock from the mantle reaches the surface. Most eruptions take place on or close to plate boundaries. What is happening in these areas to cause eruptions?

Remember that, geologically, plate margins are very active places. Here new crust forms, and old crust is destroyed. Along the mid-ocean ridges, the crust is stretched; the plates are pulled apart, allowing molten rock to well up from the mantle and spill on to the ocean floor. In Iceland we can actually see this happening on the land surface. This is because Iceland is a

Fig. 1.26 A volcanic island arc.

Fig. 1.27 A basalt lava flow from Kilauea volcano, Hawaii.

Fig. 1.28 Parinacota and Pomerape volcanoes in the Andes.

Fig. 1.29 Flood basalts in Oregon, USA.

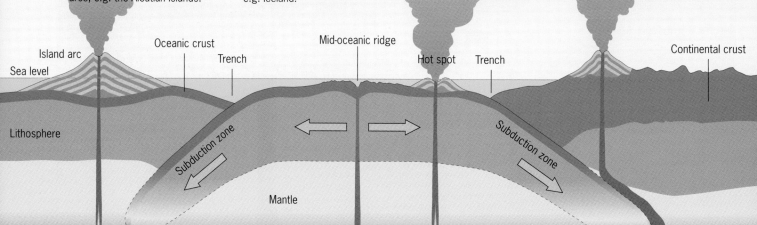

Island arcs
Where two oceanic plates converge (e.g. western Pacific). One plate is pushed downwards (subducted) into the mantle. As the subducted plate melts, magma rises to the surface forming numerous volcanoes or island arcs, e.g. the Aleutian Islands.

Mid-oceanic ridges
Tension in the crust leads to deep rifts. Magma rises up to the ocean floor along these rifts, forming new crust. The ridges form a continuous line of submarine volcanoes. In places the volcanoes rise above sea level, e.g. Iceland.

Hot spot volcanoes
Rising plumes of magma reach the surface in the centres of plates, e.g. Hawaii.

Continental-ocean plate margins
Here the oceanic plate is subducted beneath the thicker continental plate. As it melts some of the lighter oceanic plate magma forces its way to the surface, forming volcanoes, e.g. Andean volcanoes.

Island arc
Sea level
Oceanic crust
Trench
Mid-oceanic ridge
Hot spot
Trench
Continental crust
Lithosphere
Subduction zone
Subduction zone
Mantle

Fig. 1.30 Causes of volcanic eruptions.

section of the mid-Atlantic ridge above sea level. As you might expect, because it is situated on an oceanic ridge, Iceland is a relatively new landmass. Nowhere is the rock more than three million years old.

The greatest numbers of volcanoes are found close to destructive plate margins, where oceanic crust sinks into the mantle. As the crust slides down, rising temperatures cause melting. Because the crustal rock is lighter than the mantle rock, the molten rock slowly rises to the surface, forming a line of volcanoes. These volcanoes are most common on the thin oceanic crust (Figs. 1.25 and 1.35) where they form chains of islands like the Kurils, north-east of Japan, and the Aleutians (Fig. 1.26).

1.8 The effects of eruptions

Although living near to active volcanoes is often very dangerous, volcanoes also bring many benefits (Table 1.7). It is not unusual, especially in less economically developed countries (LEDCs), to find densely populated areas around active volcanoes. This is because lava and volcanic ash **weather** to form fertile soils, and people think the risks of an eruption are worth taking (Fig. 1.33). We should also remember that the gases we breathe, and the water in the oceans, are the result of volcanic eruptions over billions of years. Without these vital ingredients, life would not have evolved on the planet.

Table 1.7 The advantages of volcanoes to people.

- Rock and ash near volcanoes weather to form fertile soils. These soils attract high population densities e.g. Java. One in five Sicilians lives on the slopes of Mount Etna, even though it erupts on average once every ten years.

- Volcanically active regions, such as Iceland, provide geothermal energy through naturally created steam.

- Volcanic regions may be major tourist attractions e.g. Yellowstone (USA), Rotorua (New Zealand), and may support spa towns based on hot springs.

- Diamond and ore deposits are often found near extinct volcanoes.

REMEMBER
Living close to volcanoes has advantages as well as disadvantages.

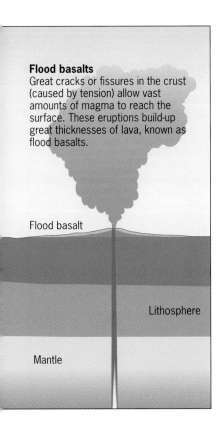

Flood basalts
Great cracks or fissures in the crust (caused by tension) allow vast amounts of magma to reach the surface. These eruptions build-up great thicknesses of lava, known as flood basalts.

Flood basalt

Lithosphere

Mantle

Climate and weather changes. The fine ash suspended in the atmosphere may block the sun's rays for several years. In 1815, following the eruption of Mount Tambora in Indonesia, harvests failed in Europe, there were frosts in June and July, and whole populations starved.

Nuées ardents: superheated clouds of gas and dust, which engulf whole communities.

Lahars: mudflows caused by rapid melting of snow and ice around the volcano summit.

Ash, pumice and fragments of rock move rapidly downhill as pyroclastic flows.

Ash falls: they smother farmland, block roads and cause buildings to collapse.

Lava flows and may endanger life and property.

360 million people live close to active volcanoes, which can erupt at any time.

Fig. 1.31 Some volcanic hazards.

CASE STUDY

1.9 Volcanic disasters – Nevado del Ruiz

Nevado del Ruiz is one of several volcanoes in the northern arc of the Andes in Colombia. On 13 November 1985, Nevado del Ruiz erupted without warning. The impact of the eruption was devastating (see Factfile).

Fig. 1.32 The major active volcanoes in the northern Andes.

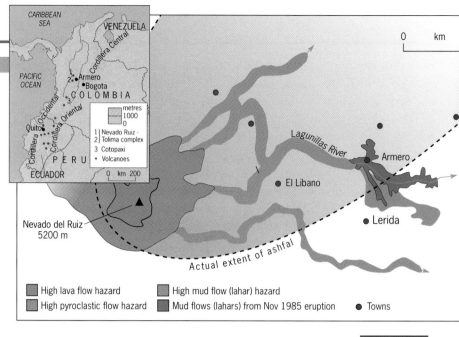

High lava flow hazard
High pyroclastic flow hazard
High mud flow (lahar) hazard
Mud flows (lahars) from Nov 1985 eruption
● Towns

FACTFILE

- *Nevado del Ruiz is an active volcano, 5200 m high, whose summit is snow clad.*
- *The volcano results from the subduction of the Nazca plate beneath the South American plate.*
- *Hot ashes and pyroclastic flows melted 20 million cubic metres of snow and glaciers on the volcano's summit.*
- *Flood water from snowmelt picked up soil and volcanic ash forming lahars.*
- **Lahars**, *40 m thick and travelling at 50 km/h, rushed down the valleys of the volcano's eastern slopes and destroyed everything in their path.*
- *The town of Armero, 74 km from the volcano, was totally destroyed.*
- *Of the 23 000 people who died, 22 000 were the inhabitants of Armero.*
- *Previous eruptions causing lahars and hundreds of deaths had occurred in 1595 and 1845.*

EXERCISES

17 Study Figure 1.32.
a State and explain two reasons why the inhabitants of Armero probably underestimated the risk from Nevado del Ruiz (see Factfile).
b Why was Armero the only town devastated by lahars?
18 Read Figure 1.33.
a How did the scale of the Nevado del Ruiz eruption compare with other eruptions in the previous one hundred years or so?
b What factors slowed the rescue and aid efforts?
c* Explain why natural disasters such as volcanic eruptions appear to have a greater impact in LEDCs, than in more economically developed countries (MEDCs). Base your answer around the following points: living conditions of the people; population densities in rural areas; road, rail and air infrastructure; government organisation; risk assessment and warning; evacuation measures.

Death toll in volcano disaster put at 20,000

Trevor Fishlock, Bogota

More than 20,000 people were reported killed yesterday in the devastating eruption of Nevado del Ruiz volcano in the Colombian Andes and the massive floods that followed.

Survivors clung to trees and rooftops as a sea of mud and ash inundated roads and settlements. Bodies were swept away in rolling sulphurous torrents.

In the town of Armero, 50 kilometres from the volcano, most of the people appeared to have died in their beds as the town was engulfed in ash and mud.

After being relatively quiet since its last major eruption 390 years ago, the 5200 metre volcano, 241 kilometres north of Bogota, the Colombian capital, suddenly roared. Rock and ash spewed hundreds of metres into the air from the blazing crater.

A terrible tide of debris rushed down the mountainside. Ice and snow melted rapidly, rivers burst their banks and torrents of flood water swept everything before them.

Rescuers trying to reach the stricken towns and settlements faced a tortuous battle against blocked roads, and fallen bridges.

It was the worst volcanic explosion since Krakatoa blew itself to pieces in Indonesia 102 years ago, killing more than 36,000 people.

'Rescue by land is impossible' said a spokesman… but rescue by air was also extremely hazardous because of the danger of volcanic dust penetrating aircraft engines.

Local authorities appealed for food, medicine, blood for transfusions and bandages to be rushed to the area. The disaster left the region with no drinkable water.

The eruption of Nevado del Ruiz was not entirely unexpected… In mid-September the Civil Aviation Authority ordered aircraft to stop flying over the mountain because of the quantities of ash it was spewing out.

On October 5… vulcanologists warned that there was a real danger of lava overflows from Nevado del Ruiz but the Government decided that there was no immediate danger…

In spite of official reassurances some panic selling of houses and farms began in the region around the volcano which is one of Colombia's main coffee producing areas.

It is a densely-populated intensively-cultivated area, with coffee farms of all sizes covering the steep hillsides.

Fig. 1.33 Report by Trevor Fishlock, *The Times*, 15.11.85.

1.10 Volcanic resources – Iceland

Iceland sits on top of the mid-Atlantic ridge and is one of the most active volcanic areas in the world (Fig. 1.35). Icelanders have not only learned to live with volcanoes, but have exploited them for their own advantage. Electricity production, recreation, leisure and tourism all rely on this geothermal resource.

Because magma is found close to the surface in Iceland, its heat can be used to generate electricity. This **geothermal energy** supplies 85 per cent of Icelandic homes with hot water for general domestic use and central heating. Most geothermal energy is generated where water stored in permeable rocks is heated by magma to form superheated steam (Figs. 1.34 and 1.36). The steam (at temperatures up to 300°C) is tapped by boreholes drilled in to the permeable rocks. This steam drives turbines, which make electricity. The potential for geothermal energy is enormous: far more than a tiny country like Iceland can use. And unlike nuclear power and **fossil fuels**, geothermal energy is both pollution-free and almost unlimited.

Iceland's hot springs attract international tourists, and some springs have healing properties. The Blue Lagoon, near Reykjavik, has a hotel and other facilities for tourists. The volcanic landscapes, with their unique combination of ice and fire, pull in the tourists who are keen to see spectacular **geysers**, such as Strokkur (Fig. 1.5), and waterfalls like Gullfoss. Market gardening uses geothermally heated glasshouses to grow flowers, vegetables and fruit. Fish farming also uses warm geothermal water to rear salmon.

EXERCISES

19 Look at the location of Iceland on an atlas map of the North Atlantic. Although Iceland has almost limitless supplies of geothermal energy, the country's geography might hinder its development. Write a brief paragraph to explain why.

Fig. 1.34 A geothermal power station at Krafla in Iceland.

Fig. 1.35 The distribution of volcanoes in Iceland.

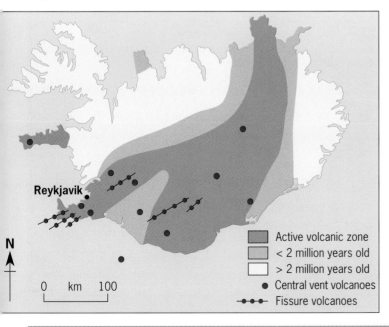

Reykjavik

N

0   km   100

Active volcanic zone
< 2 million years old
> 2 million years old
● Central vent volcanoes
–●–●– Fissure volcanoes

Fig. 1.36 Production of geothermal energy.

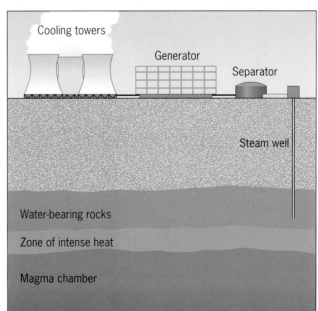

Cooling towers

Generator

Separator

Steam well

Water-bearing rocks

Zone of intense heat

Magma chamber

1.11 Summary: tectonic activity

KEY SKILLS OPPORTUNITIES
C1.2: Ex. 3, 4a, 7, 9, 14, 16a, 18, 19; **C1.3**: Ex. 18c; **C2.2**: Ex. 2a, 2b, 9, 14, 16a, 17a, 18, 19; **C1/2.3**: Ex. 16b, 18c; **N1/2.2**: Ex. 5a, 5b, 5c, 8, 11; **N1/2.3**: Ex. 11; **IT1.1**: Ex. 12, 16b; **IT1.2**: Ex. 16b; **IT2.1**: Ex. 16b; **IT2.2**: Ex. 16b; **IT2.3**: Ex. 16b.

Key ideas	Generalisations and detail
The Earth's interior is made up of several concentric layers.	• The outermost layer is the crust. This thin rocky layer includes oceanic and continental crust. • The lithosphere. • The mantle, which accounts for most of the Earth's mass. • The core. • Density and temperature increase with depth in the Earth's interior.
The Earth's crust and lithosphere are broken into large fragments, or plates.	• There are seven major plates and about 12 minor ones. • The plates are continually moving. This movement occurs along the plate margins and is responsible for most earthquakes and volcanic activity, and a wide range of landforms (e.g. fold mountains, ocean trenches, rift valleys etc.).
Important tectonic processes occur at plate margins.	• There are three types of plate margin: constructive, destructive and conservative. • New oceanic crust is formed by sea-floor spreading at constructive margins. • Old oceanic crust is destroyed at destructive plate margins. • Crust is neither formed nor destroyed at conservative margins. • The movement of plates (plate tectonics) explains continental drift and a variety of tectonic processes and landforms.
Earthquakes are the sudden release of energy from within the Earth in the form of seismic waves.	• Earthquakes result from friction between, and stretching and compression of, rocks within the crust and lithosphere. • Most earthquakes occur close to plate margins. • The energy released in earthquakes is measured on the Richter scale. The damage caused by earthquakes is measured on the Mercalli scale.
Earthquakes are major natural hazards.	• Earthquakes cause major loss of life, injury and damage to property each year. • Death and injury are caused not only by collapsed buildings, but also by fire and disease. • The human impact of earthquakes is often greater in LEDCs than in MEDCs. • In many countries that are vulnerable to earthquakes, earthquake-proof buildings help to minimise loss of life and damage to property.
Volcanoes are points of weakness in the crust where molten rock from the mantle reaches the Earth's surface.	• Like earthquakes, most volcanoes are found at plate margins. • The shape of volcanoes and the violence of eruptions depend on the type of magma and the amount of steam present.
There are several types of volcano.	• Strato-volcanoes, with alternating layers of ash and lava. • Shield volcanoes, with wide bases and low-angled slopes. • Lava domes. • Fissures, which lead to the formation of lava plateaus.
Volcanoes are major natural hazards.	• Eruptions may produce: lava flows, pyroclastic flows and avalanches, ash falls, lahars, nuées ardentes etc. • Eruptions can cause huge loss of life, injury and damage to property. • LEDCs are often hit hardest by volcanic eruptions.
Volcanoes can be used as important resources.	• Volcanoes provide: fertile soils, which allow intensive cultivation e.g. in Java; geothermal energy e.g. in Iceland; resources for recreation and tourism.

2 Rocks and landscapes

2.1 Introduction

Rocks form the 'bones' of the landscape. In the uplands this is obvious: here rocks are often exposed at the surface (Fig. 2.1). But in the lowlands and in large cities you cannot normally see rocks. They are usually hidden beneath roads and buildings and thick layers of soil. In this chapter we shall try to answer some very basic questions concerning rocks. For instance: What are rocks? How are they formed? What is their value to people? What effect do they have on **relief** and the landscape? How are they altered by **weathering** and **erosion**, and the tectonic forces that we studied in Chapter 1?

2.2 Types of rock

We can think of rocks as being like a fruit cake. Just as a fruit cake has ingredients such as sugar, sultanas, nuts and so on, so rocks are a mixture of minerals such as quartz, calcite and feldspar.

Many rocks have mineral mixtures that are similar. This enables us to recognise different kinds of rock. Granite, for example, consists of just three minerals: quartz, feldspar and mica. Limestone is even simpler: often it contains just one mineral – calcium carbonate.

Although there are hundreds of different kinds of rock, we can group them all into three main types: **igneous**, **sedimentary** and **metamorphic**. We base this simple classification on how the rocks have formed (Fig. 2.2).

Fig. 2.1 Rock type can affect the relief of an area – granite forms the Grand Teton mountains in Wyoming.

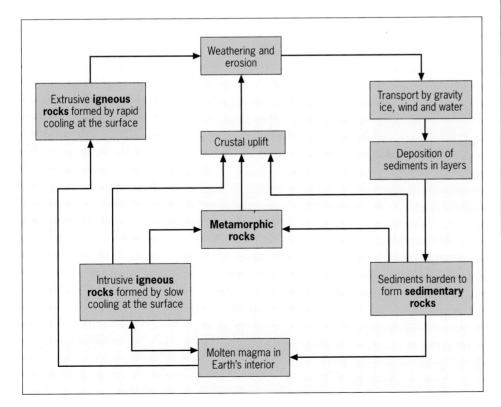

Fig. 2.2 How rocks are formed.

Weathering and erosion

Extrusive **igneous rocks** formed by rapid cooling at the surface

Transport by gravity ice, wind and water

Crustal uplift

Deposition of sediments in layers

Metamorphic rocks

Intrusive **igneous rocks** formed by slow cooling at the surface

Sediments harden to form **sedimentary rocks**

Molten magma in Earth's interior

EXERCISES

1 Find out:
a The nearest place to school where bare rock is visible at the surface.
b What type of rock is it?
c Why does it appear in that place?
d Does the rock outcrop have any effect on the relief?
2 The landscape in Figure 2.1 is made of granite. What evidence in the photograph suggests that granite is resistant to weathering and erosion?

Fig. 2.3 The mineral structure of granite.

Fig. 2.4 Fossilised remains in limestone.

Fig. 2.5 (right) Joints and bedding planes in sedimentary rocks.

Fig. 2.6 Marble, which is metamorphosed limestone.

Igneous rocks

All igneous rocks start out as magma, which eventually cools and solidifies. Cooling occurs either at the surface, to form **extrusive igneous rocks**, or within the crust, where it forms **intrusive igneous rocks**.

◆ When magma reaches the surface it is known as lava. Lava cools quickly to form rocks, such as basalt, with tiny mineral crystals.
◆ Magma cooling slowly within the crust forms igneous rocks, such as granite, with large coarse crystals. Granite is the most common igneous rock.

Sedimentary rocks

There are two kinds of sedimentary rock:

◆ Rocks like sandstone and shale formed from mineral particles weathered and eroded from older rocks. Most of these rock particles were transported by rivers, glaciers, wind and waves, and accumulated on the sea bed. Here they eventually formed new sedimentary rocks.
◆ Rocks formed from the remains of plants and animals. Limestone and chalk are made from the shells and skeletons of billions of tiny sea creatures. In contrast, coal is the fossilised remains of ancient land plants such as trees.

In general, sedimentary rocks are not as tough as igneous rocks and are more easily weathered and eroded. Some sedimentary rocks, e.g. shale, are so fragile that they can be broken by hand.

Unlike igneous and metamorphic rocks, sedimentary rocks were laid down in layers – known as **strata**. Each layer is separated from those above and below it by a **bedding plane** (Fig. 2.5). When sedimentary rocks first formed, the bedding planes were usually horizontal. However, it is common to find sedimentary rocks with tilted bedding planes. This tells us that the rocks were disturbed by earth movements, such as folding and faulting, after they were formed.

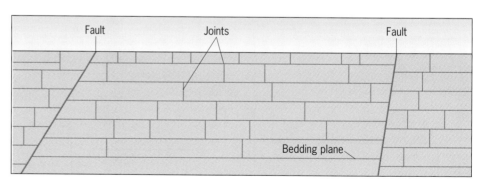

Metamorphic rocks

Metamorphic rocks have been changed either by great heat or great pressure. For instance, when a huge mass of molten granite is **intruded** into the crust, it alters the surrounding rocks. Thus, limestone in contact with the hot granite may be baked or metamorphosed into marble (Fig. 2.6). Pressure has a similar effect, but on a larger scale, changing rocks over a much wider area. The slates of the Lake District and North Wales were once shales and mudstones, and were metamorphosed by pressure.

Table 2.1 Identifying kinds of rock and rock types

Rock	Formation	Rock type
Sandstone	Sand-sized particles compressed and cemented together.	
Marble	Limestone changed by great heat and pressure (Fig. 2.6).	
Basalt	Runny lava extruded from a volcano, and which cooled quickly at the Earth's surface.	
Limestone	Remains of the shells and skeletons of small creatures deposited on the sea floor (Fig. 2.4).	
Slate	Shales and clays changed by great pressure.	
Granite	Molten rock intruded into the crust and cooled slowly.	
Coal	Fossilised remains of trees and other plants.	

EXERCISES

3a Make a larger copy of Table 2.1. Complete the table by identifying each rock type as igneous, sedimentary or metamorphic.
b* Which type of rock – igneous or sedimentary – is most likely to be altered by metamorphism? Give reasons for your answer.

EXERCISES

4 Study Figures 2.7 and 2.8.
a Describe the distribution of igneous and metamorphic rocks in Britain.
b Describe how the distribution of rock types in Britain is related to relief.
c* Suggest an explanation for this relationship.

Fig. 2.7 (below left) Distribution of rock types in the British Isles.

Fig. 2.8 (below right) The relief of the British Isles.

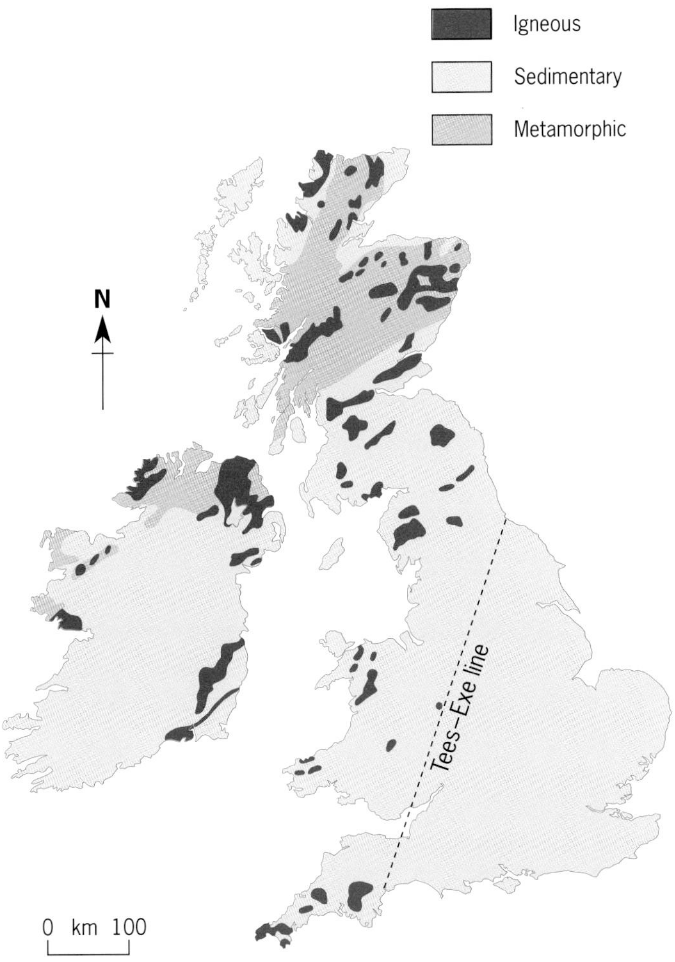

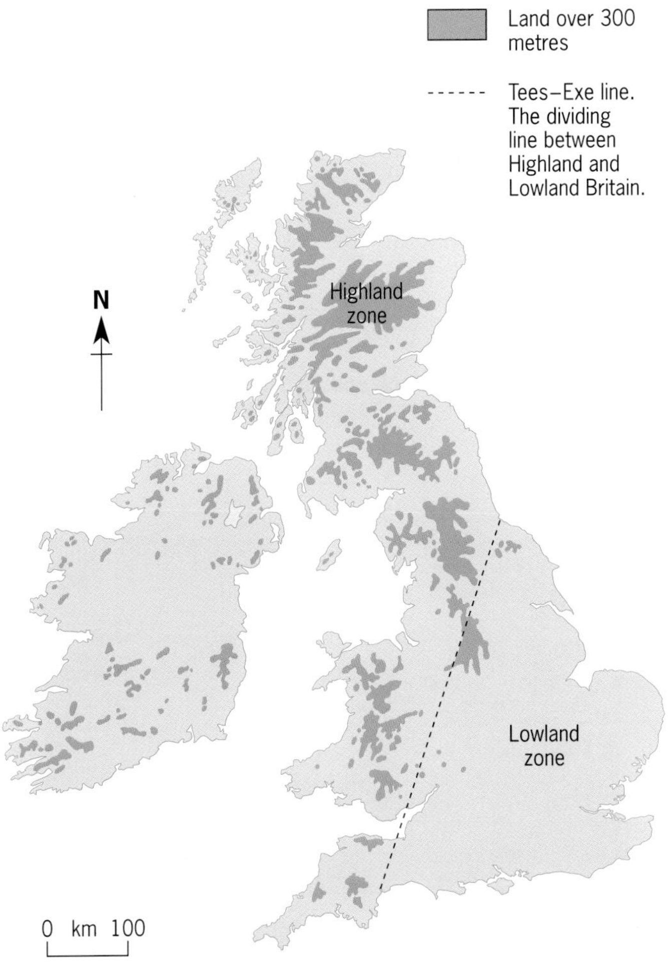

Igneous
Sedimentary
Metamorphic

Land over 300 metres

Tees–Exe line. The dividing line between Highland and Lowland Britain.

N

N

Highland zone

Lowland zone

Tees–Exe line

0 km 100

0 km 100

Fig.2.9 Screees and scars in Littondale, North Yorkshire.

Fig. 2.10 A gritstone block split by frost action, Norber, North Yorkshire.

Fig. 2.11 A granite blockfield in the Cairngorms.

2.3 Rock weaknesses

We often use the term 'rock hard' for something that is very difficult to break. This description fits most rocks, especially igneous and metamorphic ones. And yet along the coast and in the uplands we often come across large areas of rock (Figs 2.9 and 2.11) that have been broken up by natural forces, such as waves and frost.

This suggests that rocks are not always as tough as they seem. The reason is that rocks have cracks and lines of weakness called joints and bedding planes (Fig. 2.5). It is here that the processes of weathering and erosion act most strongly. Even the hardest rocks eventually break down.

2.4 Weathering

Rocks at or near the surface experience changes in heat and moisture. These changes slowly cause the rocks to break down by a process called weathering. Some types of weathering simply break up the rocks into smaller pieces. This is physical weathering. Chemical weathering causes breakdown by altering the minerals in rocks.

Rocks are also eroded by ice, wind, water and the action of animals and plants.

Physical weathering

Frost

In high latitudes, frost action is the most common type of physical weathering. Consider what happens to rainwater falling on to a rock surface in winter. First it seeps into joints and cracks in the rocks. Then, if the temperature drops below zero, the water freezes and turns to ice. Water expands by 9 per cent when it freezes (which in the uplands is on most winter nights). If confined to a narrow crack, the force of expanding water can split the rocks apart (Fig. 2.10).

If freeze-thaw occurs on a cliff where the rock is well jointed, small rock fragments broken off by the frost roll downslope. They build up to form scree (Fig. 2.9). On flatter surfaces, especially where the joints in the rocks are widely spaced, frost has a different effect. It breaks up the rock into massive boulders to form a feature that is called a **blockfield** (Fig. 2.11).

Plants

Tree roots cause physical weathering. They penetrate and widen rock joints (Figs. 2.12 and 2.14). And, if a tree falls over in a gale, its roots may lift out great blocks of rock.

Insolation

In hot deserts like the Sahara, where there is little plant cover, we find a different type of physical weathering. Insolation weathering occurs when rocks are exposed to the powerful rays of the sun in the day and to rapid cooling at night. The surface minerals of rocks heat up and expand at different rates. This sets up stresses, weakening the rock and causing the outer layers to peel away. The effect is much greater if the rock is occasionally wetted by rain, dew or mist. This process is known as **exfoliation** or 'onion peel' weathering, and produces boulders and rock outcrops with unusual rounded shapes (Fig. 2.13).

> **REMEMBER**
> Weathering is the breakdown of rocks exposed to changes in temperature and moisture. Erosion is the removal of rock particles and the wearing away of the land surface by rivers, glaciers, waves and winds.

Fig. 2.12 Biological weathering by a tree's roots.

Fig. 2.13 Exfoliated granite rocks in California, USA.

Fig. 2.14 Rocks shattered by the roots of a fallen tree.

Chemical weathering

Chemical weathering takes place both on the surface and below it, wherever moisture is present. It covers a wide range of complex chemical reactions that alter rock minerals and cause the rocks to disintegrate.

One of the most common forms of chemical weathering is solution. Some rock minerals, such as calcium carbonate, dissolve easily in water that contains carbon dioxide. Others react with oxygen (oxidation) or water, and are weakened and break down. Most chemical reactions operate best at high temperatures. That is why chemical weathering is most effective in warm, wet climates, such as those near the Equator.

EXERCISES

5 Draw a sketch of Figure 2.9 to explain how frost action on a cliff face causes weathering and the formation of scree.
6 List the different types of weathering taking place in each of the areas shown in Figures 2.10–2.14.

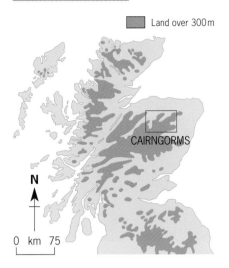

☐ Land over 300m

Fig. 2.15 The location of the Cairngorms.

Fig. 2.16 A granite tor in the Cairngorms.

2.5 Granite landscape: the Cairngorms

The Cairngorms in north-east Scotland form a plateau more than 1200 m high. This upland has four of the five highest mountains in the British Isles (Fig. 2.15). The plateau has a severe, almost arctic-like climate. Its average annual temperature is just below freezing, which allows patches of snow to survive throughout the summer. (If the world's climate were to cool by a degree or so, these snow patches would quickly become glaciers.)

The Cairngorms are made entirely from granite, one of the toughest of all rocks. The sequence of events that formed the Cairngorm plateau (Fig. 2.17) include:
◆ the intrusion of molten granite into the crust, which, when it cooled and solidified, formed what is called a **batholith**;
◆ the removal, by weathering and erosion, of the less resistant rocks above the granite;
◆ the more rapid rates of weathering and erosion of the rocks surrounding the granite, leaving the granite as an 'island' of high ground.

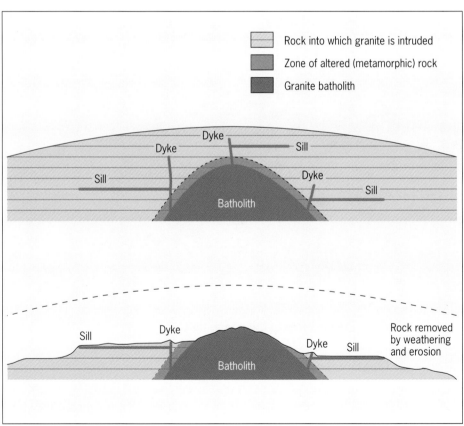

☐ Rock into which granite is intruded
☐ Zone of altered (metamorphic) rock
☐ Granite batholith

Fig. 2.17 Formation of a batholith.

Around the edges of the plateau, glaciers have carved deep U-shaped valleys. Vertical cliffs on the valley sides have been weathered by frost action, leaving screes and boulder fields on the lower slopes. There are glacial deposits on the valley floor.

Meanwhile, on the plateau surface, frost has broken the granite into a chaotic boulder-strewn landscape forming blockfields. Also, on high ground, isolated outcrops of granite called tors rise above the plateau surface (Fig. 2.16). Geologists think that these features were formed mainly by chemical weathering. This weathering was concentrated on where the vertical joints were close together (Fig. 2.18). Later, erosion removed the weathered granite, and frost action dislodged large blocks of granite from the tors.

Fig. 2.18 (right) Formation of a granite tor.

Fig. 2.19 (below) 1:50 000 OS map extract of the Cairngorms.

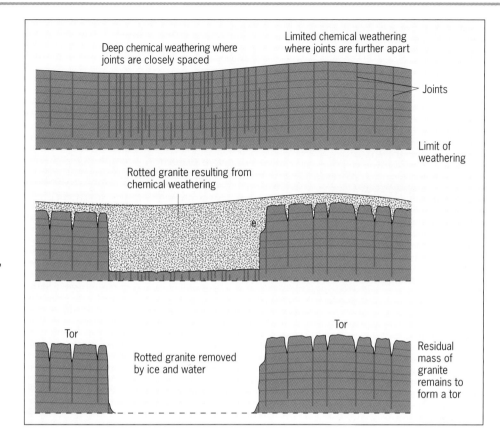

Deep chemical weathering where joints are closely spaced

Limited chemical weathering where joints are further apart

Joints

Limit of weathering

Rotted granite resulting from chemical weathering

Tor

Rotted granite removed by ice and water

Tor

Residual mass of granite remains to form a tor

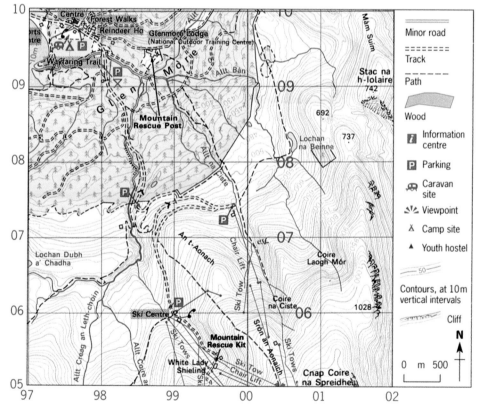

Legend:
Minor road
Track
Path
Wood
Information centre
Parking
Caravan site
Viewpoint
Camp site
Youth hostel
Contours, at 10m vertical intervals
Cliff
N
0 m 500

EXERCISES

8 Study Figure 2.19.

a Give six-figure references and the height of the three highest points on the map.

b* What evidence suggests that the rock type in some areas might be granite?

c What evidence can you find for tourism in this area? Give examples and grid references.

d With reference to the map, name one recreational activity other than skiing.

e* Using Figure 2.19, explain how the physical geography of the Cairngorms influences recreation in the area.

f What types of work would be available to people who live in this area? Give examples from the map.

Minor igneous intrusions and the landscape

Areas of igneous rock that cooled slowly within the Earth's crust are known as intrusions. Some of these intrusions such as the granite batholiths of the Cairngorms and Dartmoor, are huge. Others are small. These minor intrusions are called **sills** and **dykes** (Fig. 2.17).

◆ Sills are sheets of igneous rock (especially dolerite) that have been forced between the bedding planes of older rocks. They often cover large areas. Because dolerite is usually harder than the surrounding rock, sills often form steep slopes. On valley sides, a sill may crop out as a cliff. Where it crosses a river, it creates a band of resistant rock and forms waterfalls (e.g. High Force in Teesdale). The Great Whin Sill has a strong influence on the landscape of the North Pennines. In Northumberland, it forms a steep ridge along which runs part of Hadrian's Wall (built in Roman times) (Figs. 2.20 and 2.21). It also forms the Farne Islands in Northumberland and the sheer cliffs of High Cup Nick in Cumbria.

◆ Dykes are similar to sills, except that they cut across the bedding planes of older rocks. As a result, they crop out vertically, in long narrow bands, which sometimes run for tens of kilometres across the landscape.

Fig. 2.20 (right) An aerial view of the Roman Wall at Housesteads.

Fig. 2.21 (below) A geological section through the Great Whin Sill at Housesteads.

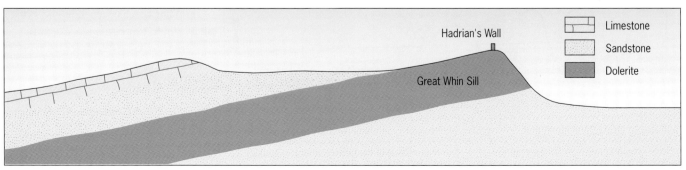

Hadrian's Wall

Great Whin Sill

Limestone

Sandstone

Dolerite

2.6 Limestone landscape: the Yorkshire Dales

In the Yorkshire Dales (Fig. 2.27), a hard mountain limestone known as Carboniferous Limestone is found. This rock slowly dissolves in rainwater. How does this chemical weathering happen?

As rain falls from clouds and soaks into the soil, it absorbs carbon dioxide to become dilute carbonic acid. This acid then reacts with the main mineral in Carboniferous Limestone – calcium carbonate – to make calcium bicarbonate, which is removed in solution. The rock is dissolved at a rate of about 4 cm every 1000 years. This solution acts most strongly along the lines of weakness in the limestone (i.e. joints and bedding planes). The result of solution is scenery known as **karst**.

Fig. 2.23 (below) The formation of karst scenery.

Fig. 2.22 (above) A limestone pavement at Conistone in Upper Wharfedale, North Yorkshire.

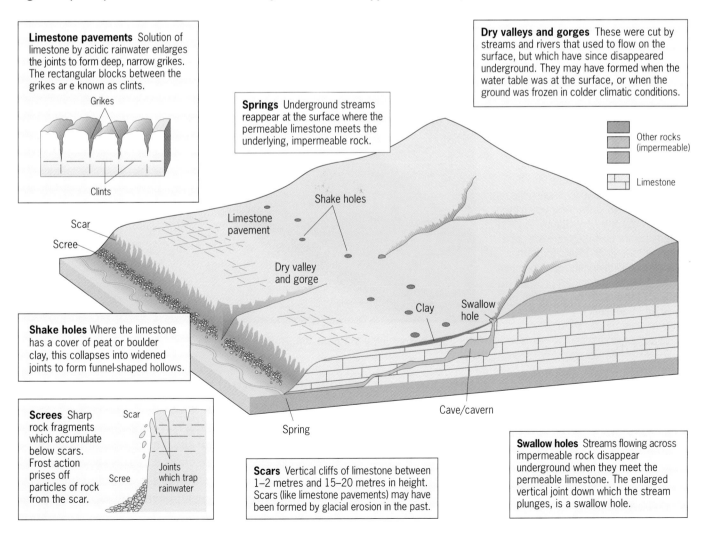

Limestone pavements Solution of limestone by acidic rainwater enlarges the joints to form deep, narrow grikes. The rectangular blocks between the grikes are known as clints.

Grikes

Clints

Springs Underground streams reappear at the surface where the permeable limestone meets the underlying, impermeable rock.

Dry valleys and gorges These were cut by streams and rivers that used to flow on the surface, but which have since disappeared underground. They may have formed when the water table was at the surface, or when the ground was frozen in colder climatic conditions.

Other rocks (impermeable)

Limestone

Scar

Scree

Limestone pavement

Shake holes

Dry valley and gorge

Clay

Swallow hole

Cave/cavern

Spring

Shake holes Where the limestone has a cover of peat or boulder clay, this collapses into widened joints to form funnel-shaped hollows.

Screes Sharp rock fragments which accumulate below scars. Frost action prises off particles of rock from the scar.

Scar

Scree

Joints which trap rainwater

Scars Vertical cliffs of limestone between 1–2 metres and 15–20 metres in height. Scars (like limestone pavements) may have been formed by glacial erosion in the past.

Swallow holes Streams flowing across impermeable rock disappear underground when they meet the permeable limestone. The enlarged vertical joint down which the stream plunges, is a swallow hole.

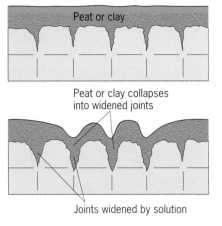

Shake holes Funnel-shaped hollows

Fig. 2.24 (above) How shake holes form.

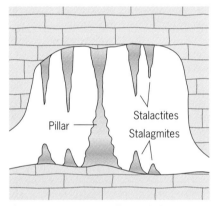

Caves and caverns The solution along joints and bedding planes leads to the formation of caves and underground features. Dissolved limestone may be deposited as dripstone (or tufa) in the form of finger-like stalactites, which hang from the roofs of caves. Stubby stalagmites are built up where the drips fall on the cave floor. Pillars form when stalactites and stalagmites join together.

Fig. 2.25 (above) The formation of caves and caverns.

EXERCISES

10a Study Figure 2.26 and draw a sketch of the valley. Add the following labels: dry valley, scree, and cliff.
b* Include a few notes on your sketch explaining how these features were formed, and what possible difficulties there are for farming in this area.

Karst landforms

The main karst landforms are: limestone pavements, dry valleys, caves, caverns and gorges.

◆ Limestone pavements are horizontal platforms of limestone. They consist of bare rock, broken into rectangular blocks, or clints. Between the clints are deep cracks known as grikes. Grikes are joints widened by solution.

◆ Limestone is a permeable rock. As a result, limestone areas have few surface streams. However, valleys without streams are common in limestone areas. These dry valleys tell us that streams once flowed on the surface. How did this happen? Ten thousand years ago, the climate was much colder and the ground was permanently frozen. During the summer, the top metre or so thawed. Thus, for a few months each year, streams flowed across the limestone, and carved the dry valleys we see today.

◆ Limestone areas have complex underground drainage systems. Surface streams flowing on to the limestone quickly disappear underground down enlarged joints or swallow holes. They flow through caves and caverns and eventually re-emerge at the surface as springs.

◆ Where surface streams occur in limestone areas they often flow in very steep-sided valleys or gorges. Gorges develop because there is so little surface water on the limestone slopes to wear back the valley sides.

Fig 2.26 A dry valley in Upper Wharfedale, North Yorkshire.

Limestone quarrying: conservation or jobs?

Limestone is a valuable mineral (Table 2.2). It is so valuable that it is even quarried in National Parks – areas of outstanding scenery supposedly protected against such development. There are eight limestone quarries in the Yorkshire Dales National Park and they are controversial. They destroy the landscape, are an eyesore, and generate a lot of noise, dust and lorry traffic (Fig. 2.29). However, quarrying is often supported by local people because it creates much-needed jobs.

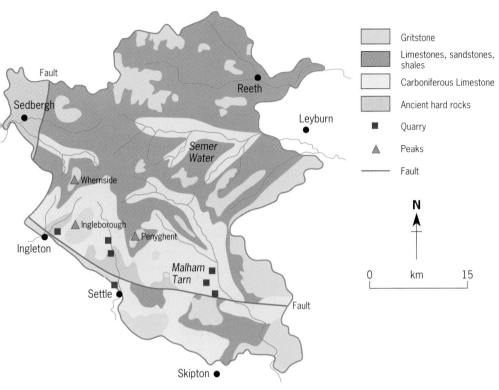

Fig. 2.27 (above) Yorkshire Dales National Park.

Gritstone
Limestones, sandstones, shales
Carboniferous Limestone
Ancient hard rocks
■ Quarry
▲ Peaks
— Fault

N

0   km   15

EXERCISES

11 Read Figures 2.28 and 2.29.
a What will the quarry owners do to reduce inconvenience to residents and damage to the environment?
b In your own words, summarise the views of those in favour and those against the proposal.
c The issue of quarrying is about the conflict between jobs for local people and conservation. What is your view on this issue? Give a brief talk to the class stating your opinion and explain why you hold it.

Quarry extension wins approval

Chairman uses casting vote to decide contentious plan

by Sue Marshall

Quarrying at Cracoe is set to continue to the year 2000 after the national park gave the go-ahead to Tilcon's controversial plans to push extraction 100 metres deeper into the bowels of Swinden Quarry.

Following a two hour debate on Tuesday the park's planning committee was evenly split with the balance tipped in Tilcon's favour by chairman Robert Heseltine's casting vote.

Initial extraction will be at the Threshfield end of the quarry and in five to six years time plant and machinery will be hidden from view. Landscaping will restore

much of the hillside and Tilcon has set aside £500,000 to help turn the site into a nature reserve on completion of quarrying. Officers had recommended refusal of the scheme to extract a further 37 million tonnes of Dales limestone on the grounds that it contravened environmental and traffic policies.

They felt there were already adequate reserves of stone and the development could not be carried out without detriment to water supplies.

But Tilcon has pledged to sink new bore holes should the supply be affected and ward councillor Shelagh Marshall proposed the plan be approved.

Fig. 2.28 (above) Report by Sue Marshall in the *Craven Herald and Pioneer*.

'There is no doubt that the extent of present quarrying has scarred our landscape and pollution by dust and of water has been significant. But quarrying companies today fully realise the need to be good neighbours and take all possible measures to minimise inconvenience.'
Local councillor

'If we allow this we will be continuing the misery for those people who live in the area and risking their water supply. There are only seven employees resident in the National Park on the company's payroll.'
Local resident

'We are trying to give local employment some protection. We are talking about wage earners, who aren't very highly paid, who support a family. These are hardworking Dales people.'
Local councillor

'My 11 hectares of land are likely to be flooded as there will be a 78 per cent increase in water going down the Beck. The Beck just won't be able to take it.'
Local farmer

'The development is contrary to what should be the policy of the national parks, to look after our finest landscapes.'
Secretary, Craven branch of the Council for the Protection of Rural England

'Much of the material extracted from the quarry will be used as aggregate to make more roads to further destroy the countryside. The great majority of people in Cracoe will be disappointed.'
Chairman of the parish council

'Local residents will benefit from the visual improvement and reduced hours of transport. There will be a cessation of almost all night-time lorries leaving the quarry.'
Spokeswoman for quarry company

Fig. 2.29 (left) Reactions to Swinden Quarry.

CASE STUDY

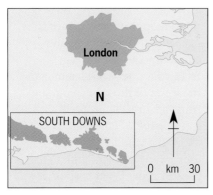

Fig. 2.30 The location of the South Downs.

2.7 Chalk landscape: the South Downs

Chalk is a soft type of limestone. It is also **porous** because it contains tiny air spaces, or pores, between its mineral particles which absorb water, rather like a sponge. As a result, there are very few permanent streams and rivers in chalklands.

This lack of surface water has always been a problem for settlement in these areas (see Chapter 5). It has forced settlements to cluster around springs where there is a permanent water supply. There are two places where springs are often found in chalklands: at the foot of scarp slopes, where the chalk rests on an impermeable rock, such as clay; and on dip slopes, where the zone of saturated rock (**water table**) reaches the surface (Fig. 2.31).

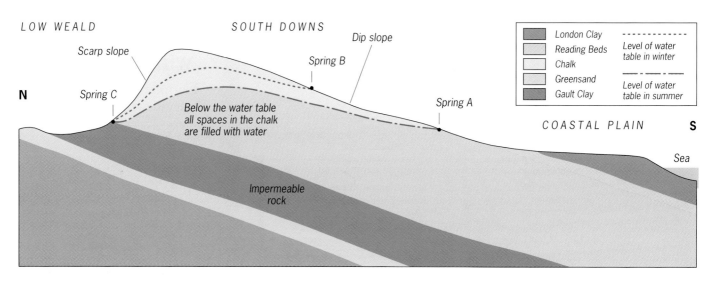

Fig. 2.31 The water table in a chalk escarpment.

EXERCISES

12 Explain the difference between the **permeability** of chalk and Carboniferous Limestone.

13 Study Figure 2.31.

a Why does the height of the water table vary between summer and winter?

b What will happen to the stream that flows from spring A in (1) summer, (2) winter?

c What will happen to the stream flowing from spring B?

d Why is spring B unlikely to attract settlement?

e Which spring is likely to be most attractive to settlement? Give your reasons.

The South Downs are a chalk upland, or an **escarpment**, stretching from Hampshire to Beachy Head near Brighton (Fig. 2.30). Although the Downs are, on average, only 200 m high, they are an impressive feature. Like all escarpments, the South Downs have two distinctive slopes:

◆ Most striking is the steep, north-facing scarp slope rising abruptly from the Low Weald (Fig. 2.31).

◆ Beyond the scarp, a gentle dip slope runs down to the Channel coast. In several places the escarpment is cut by the valleys of southward-flowing rivers, such as the Arun, Ouse and Cuckmere.

How can chalk, which is a less resistant rock, form such a prominent relief feature? There are two reasons. Firstly, the surrounding rocks (Figs. 2.31 and 2.36) are more easily eroded than chalk and are therefore worn down more quickly. Secondly, because streams and rivers are rare in chalklands today, the chalk is not being worn away by rivers. This was not always so. The dip slope of the South Downs is criss-crossed by dry valleys. They formed during the ice age when the chalk was permanently frozen, allowing rivers to flow on the surface during the brief arctic summers.

Fig. 2.32 An aerial view of the South Downs near Truleigh Hill, Sussex. The steep scarp slopes in on the right.

2.8 Clay landscapes

Clay is a less resistant rock. Because it is so easily worn down by rivers and glaciers, it often forms lowlands with gentle slopes. In northern Britain and East Anglia, many lowlands are covered with a thick layer of till, or boulder clay. This sticky, easily moulded material was left behind more than 13 000 years ago by great ice sheets and glaciers. In southern Britain, the clay is much older. It is sandwiched between more resistant rocks like chalk and limestone. This clay often forms broad valleys such as the Vale of Oxford and the Vale of the White Horse in Wiltshire.

EXERCISES

14a Make a sketch of Figure 2.32. Label the chalk scarp, clay lowlands and different types of land use. Mark on the principal settlements.
b* Add notes to your sketch to explain the differences in land use and possible reasons for the location of settlements.

Table 2.2 The economic value of rocks

Rock type	Economic value and use
Granite	Upland areas with steep slopes and poor soils. Rough grazing for sheep. Water catchment. Recreation (hill walking, climbing). Quarrying for roadstone, ornamental stone and china clay.
Limestone	Quarrying for roadstone, lime for cement, steelmaking etc. Thin soils and lack of surface water support only rough grazing and pasture land for sheep and cattle. Many limestone areas (Yorkshire Dales, Peak District, Mendips) are very scenic and are important for recreation.
Chalk	Lack of water and thin soils. Not much settlement. Mainly rough grazing and permanent pasture, though better soils may be cultivated. Chalk is quarried for lime and cement.
Dolerite	Mainly quarried for roadstone. Outcrops of dolerite cover only small areas and therefore have little effect on land use.
Clay	Produces heavy soils suitable for livestock farming, especially dairying and beef. Clay (e.g. Gault Clay and Wealden Clay, Fig. 2.36) is quarried to make bricks in many parts of the UK.

Fig. 2.33 Folded limestone rocks, Dorset.

●●●●●●●●●●●●●●●●
● **REMEMBER**
Uplands may result from:
● • resistant rocks that erode
   more slowly than
   surrounding less-resistant
   rocks;
● • folding e.g. anticlines;
● • faulting e.g. uplift along
   fault lines.
●●●●●●●●●●●●●●●●

Fig. 2.34 World distribution of fold mountains and rift valleys.

EXERCISES

15a Using an atlas and Figure 2.34, identify the major fold mountain ranges in Asia, North America, South America and Europe.
b* Compare the distribution of fold mountains (Fig. 2.34) with the boundaries of the main plates (Fig. 1.7). Describe the similarities and suggest possible reasons for them.

2.9 Folding and faulting

Folding

At first, most sedimentary rocks form in horizontal layers. Sometimes these rocks lie undisturbed for millions of years. We know this because today many layers are still in their original horizontal position. Often, however, tectonic forces within the crust (see Chapter 1) compress the rocks and fold them into new shapes. These forces have **folded** sedimentary rocks into some of the highest mountain ranges in the world (Fig. 2.38).

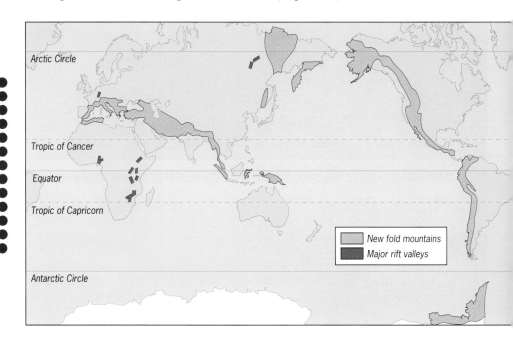

Anticlines and synclines

If you put a sheet of A4 paper on a flat surface and apply gentle pressure from both ends, the paper will form a simple arch, or upfold. In a similar way, rocks are folded by powerful tectonic forces. We refer to these upfolds as **anticlines** (Fig. 2.35).

In south-east England, the Weald in Kent and Sussex was originally a dome-shaped anticline (Fig. 2.36). After the dome was formed, the forces of weathering and erosion got to work. Rivers stripped away the outermost layers of rock, so that today we are left with an eroded anticline. The removal of the covering of chalk caused the inward facing escarpments of the North and South Downs (Fig. 2.31). Sometimes, instead of pushing the rocks up, folding creates a downfold or **syncline** (Fig. 2.35). Both London and Paris are located in the centre of basins, or synclines.

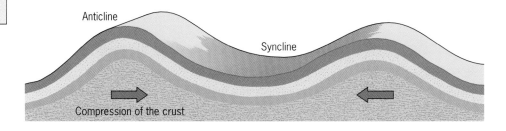

Fig. 2.35 An anticline and syncline.

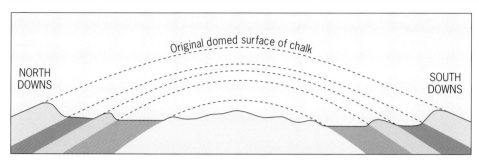

Fig. 2.36 A cross-section of the Weald, an eroded anticline.

Tertiary beds
Chalk
Greensand
Gault clay
Wealden clay
Hastings sands

Fig. 2.37 Tourists in the main street of Gruyères in the Alps, Switzerland.

Fold mountains

To understand folding we must go back to the ideas of plate tectonics in Chapter 1. Imagine two continents, separated by a shallow sea and moving together. As the continents get closer, the sedimentary rocks on the sea bed crumple upwards to form fold mountains. This is exactly how the Himalayas were formed as India was transported on the Indo-Australian plate northwards towards Eurasia (Fig. 2.38). Fold mountains such as the Alps provide important resources for economic activities (Table 2.3).

EXERCISES

16a Why are the North and South Downs tilted structures (Fig. 2.36)?

b What name do we give to tilted uplands like the North and South Downs?

c* If the Weald were a syncline, how and why would the ages of rocks on the rim differ from those at the centre? Draw a sketch to help explain your answer.

d* Suggest how folded mountain regions create disadvantages as well as advantages for human activities.

Table 2.3 Fold mountains and economic activities: The Swiss Alps

The Alps	The Alps have formed in the past 50 million years by the pressure of the African plate pushing northwards against the Eurasian plate. The Alps cover 60 per cent of the area of Switzerland, average 1700 m, and have more than 100 summits at about 4000 m.
Tourism	The Alps are the main centre of tourism in Switzerland (Fig. 2.37). Swiss tourism is an all-year-round industry, dominated by skiing in winter, and sightseeing and hiking in summer. Water-based activities (e.g. boating, wind surfing etc.) are important on many alpine lakes in summer. Tourism employs 12 per cent of the Swiss workforce and accounts for between 5 and 6 per cent of Switzerland's gross domestic product (GDP).
Hydro-electric power (HEP)	HEP provides 53 per cent of Switzerland's electricity. The Alps have plentiful HEP resources owing to their high precipitation, many natural lakes, and large differences in relief between the valleys and the mountains.
Agriculture	The alpine valleys provide scope for high-quality pasture for livestock farming (especially dairying). Upland pastures (known as alps) are used for summer grazing.

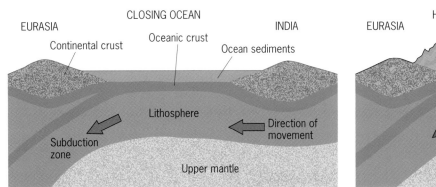
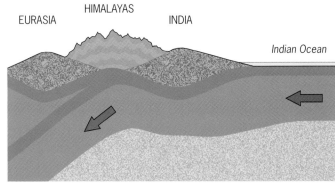

Fig. 2.38 The formation of the Himalayas.

Faulting

The tectonic forces within the crust do not always lead to folding. Some rocks are either too rigid or too brittle to fold. Instead, when they are put under pressure, they snap. When this happens we call it **faulting**.

Faulting occurs most often when the crust is being stretched and pulled apart. This happens at constructive plate margins, where rising magma from the mantle forces its way to the surface. The most spectacular effects of this tension are **rift valleys** (Fig. 2.39), such as those found in the mid-ocean ridges, and the East African Rift Valley (Fig. 2.41). Volcanic eruptions often take place when rift valleys are formed. Simpler types of faulting are normal faults, reverse faults and tear faults (Fig. 2.40). Both normal and reverse faults can create steep slopes known as fault scarps.

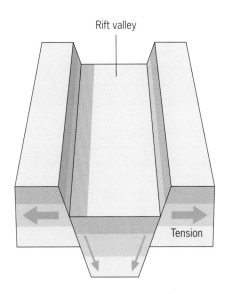

Fig. 2.39 The formation of a rift valley.

Fig. 2.40 Types of fault.

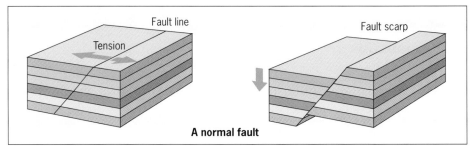

A normal fault

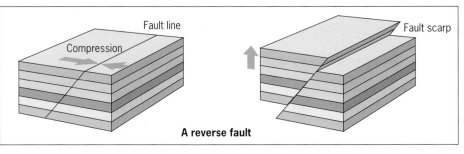

A reverse fault

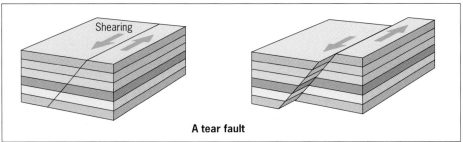

A tear fault

2.10 Summary: rocks and landscapes

KEY SKILLS OPPORTUNITIES
C1.1: Ex. 11b; **C1.2**: Ex. 3a, 3b, 8a, 8b, 8d, 8e, 8f, 9, 11a, 12, 13, 15, 16, 17; **C1/2.3**: Ex. 4a, 4b, 11b; **C2.1**: Ex. 11c; **C2.2**: Ex. 11b.

Key ideas	Generalisations and detail
Rocks are made from a mixture of minerals.	• Granite is made up of quartz, feldspar and mica; limestone of calcium carbonate.
There are three main types of rock: igneous, sedimentary and metamorphic.	• Igneous rocks such as granite and basalt are formed from molten rock, or magma. • Sedimentary rocks result either from the breakdown of pre-existing rocks (e.g. sandstone) or from the build up of plant and animal remains on the sea floor (e.g. limestone). • Metamorphic rocks (e.g. slate and marble) have been altered by great heat and/or pressure.
Rocks have a structure.	• Rocks contain lines of weakness such as joints and bedding planes. Sedimentary rocks were deposited in layers, or strata.
Rocks are changed by the process of weathering.	• Physical weathering by frost or the sun breaks down rocks into smaller fragments. • Chemical weathering destroys rocks by altering their mineral composition.
Some rocks produce distinctive landscapes.	• Granite often produces upland landscapes (e.g. Cairngorm plateau) with features such as tors, blockfields and screes. Land use is mainly restricted to rough grazing and recreation. • Minor igneous intrusions, such as sills and dykes, form important local features such as vertical scars and waterfalls. • Limestone produces upland landscapes known as karst. They include pavements, scars, dry valleys, shake holes, caves and caverns. Soils are thin and not suited to cultivation, though recreation is often important. • Chalk is associated with gentle uplands or escarpments. These consist of a steep scarp slope and a gentle dip slope. There is little surface drainage today. • Clay gives rise to gentle lowland landscapes of great value to agriculture.
Rocks have great economic value.	• Hard rocks such as dolerite and granite may be used as roadstone. Clay baked into bricks is a valuable building material, and so is sandstone. Limestone is a vital raw material used in the chemical, steel and agricultural industries. Weathered granite forms china clay, which is used for pottery manufacture (Fig. 2.42).
Rock structure and scenery is influenced by folding and faulting.	• Pressure caused by plate movements produces simple upfolds, or anticlines (e.g. the Weald), and downfolds, or synclines (e.g. the London Basin), as well as major fold mountain ranges, such as the Himalayas. When rocks fracture instead of folding, they form rift valleys (e.g. East African Rift Valley) and fault scarps.
Fold mountains present advantages and disadvantages for human activities.	• The possible advantages of fold mountain areas include: resources for tourism (snow, scenery, lakes), hydro-electric power, pasture for livestock, water supply, forestry, mineral ores etc. The disadvantages include: steep slopes, thin soils, cold climate and a short growing season, which limit farming and settlement; poor accessibility; and fragile ecosystems easily damaged by tourism and farming.

Fig. 2.41 Hell's Gate, Kenya, in the East African Rift Valley.

Fig. 2.42 China clay quarry, Cornwall.

3 Weather and climate

EXERCISES

1a Study Figures 3.1–3.6 and suggest ways in which the type of weather shown might affect human activities.

b Search the newspapers or the internet for information on the recent weather events. Why did the weather make the news? Was its impact good or bad?

3.1 Introduction

For British people, the weather is an endless topic of conversation. More often than not, we complain about our weather: it's either too cold or too wet, or more rarely too hot or too dry. And we do not trust our climate. Every year, millions of Britons go to the Mediterranean, because they expect the summer at home to be cool and damp.

In this chapter, we begin by focusing on the features of weather and climate, then on the climate of the British Isles. Finally, we study extreme weather events such as tropical storms and droughts. However, first we need to be clear about the difference between weather and climate.

Figs. 3.1–3.6 Many different types of weather.

3.2 What are weather and climate?

Weather and climate are about the same things: temperature, rainfall, wind speed, sunshine, the amount of cloud and so on. And yet weather and climate are not the same. The difference is one of timescale. Weather is about the short term: what's going to happen to temperature and **precipitation** (rain, snow, sleet etc.) today or tomorrow. Climate involves longer timescales. It is the seasonal pattern of weather we can expect on the basis of past experience. We could say that climate is only weather averaged out over 30 or more years.

In many parts of the world, the climate has a definite pattern. For example, at the Equator almost every day is hot and sunny with heavy rainfall in the late afternoon. In much of tropical Africa and South Asia, summers are wet and winters are dry. In the Mediterranean it is the other way round. But in the British Isles it is not nearly so simple. Someone once said that in the British Isles there is no climate, only weather. For example, as I write this, it is late April and it's snowing hard, but a week ago the temperature touched 20°C.

Table 3.1 Average daily maximum temperatures in London

Month	°C	Month	°C
January	6	July	22
February	7	August	21
March	10	September	19
April	13	October	14
May	17	November	10
June	20	December	7

3.3 The global climate

Large parts of the world have similar patterns of temperature and precipitation. This enables us to recognise climate regions (Fig. 3.7).

Fig. 3.7 World climate regions

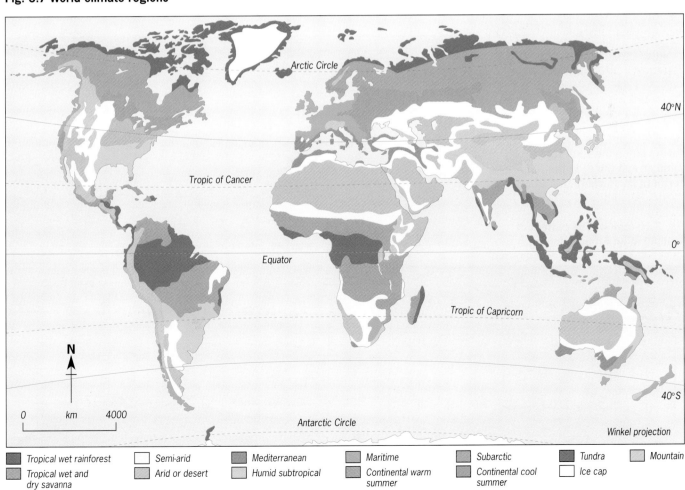

Tropical wet rainforest · Tropical wet and dry savanna · Semi-arid · Arid or desert · Mediterranean · Humid subtropical · Maritime · Continental warm summer · Subarctic · Continental cool summer · Tundra · Ice cap · Mountain

EXERCISES

2a Using the daily weather report in a national newspaper, keep a record of London's maximum temperatures for a week.
b How do the week's temperatures compare with the climatic average in Table 3. 1 ?
c* Explain why it is unlikely that your week's record will match the monthly average temperature exactly.

EXERCISES

3 Study Figure 3.7. What type of climate does the British Isles have? Which other countries have a similar climate?

EXERCISES

Study figure 3.9.

4 Along which line of latitude is the sun overhead on 21 June and 21 December? What season of the year is it in Britain?

5 Explain why the south pole is warmer than the north pole on 21 December.

6* Imagine an area of land extending from the Equator to the North Pole. Draw this continent and mark on it the following lines of latitude: Equator, tropics, polar circles. Draw in the areas that would have equatorial, tropical, temperate and polar climates if latitude was the only influence on the climate.

Fig. 3.8 (above right) The effect of latitude on temperature.

EXERCISES

7 Study Figures 3.9 and 3.10. Suggest why the area inside the Arctic Circle is often called the 'land of the midnight sun'.

Fig. 3.9 (right) The effect of the Earth's tilt on the sun's rays in summer and winter in the northern hemisphere.

Fig. 3.10 (below) The pattern of daylight in an Arctic summer.

Latitude and climate

On a global scale, latitude is the biggest influence on climate. This is because the sun's angle changes with latitude, and the amount of heat energy received at the Earth's surface changes too. The simple rule is that the higher the sun is in the sky, the more concentrated are its rays, and the higher the temperature. Figure 3.8 shows how this happens.

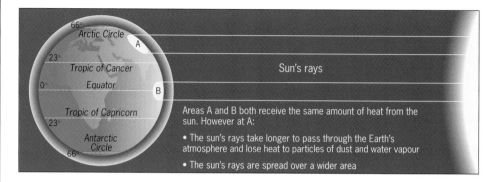

Areas A and B both receive the same amount of heat from the sun. However at A:

• The sun's rays take longer to pass through the Earth's atmosphere and lose heat to particles of dust and water vapour

• The sun's rays are spread over a wider area

Latitude also affects temperature by influencing day length (see Fig. 3.9). The length of day does not vary much in the tropics, but as latitude increases it becomes more important. In the British Isles in winter, days are short and nights are long, and this contributes to low temperatures. Further north, inside the Arctic Circle (66.5°N) the winter days become so short that for several weeks the sun does not rise at all. However, in summer there is a similar period with 24 hours of daylight.

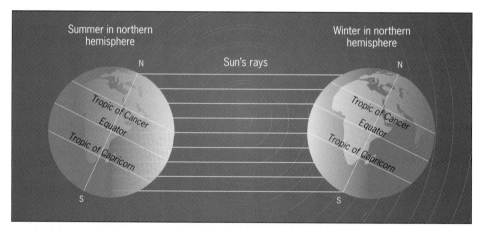

Land, sea and wind direction

The climate of a place is also affected by how far it is from the sea. The sea heats up and cools down more slowly than the land so it has a moderating influence on the climate. If the prevailing winds (those that blow most often) are from the sea, temperatures will be cooler in summer and warmer in winter than at places at the same latitude but in the centre of a continent.

Pressure and winds

Winds are horizontal movements of air over the Earth's surface and within the atmosphere. They are caused by differences in pressure, and blow from areas of high pressure to areas of low pressure. On a global scale, these variations in pressure are caused by differences in temperature.

- Where air is warmed it expands, becomes lighter and rises. The result is low pressure at the surface.
- Where air is cooled it contracts, becomes denser and sinks. This produces high pressure.
  Areas of permanent low pressure occur around the Equator and around the polar circles.
- Low pressure around the Equator results from high temperatures and rising columns of warm air.
- Low pressure around the polar circles develops where cold air meets warm tropical air (the polar front). The cold air undercuts the warm air, forcing the warm air to rise.
  Belts of permanent high pressure encircle the globe in two places:
- at the sub-tropics between 30 and 40 degrees of latitude;
- at the poles.
  The result of these pressure belts is a system of global winds (Fig. 3.11).

> **EXERCISES**
>
> 8 Suggest why Shannon in Eire (52°41′ N) has an average January temperature of 5°C but Minsk in the Russian Federation (52°50′ N) has an average temperature of -8°C

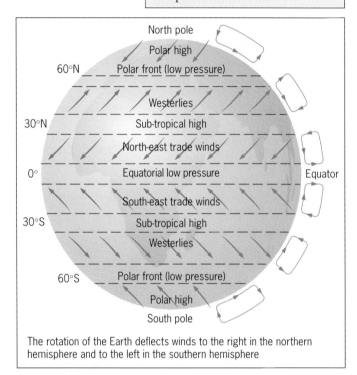

North pole
Polar high
60°N — Polar front (low pressure)

Westerlies
30°N — Sub-tropical high
North-east trade winds
0° — Equatorial low pressure — Equator
South-east trade winds
30°S — Sub-tropical high
Westerlies
60°S — Polar front (low pressure)
Polar high
South pole

The rotation of the Earth deflects winds to the right in the northern hemisphere and to the left in the southern hemisphere

Fig. 3.11 World wind belts.

Fig. 3.12 Cumulus clouds, formed on a warm afternoon in October.

3.4 Precipitation

Precipitation is the moisture that falls from clouds. In the British Isles, most precipitation at sea level falls as rain, though in winter and spring, snow and sleet also fall. Other forms of precipitation include hail and drizzle. About 4 per cent of the atmosphere close to sea level is water vapour, and this is what forms precipitation. (Fig. 3.12).

- Warm air rises and cools.
- Cooling continues until the air reaches the temperature known as the **dew-point**. At this temperature the air is saturated: it cannot hold any more vapour.
- At saturation, the water vapour condenses to make tiny water droplets, which form clouds. Usually clouds form well above the ground, but when they form at ground level we call them fog.
- By a complex process, the droplets grow until they fall as precipitation.

water vapour condenses to form clouds

dew-point

warm air rising

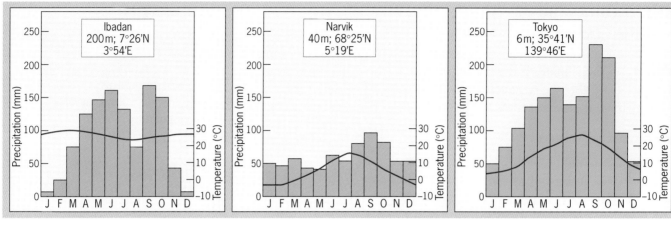

Figs. 3.13, 3.14, 3.15 Climate graphs: Ibadan, Nigeria (left), Narvik, Norway (centre), Tokyo, Japan (right).

EXERCISES

9a Using the figures in Table 3.2, plot a climate graph for place A, either manually or using Excel. Then calculate: (1) the mean monthly temperature, (2) the mean annual range of temperature, (3) the mean annual precipitation.
b Is place A in the northern or southern hemisphere? Explain your answer.
c Compared with the climate at Ibadan, Tokyo and Narvik, does place A have a tropical, temperate or cold climate?

3.5 Climate graphs

We can summarise the main features of climate at a place by using climate graphs (Figs. 3.13–3.15). We plot the mean monthly temperatures as a line graph, and the mean monthly precipitation as a bar graph.

Table 3.2 Climatic data for place A (54 m above sea level)

	Temperature °c Average max.	Monthly min.	Mean monthly precipitation (mm)
January	21	12	48
February	22	12	38
March	20	11	46
April	17	9	48
May	14	7	46
June	12	5	56
July	11	4	48
August	13	5	48
September	15	6	53
October	17	8	58
November	19	9	61
December	21	11	53

Table 3.3 Temperature and altitude

	Altitude (m)	Temperature (°c)
Fort William	0	4
Ben Nevis	1347	?
Bangor	0	7
Snowdon	1085	?
Whitehaven	0	19
Scafell Pike	978	?

3.6 Influence of altitude and aspect

So far we have assumed that altitude has no effect on temperature. This is far from the case. Air is warmed mainly by heat radiated from the ground. As height increases, the air becomes less dense and so it is less able to retain the heat from the ground. Temperatures fall on average by 6.5°C for every 1000 metres of altitude. This is called the **lapse rate**.

Aspect

On a local scale, differences in temperature are often due to **aspect**. Aspect refers to the direction in which a slope faces. Normally, we expect the warmest slopes to be those facing the sun. Not only do these slopes receive sun rays that are more concentrated (Fig. 3.16), but they also have longer hours of direct sunlight, especially in winter. In northern Europe, settlements in upland valleys are usually found on south-facing slopes, as are any vineyards (Fig. 3.17).

EXERCISES

10a Copy Table 3.3 and complete the calculations.
b Explain why temperatures at sea level are higher than in nearby mountains.
c If it's raining at Fort William, describe the likely weather on the summit of Ben Nevis.

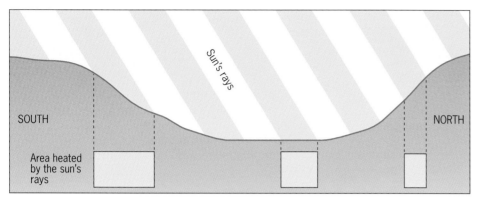

Fig. 3.16 The effect of aspect on solar radiation in Britain, in June.

Fig. 3.17 Vines growing on a south-facing slope at Esslingen, Germany.

3.7 | The climate of the British Isles

Look at the position of the British Isles on a world map. We are on the western edge of the Eurasian landmass. To the west, for 5000 kilometres, there is just open ocean. On three days out of four, the winds blow from this direction, so it's not surprising that the British Isles, exposed to the full influence of the Atlantic Ocean, have a mild, damp climate.

Although the distance from north to south of the British Isles (from the Scillies to Shetland) is only 1000 kilometres, and from east to west less than 300 kilometres, there are large regional differences in climate.

Temperature

Given the relatively high latitude of the British Isles, the sun gives only moderate average temperatures. But the range of latitude is large enough to have some influence on temperature. The Scilly Isles (50°N) in the far south-west have an average annual temperature of 11.9°C. This compares with 7.5°C in the Shetland Isles, ten degrees of latitude further north.

Seasonal differences in temperature

The most remarkable feature of the climate of the British Isles is the mild winters. We can thank the Atlantic Ocean, and the prevailing westerly winds for this. The warmth of the ocean keeps our winter temperatures well above the average for the latitude (Fig. 3.18). Unfortunately, there is a price: cool summers. Throughout the summer, the ocean stays cooler than the land, keeping temperatures below average for the latitude. The warmest area in summer (London) averages only 18°C in July, and many parts of northern Britain do not even reach 15°C (Fig. 3.19). This gives the British Isles a small ('equable') range of temperature, with only 10–12°C difference between the warmest and coldest months.

Continentality

As we move eastwards into Europe, the effect of the ocean on temperatures decreases. The continental landmass is quick to heat up in summer and quick to cool down in winter. Places in eastern Europe have warmer summers and colder winters compared to those on the Atlantic fringe. We refer to this effect as **continentality**. In central Siberia, continentality reaches an extreme, with annual temperature ranges exceeding 50°C.

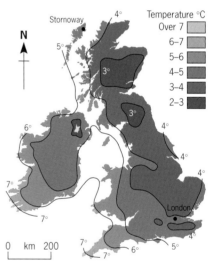

Fig. 3.18 (above) January temperatures in the British Isles.

Fig. 3.19 (below) July temperatures in the British Isles.

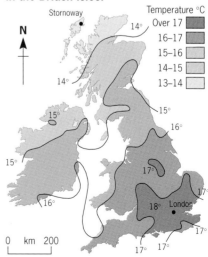

EXERCISES

11 Study Figures 3.18 and 3.19. Then copy the paragraph opposite and fill in the missing words.

EXERCISES

12a Make a table to summarise how the following factors influence the climate of the British Isles: (1) latitude, (2) Atlantic Ocean, (3) westerly winds, (4) North Atlantic Drift.
b* Which of these factors would you say is most important? Explain your answer.

In January, the isotherms run approximately from .... to ....The warmest part of the British Isles is the .... region: the coldest is in .... Thus, in January, the closer a place is to the warming influence of the .... the higher its temperature. In spite of its lower latitude, London is no warmer than .... in January.

In July, the isotherms run .... to .... Now temperatures fall with .... The warmest areas are in .... and the coldest are in ....

In summer, London, with an average July temperature of .... is appreciably warmer than Stornoway, with a temperature of ....

Missing words: north, south, east, west, south-west, southern Britain, Atlantic Ocean, Stornoway, latitude, northern Britain, Scotland, 18°c, 13°c.

Fig. 3.20 January temperatures in the North Atlantic.

●●●●●●●●●●●●●●●●
● **REMEMBER**
● There are three major
● influences on the climate
● of the British Isles:
● • latitude;
● • situation on the edge of
●   a landmass surrounded
●   by sea and ocean;
● • prevailing winds that
●   spread the influence of
●   the ocean on shore.
●●●●●●●●●●●●●●●●

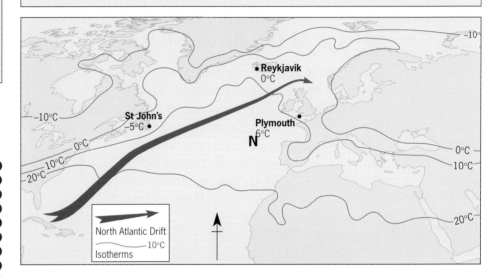

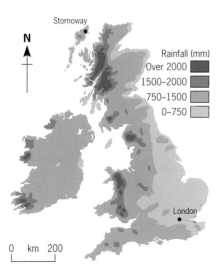

Fig. 3.21 Distribution of precipitation in the British Isles.

Westerly winds and the North Atlantic Drift

The mild winters of the British Isles are not due only to the nearness of the ocean. In Figure 3.20 you can see that eastern Canada, at the same latitude as the British Isles but on the other side of the Atlantic Ocean, has very severe winters. Why?

◆ In the British Isles, the prevailing westerly winds blow on-shore (i.e. from the ocean onto the land) spreading the warming influence of the ocean deep into the continent in winter. In eastern Canada, these same westerlies are off-shore winds, bringing bitterly cold air from the continental interior.

◆ A warm ocean current – the North Atlantic Drift – brings tropical water from the Caribbean to northern Europe. Thus, while the coast of eastern Canada is gripped by sea ice during the winter, the shores of the British Isles (and Iceland and northern Norway) remain ice-free (Fig. 3.20).

Distribution of precipitation over the British Isles

The distribution of precipitation over the British Isles is uneven (Fig. 3.21). The driest regions are in the south-east and have as little as 600 mm of precipitation a year. Compare this with the mountains of the north and west, which may have more than 5000 mm. Two factors dominate the distribution of precipitation: relief and distance from the Atlantic Ocean. In simple terms western Britain is wetter than eastern Britain, and upland Britain is wetter than lowland Britain.

Table 3.4 The effects of relief and longitude on precipitation in the British Isles

	West	East
Upland	1500 – 5000 mm *Brecon Beacons*	1000 – 2000 mm
Lowland	900 – 1500 mm	600 – 900 mm

In the British Isles, mean annual precipitation is high and spread throughout the year, unlike in the Mediterranean, where there is a wet and a dry season.

Types of precipitation

High precipitation in the British Isles is easily explained. The prevailing westerly winds pick up moisture from the ocean and, as they sweep in from the Atlantic, the British Isles are the first obstacle in their path. When this moist air hits the western mountains, it sheds large amounts of precipitation. We call this relief, or **orographic,** precipitation (Fig. 3.22).

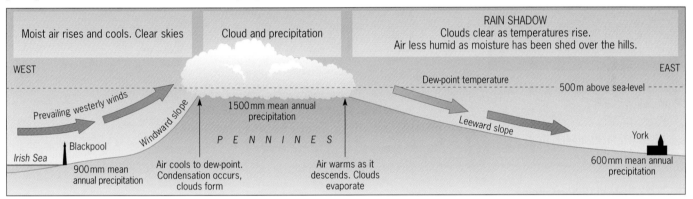

In the lowlands there is less precipitation, and amounts decrease eastwards. In part, this is because so much moisture has been 'spent' in the uplands. However, this is not the whole story: as the moist air descends from the mountains, it warms up and the moisture evaporates reducing precipitation and creating a **rain shadow** (Fig. 3.22). Many parts of eastern England and eastern Scotland lie in a rain shadow.

Most precipitation in the British Isles comes from mid-latitude storms

Fig. 3.22 (above) Relief precipitation and the rain shadow effect in northern England.

Fig. 3.23 (below left) Mean annual precipitation for southern England.

Fig. 3.24 (bottom left) Relief cross-section from Wales to southern England.

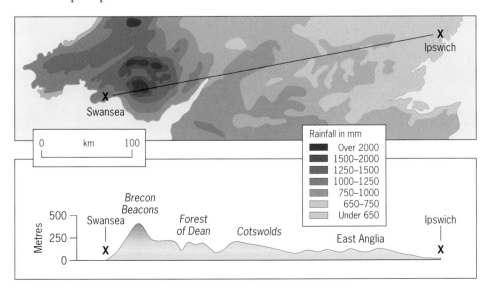

known as depressions (see Section 3.9). However, in eastern England thunderstorms also contribute significant amounts of **convectional** precipitation (Fig. 3.26), especially in summer. In summer, the sun heats the ground, causing the warm air to rise in a column, or convection current. As the air rises, it cools until it forms towering thunderstorm (cumulo-nimbus) clouds (Fig. 3.25). Because of their great thickness, these clouds completely blot out the sun and often produce lightning, thunder and very heavy showers of rain and hail.

Fig. 3.25 (above) A cumulo-nimbus cloud.

Fig. 3.26 (right) Convectional precipitation and thunderstorms.

Fig. 3.27 (below) Understanding weather charts.

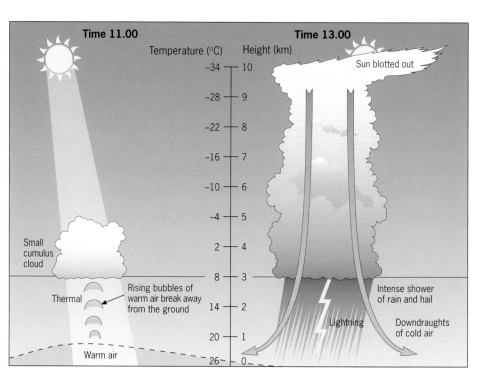

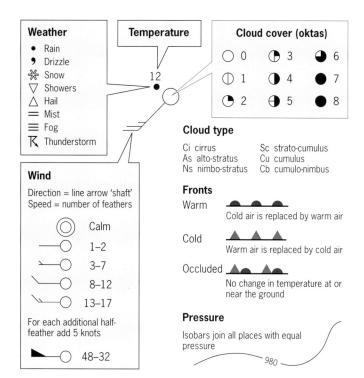

3.8 Weather charts

If you look at the weather forecast on television or in newspapers you will see weather charts (Fig. 3.28). The most important feature on these charts are **isobars** – lines joining places of equal pressure. Circular patterns of isobars pick out areas of low pressure (**depressions**) and high pressure (**anticyclones**). Sometimes the isobars are packed closely together. This indicates strong winds. When the isobars are spaced widely apart, they show light winds or calm conditions. Isobars on maps can also help us to tell the wind direction, because surface winds blow from areas of high pressure to areas of low pressure.

Weather charts provide information about other weather conditions too, especially temperature, cloud cover and precipitation. This information is given as a series of symbols for each weather station (Figs. 3.27–3.29).

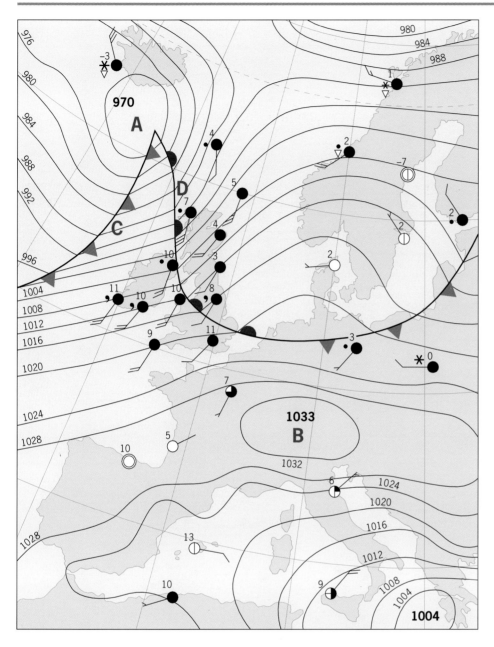

Fig. 3.28 (left) Weather chart for 15.1.95.

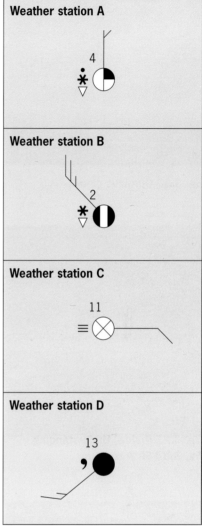

Fig. 3.29 (above) Weather station plotting models.

3.9 Depressions and anticyclones

Air masses are large bodies of air with uniform temperature and humidity. Several different air masses meet over the British Isles, some originating in the tropics and others in the Arctic. This is why the British Isles have changeable weather. On most days, the weather charts for the British Isles and the North Atlantic are dominated either by depressions or anticyclones.

Depressions

Depressions are large areas of low pressure. They form over northern Canada and the Atlantic Ocean where warm tropical air meets cold polar air. They may be up to 2000 kilometres across. Normally, they move rapidly eastwards, often crossing the Atlantic in two or three days. On three days out of four, depressions are responsible for our weather. They bring mild, wet, stormy conditions, followed by brief intervals of bright, sunny weather.

EXERCISES

15a Study Figure 3.27 and then describe the weather conditions at each station in Figure 3.29.
b Visit the website grytviken. leeds.ac.uk~charlie/met/_ charts.html Download the current weather chart for the British Isles. Write a brief report describing the main weather features across the British Isles.

Fig. 3.30 Cumulus cloud.

Fig. 3.31 Stratus cloud.

Fig. 3.32 Cirrus clouds.

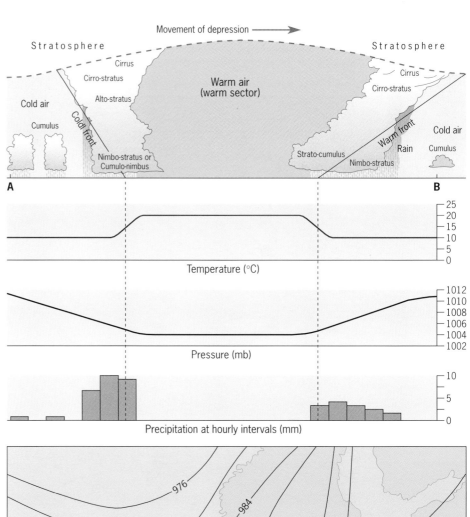

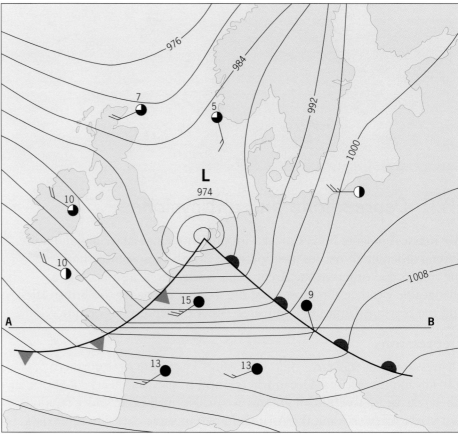

Fig. 3.33 Weather conditions in a depression.

Fig. 3.33 shows the cause of wet and cloudy weather in depressions. Air rises along **fronts** where warm and cold air meet. Warm air is confined to a wedge-shaped area known as the warm sector. The warm air gradually slides above the cold air. We already know that when air rises it cools and forms clouds and precipitation. Thus, the warm and cold fronts in depressions are marked by great swirls of thick rain-bearing clouds (Fig. 3.35). Eventually, the warm air is undercut by the faster-moving cold air and lifted off the ground. It is then called an occluded front.

Anticyclones

In many respects, anticyclones (Fig. 3.34) are the exact opposite of depressions (Table 3.5). Often they bring extreme temperatures. In summer, temperatures may rise into the mid 20s and above, while in winter, cold and frosty weather is common. The most difficult aspect of anticyclonic weather to predict is sunshine. Winter anticyclones may be either clear and bright, or overcast with extensive low cloud and fog. The sun may be hidden behind a cloud blanket for several days. People call such weather 'anticyclonic gloom'.

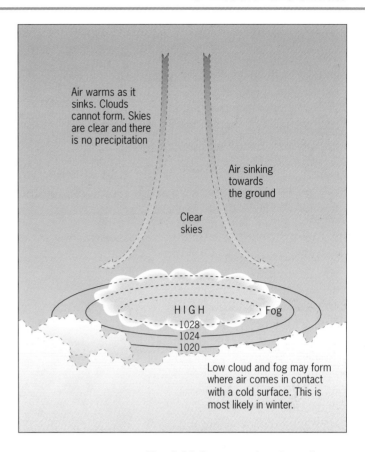

Fig. 3.34 Cross-section through an anticyclone.

Table 3.5 Comparison of depressions and anticyclones

	Depressions	Anticyclones
Pressure	Low	High
Winds	Strong	Light
Wind circulation	Anticlockwise	Clockwise
Precipitation	Steady at the warm front Heavy showers at the cold front	Usually none
Air masses	Two: warm and cold separated by fronts	One: there are no fronts

Table 3.6 The weather pattern in a depression

	As warm front approaches	In the warm sector	As the cold front approaches	Behind the cold front
Temperature				
Pressure				
Wind direction				
Cloud				
Precipitation				

3.10 Satellite images

Since the 1960s, weather forecasters have used satellite images of clouds as well as charts. A number of satellites transmit visible and infra-red images.

◆ Visible images record the Earth's atmosphere and surface as we would see them from space. The more a surface reflects light, the brighter it

EXERCISES

16* Study Figure 3.33. Then copy Table 3.6 and fill it in to describe how temperature, pressure, wind direction, cloud and precipitation change as a depression moves across an area.

17 Study the weather chart in Figure 3.28.

a Name features A and B.

b Name fronts C and D.

c Why are the winds stronger at C than at D?

d Describe the weather conditions in the south and north of the British Isles.

e* Why is it warmer in Ireland than in north-east England?

appears on a visible image. Thus, thick clouds and ice sheets are white, while seas and oceans are black.

- Infra-red images (Fig. 3.35) tell us about the temperature of clouds and the Earth's surface. The darker the surface, the warmer it is. This information is useful to weather forecasters, because it tells them about the height of clouds, and the temperature of land and sea surfaces.

Depressions often form striking images when seen from space (Fig. 3.35). The fronts are picked out by great swirling bands of rain-laden cloud, like a giant catherine-wheel. Behind the fronts, shower clouds have a mottled appearance, with each individual cumulus cloud standing out as a tiny parcel.

Fig. 3.35 (right) A satellite image of a depression, 15.1.95.

Table 3.7 Interpreting visible light and infra-red images

Tone	Visible	Infra-red
Black	Surfaces that absorb light e.g. oceans, seas lakes.	Warm/hot surfaces e.g. tropical oceans, hot deserts.
Grey	Moderately absorptive surfaces e.g. vegetation, crops	Moderate temperatures: low clouds; western Europe in winter.
White	Highly reflective surfaces e.g. snow, ice, thick cloud, deserts.	Cool/cold surfaces: land and sea in high latitudes; high clouds.

3.11 Weather hazards

Tropical cyclones

Tropical cyclone is the name given in South Asia to a violent storm that is generated over a warm tropical ocean. In the Caribbean and USA, the same type of storm is called a hurricane, while in East Asia and South-east Asia, it is known as a typhoon.

Tropical cyclones are more-powerful versions of mid-latitude depressions. They are areas of intense low pressure, around which very strong winds, cloud and heavy rain rotate (Fig. 3.37). Wind speeds commonly exceed 150 km/h and can cause immense damage (Table 3.8). Over the sea, the winds pile up the water into enormous waves, or surges, which often flood low-lying coastal areas.

Cyclones usually develop over the oceans in late summer and early autumn, when the surface water is at its warmest (at least 27°C). At these temperatures, water rapidly evaporates. The rising air cools and, as it condenses, releases huge amounts of heat. This heat provides the energy to power these tropical storms. However, once over a landmass, and deprived of their energy supply, tropical cyclones quickly blow themselves out.

Fig. 3.36 A satellite image of hurricane Andrew over the east coast of the USA.

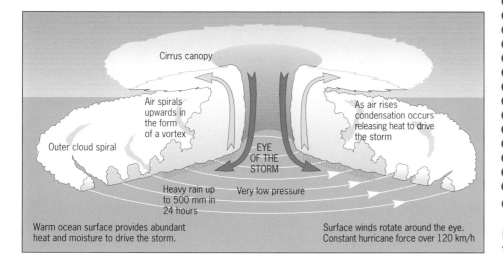

Cirrus canopy

Air spirals upwards in the form of a vortex

As air rises condensation occurs releasing heat to drive the storm

Outer cloud spiral

EYE OF THE STORM

Heavy rain up to 500 mm in 24 hours

Very low pressure

Warm ocean surface provides abundant heat and moisture to drive the storm.

Surface winds rotate around the eye. Constant hurricane force over 120 km/h

Fig. 3.37 Cross-section through a tropical cyclone.

Table 3.8 Major cyclone disasters

Date	Deaths	Location
1780	20 000	West Indies
1881	300 000	East China-Vietnam
1900	6000	Galveston, Texas
1935	800	Florida Keys
1970	450 000	Bangladesh
1990	28	Caribbean, N and S Carolina
1991	125 000	Bangladesh
1992	22	Florida

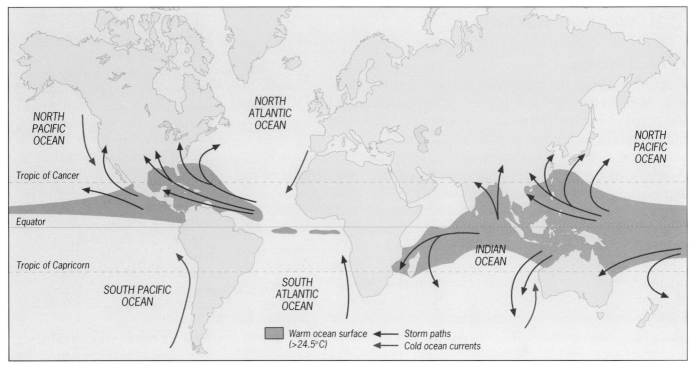

Fig. 3.38 Regions where tropical cyclones develop.

3.12 The 1991 Bangladesh cyclone disaster

FACTFILE

- *Population of Bangladesh: 130 million.*
- *Land area: 144 000 sq km (half the size of the UK).*
- *Population density: 900/sq km – one of the highest in the world.*
- *90 per cent of the population lives in rural areas.*
- *GDP per head: $1290. Bangladesh is one of the poorest LEDCs though its economic position improved significantly in the 1990s.*
- *Most of Bangladesh occupies a* **delta** *formed by the convergence of three great rivers: the Ganges, the Brahmaputra, and the Meghna.*
- *80 per cent of the country is less that 1.5 metres above sea level.*
- *Every year, rivers flood half the country to a depth of 30 centimetres.*
- *Bangladesh is also vulnerable to flooding by tidal surges caused by tropical cyclones in the Bay of Bengal.*

River floods are an annual event in Bangladesh. Although they cause great disruption, their impact is small compared to the disastrous floods caused by tropical cyclones. In 1970, a tropical cyclone and tidal surge killed more than 450 000 people.

A similar disaster occurred in 1991 (Fig. 3.39) when a cyclone hit the south-east coast. A 7m-high tidal wave, whipped up by winds of more than 200 km/h, killed 125 000 people.

Diary of a disaster

30 April, 1991
Survivors in the south-east of Bangladesh are already faced with shortages of food and safe drinking water.

2 May
There is a serious risk of cholera and other diseases. Lack of hygiene, and water supplies contaminated by sewage and dead bodies, spread the fear of epidemics. Famine and starvation are a threat in remote areas without road links. The government is hampered in its relief effort by a lack of helicopters, and appeals for international aid.

6 May
Food shortages are more widespread. Four million survivors face starvation and disease. Lack of food is serious because the cyclone struck just before the harvest, when food reserves were already low.

7 May
The government asks the world community for $1.4bn. $200bn of aid is pledged by Saudi Arabia, the European Community, the United Kingdom, Germany, France, Italy, Canada and Japan.

9 May
The Red Cross and the government step up relief efforts. Diarrhoea and dysentery affect thousands of children in the islands and in the south-east.

"The whole sky turned black and cold winds started to blow. There was such a roar, I thought my eardrums would burst. Somehow I survived the night clinging to a tree. In the morning I returned home to find my father weeping. My brother and sister were dead." (Khairal Amin, survivor of the 1991 cyclone disaster)

The loss of life was only part of the disaster. Crops, livestock, roads, bridges and electricity pylons were also destroyed. Salt water contaminated farmland, and drinking-water supplies were polluted. The Bangladesh government estimated the damage at US$ 1.5bn. The cyclone's main impact was felt along the south-east coast and in remote islands, such as Sandvip and Hatia in the delta, where evacuation was impossible (Fig. 3.40).

> ## EXERCISES
>
> **21** Imagine that you are a journalist covering the Bangladesh cyclone disaster. Write a short article entitled 'countdown to a disaster' explaining the background to the disaster. Suggest what might be done to avoid a similar disaster in future.

Fig. 3.39 After the cyclone.

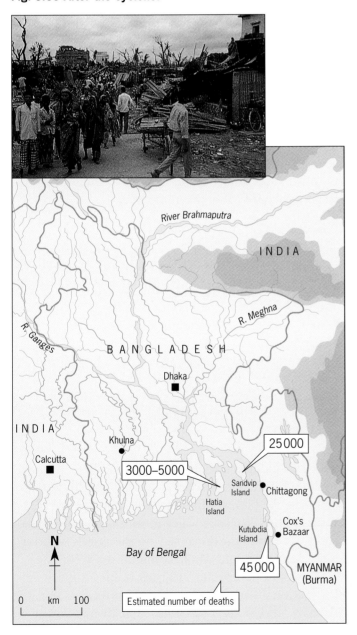

Fig. 3.40 Bangladesh after the flood.

Where natural disasters hit hardest

In 1992, hurricane Andrew devastated the coast of Florida in the USA (Fig. 3.36). It was one of the most powerful storms on record, and yet it killed fewer than 30 people. Why do natural hazards like cyclones hit poor countries so much harder?

The answer is poverty. Two-thirds of the people in Bangladesh live below the World Health Organisation's poverty line, half the rural population does not get enough to eat, and most rural dwellers are landless. Desperate people settle anywhere – even on temporary silt islands that emerge each year after the floods.

Loss of life in the 1991 disaster was high also because of government incompetence. Between 1970 and 1991, only 137 cyclone shelters were built. These saved many lives but thousands of poor people, unable to afford radios, were unaware of the approaching cyclone, and did not look for shelter.

Monpura Island and Rahim Sarkar

Monpura Island appeared suddenly when the Meghna River deposited silt in its shifting channel, and it was quickly settled by farmers. Its fertile soils promised good harvests of rice, string beans and water melons.

Rahim Sarkar is a rice farmer on Monpura Island. Landless, he had settled on the island with his family three years before the 1991 cyclone, after his landlord had driven him out of his smallholding on the mainland. Mr Sarkar had known the risk he was taking. Monpura Island is extremely vulnerable. It lies directly in the path of cyclones, and is barely above sea level. Its remoteness makes evacuation impossible. Mr Sarkar's house was a straw hut built on a raised mud platform, which gave no protection. But along with the 7 million other people who live on this disaster coast, poverty had left him no choice. Tragically, he lost his wife and three children in the disaster.

CASE STUDY

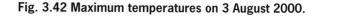

	41°C
	38°C
	35°C
	32°C
	29°C
	27°C
	24°C
	21°C
	18°C

Fig. 3.41 The distribution of wildfires, 3 August 2000.

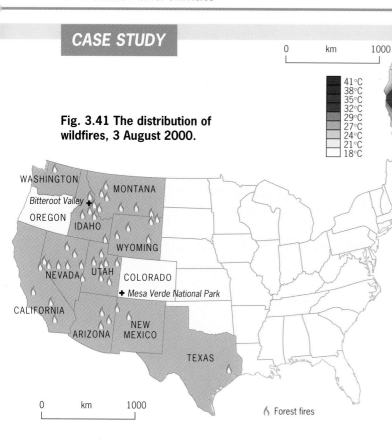

0 km 1000

Fig. 3.42 Maximum temperatures on 3 August 2000.

Fig. 3.43 Firefighting in Colorado USA, June 2000.

3.13 Drought and wildfires in the USA

In the summer of 2000, the western USA was hit by the worst wildfires for more than 50 years. Major fires burned out of control throughout June, July and August, from California and Arizona in the south, to Washington and Montana in the north.

Causes

The fire season in the USA was one of the worst on record because of:

◆ prolonged drought – the rain that fell in Las Vegas on 2 August was the first for 146 days;
◆ high temperatures, often in excess of 38°C;
◆ strong winds.

Most of the fires were natural – sparked by lightning strikes in tinder-dry forest areas – although a significant number were also the result of discarded cigarettes and campground fires.

Impact

By early August, more than 1.75 million hectares of forest had been burned, and 66 major fires continued to blaze out of control. More than 20 000 firefighters struggled to contain the blazes. Montana was the worst affected state. Fifty thousand hectares in the Bitteroot Valley in south-west Montana were blackened. Power lines were brought down leaving thousands without electricity. Fifty homes were destroyed, and whole communities were evacuated. Many feared they would never return to their homes. In Colorado, the Mesa Verde National Park was closed to the public, as fire threatened the historic Anasazi (Indian) cliff dwellings. The overall cost of fire damage to the US economy was estimated to run into billions of dollars.

EXERCISES

22 Study the distribution of wildfires (Fig. 3.41) and maximum daily temperatures in the USA (Fig. 3.42).

a Describe the distribution of wildfires.

b Explain why wildfires and high temperatures have a similar distribution.

c Suggest one possible reason, apart from temperature, that explains the distribution of wildfires.

3.14 Europe under water: the floods of January 1995

Towards the end of January 1995, there were severe floods in many parts of France, Belgium, the Netherlands and the UK. Rivers such as the Rhine and Maas rose to record levels. More than 250 000 people were evacuated when the Rhine threatened to burst through the dykes in the Netherlands (Fig. 3.44), and in Belgium the floods were the worst for 60 years.

The main reason for the floods was the unusually high precipitation between November and January. In the UK, January 1995 was the fifth-wettest month on record. During a normal winter we expect several spells of high pressure. These periods bring dry and quiet weather as the Atlantic storms are kept away from western Europe by the high pressure. In the winter of 1994–5 this didn't happen. Instead, a succession of storms brought heavy rainfall. By the end of January, large areas of the lowlands of western Europe were flooded. There was enormous damage to property and some loss of life.

The Netherlands has evacuated some 100 000 people from Gelderland, the biggest movement of people since the floods of 1953.

Eastern Netherlands
85000 evacuated. Low-lying ground around Nijmegen is declared a no go area. The Rhine at Lobith is nearly 17m above sea level.

River Maas
8000 people evacuated along river.

Namur area, Belgium
300 people evacuated, 6 killed.

Charleville–Mezieres
Red alert as River Meuse rises to above 5m above sea level.

Cologne
Rhine is nearly 10m above sea level, flooding the old town.

Fig. 3.44 Flooding in the Low Countries: January 1995.

So who's to blame, then?

The water is up to the skirting boards, the dishwasher has shorted, the carpets are ruined and you never could afford the extra premiums the insurance company wanted against flooding. Who, if anyone, can be blamed for this fine mess?

How about fingering the usual suspects – governments? Politicians have pursued economic goals with startling ecological illiteracy for years; forests have been razed, watersheds mucked around with, hedges ripped out, ditches filled in and farmers encouraged to take land out of production. Fine, but all this leaves land more or less bare, which in turn means that water runs off hills or saturated earth into rivers faster than ever.

As rivers can't always cope, should we blame civil engineers? Since Victorian times they have argued that water should be drained from catchment areas as efficiently (ie, fast) as possible. Many billions of pounds have been spent raising river banks, canalising, channelling and diking almost everything that flows.

The Rhine alone has had 70 kilometres of meanders and bends straightened out; the Meuse, Waal and Lek proportionately fewer. But this means that these rivers now empty into Holland fuller and faster than ever before. If anything goes wrong, the damage is potentially worse than before. Mathematical models and historical data show that conditions which caused medium-scale floods in Victorian times would cause major floods today.

What about blaming metropolitan authorities? Just because you can't see many rivers or streams in towns doesn't mean they aren't there; in fact, they're mostly encased in concrete and taking more water than they ever used to straight into larger rivers or the sea. The more concrete and tarmac there is, the more rapid water run off there is. It now takes far less time for water to get from one end of the Rhine or the Thames to the other than it used to.

Planners and rural authorities might be kicked too, for allowing developers to build on land that always used to flood and farmers to claim land that rivers needed once a year. From Tewkesbury to Delft, water meadows have been filled in, flood corridors have become prime sites for new roads, and low-lying farmland near towns has been taken over by supermarkets, housing and trading estates.

Fig. 3.45 An article from *The Guardian* 3.2.95.

EXERCISES

23 Although the winter of 1994–5 was exceptionally wet, the floods were not caused just by high rainfall. Read Figure 3.45 and explain how the following made flooding worse: (1) deforestation, (2) straightening the rivers' courses; (3) urbanisation, (4) planners.

3.15 Summary: Weather and climate

KEY SKILLS OPPORTUNITIES
C1.2: Ex. 1b, 2a, 3, 4, 5, 7, 11, 13, 16, 20a, 20b, 22;
C1/2.3: Ex. 16, 21; **C2.2**: Ex. 12a; **N1/2.1**: Ex. 7, 8, 10b, 10c, 15, 17, 18, 20c, 22, 23; **N1/2.2**: Ex. 9a, 10a; **IT 1/2.1**: Ex. 1b;
IT1.2: Ex. 9a, 15b, 19b;
IT2.2: Ex. 1b

Key ideas	Generalisations and detail
Weather is the day-to-day state of the atmosphere.	• Weather in the British Isles and north-west Europe is very variable. In other parts of the world (e.g. around the Equator) the weather is very constant.
Climate Is the long-term (seasonal) pattern of weather.	• The main feature of climate is seasonal change in temperature and precipitation. Outside the tropics, climates have a warm and cold season. Within the tropics, seasonal differences in precipitation (wet and dry seasons) are more significant.
Weather has an important impact on human activities.	• Transport movements are disrupted by snow, ice and fog. Summer droughts affect agriculture and water supplies. Heavy precipitation causes rivers to flood in winter, as happened in The Netherlands in January 1995.
On the global scale, there are broad climate regions corresponding with belts of latitude.	• Latitude is the main influence on temperature. It determines the sun's angle in the sky and the amounts of solar radiation received by a place. From the Equator to the poles, climate changes from equatorial to tropical continental, hot desert, Mediterranean, cool continental/maritime, cold continental and polar.
The British Isles have a mild damp climate.	• The main influences on climate in the British Isles are: latitude, distance from the ocean, the North Atlantic Drift, the prevailing westerlies, altitude and aspect.
The climate of the British Isles has significant regional differences.	• The west is milder and wetter than the east; the south is warmer than the north. Highland Britain is both wetter and colder than Lowland Britain.
Precipitation – the moisture that falls from clouds.	• Precipitation includes rain, drizzle, snow, sleet and hail.
Precipitation occurs In three situations: when air is forced to cross mountains; in depressions along fronts; when air is heated and rises by convection.	• Precipitation in mountainous areas is called relief, or orographic precipitation. It gives high precipitation in British uplands. Frontal precipitation occurs in depressions when air is forced to rise at warm and cold fronts. Most precipitation in the British Isles is frontal. Convectional precipitation follows intense heating of the ground by the sun. It causes showers and thunderstorms and is particularly important in the tropics.
Weather charts provide a daily summary.	• Weather charts summarise temperature, precipitation, cloud cover, wind direction/speed, pressure etc. These charts are essential for making forecasts. They are updated every six hours. The main features on these charts are isobars and fronts.
Depressions and anticyclones dominate Atlantic weather charts.	• Depressions are mid-latitude storms bringing mild, wet, cloudy conditions to north-west Europe. • Anticyclones are areas of high pressure bringing usually dry, settled weather. Temperatures are often extreme (cold in winter, warm in summer) with very variable amounts of sunshine.
Weather forecasters rely increasingly on satellite images.	• Both visible and infra-red images are used. They provide information on cloud patterns and temperature.
Tropical cyclones are violent storms that form over warm oceans.	• Tropical cyclones bring very strong winds and heavy rain. Every year they cause immense loss of life and damage to property in the tropics and sub-tropics.
Tropical cyclones hit poorer countries hardest.	• Hurricane Andrew (Florida 1992) was responsible for 22 deaths. The less-powerful cyclone that struck Bangladesh in 1991 killed 125 000 people. Poverty, lack of early warning, lack of shelters and remoteness mean greater destruction in LEDCs.
Climatic hazards can also have a severe impact on MEDCs.	• The drought in the USA in the first half of 2000 was responsible for the worst forest fires for more than 50 years.

4 Ecosystems

4.1 Introduction

If you look in an atlas of maps showing the global distribution of climate, vegetation and soil, one feature stands out: their similarity. To a geographer, this suggests that these three components are all closely related (Fig. 4.1). The relationships between living things and their environment – **ecosystems** – are the focus of this chapter. We shall illustrate them with reference to one small-scale ecosystem – moorland, and three large-scale ecosystems: the tropical rainforest, the savanna grassland, and the northern coniferous forest (Fig. 4.2). We shall also consider the human impact on these ecosystems, which today is responsible for immense and far-reaching changes.

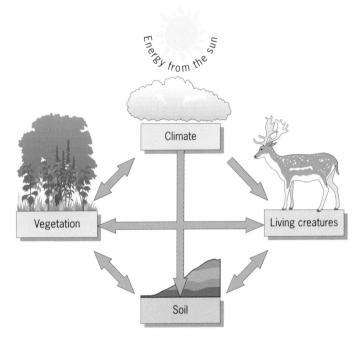

Fig. 4.1 (right) The parts of an ecosystem.

Fig. 4.2 (below) World distribution of forest ecosystems.

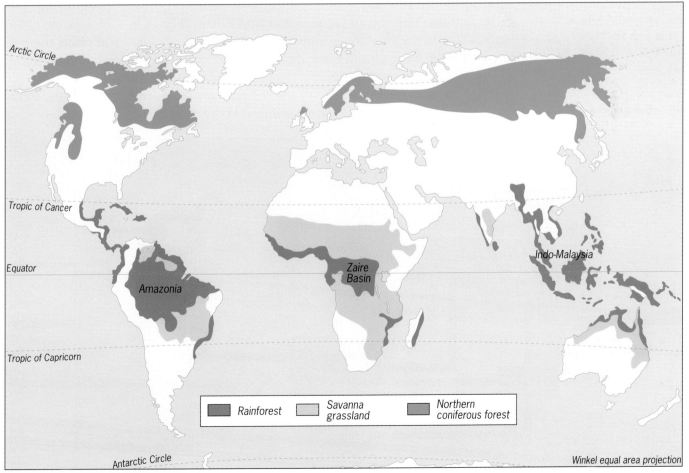

Fig. 4.3 (left) An ecosystem in southern California, USA.

Fig. 4.4 (right) An ecosystem in Yukon, northern Canada.

EXERCISES

1a Study Figures 4.3 and 4.4. Identify the ecosystems shown using Figure 4.6 to help you.
b With reference to Figure 4.6, describe the climatic conditions that give rise to the vegetation in Figures 4.3 and 4.4.

Fig. 4.5 A moorland ecosystem.

4.2 Local ecosystems: moorland

Ecosystems are groups of plants, animals and decomposers, such as fungi and bacteria, and their physical environment. The main feature of an ecosystem is that the various parts depend on each other. Plants, animals and decomposers are linked to each other, and to the physical environment, by complex flows of energy and cycles of matter.

Energy flows

Moorland ecosystems are dominated by herbs, grasses and low-growing shrubs. They are common in highland Britain (Figs. 4.5, 4.7). Like all ecosystems, they are powered by sunlight. The green leaves of plants trap the sun's energy and combine it with CO_2, water and mineral nutrients to make sugars and starches. We call this process photosynthesis. The plants, such as heather and bilberry, are the **primary producers**, and the basic food source for all animals (i.e. consumers) in the ecosystem.

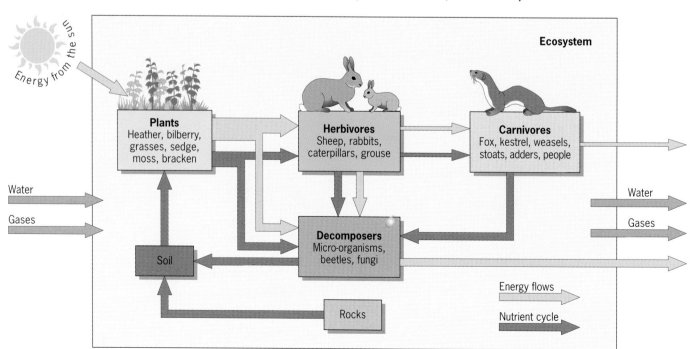

Some animals, e.g. caterpillars and rabbits, are herbivores, which feed directly on the moorland plants. Others, e.g. insect-eating birds and foxes, feed on the herbivores and are known as carnivores. In this way energy is transferred through the ecosystem in a **food chain** or **food web** (Fig. 4.8). At each stage in a food chain, there is less energy available. This is because plants and animals use energy in respiration, and simply in keeping alive.

Nutrient cycles

Ecosystems cycle mineral nutrients, such as phosphorus, potassium and calcium. Most mineral nutrients come from the weathering of rocks. Released into the soil, they are taken up by the roots of plants and are transferred by herbivores and carnivores along food chains. Eventually, most nutrients are returned to the soil when an organism dies. Here, dead plants and animals are broken down by fungi, bacteria and other decomposers. This makes them available for re-cycling. Without decomposers, ecosystems would quickly run out of mineral nutrients.

> **EXERCISES**
>
> **2a** Study Figure 4.8 and name a primary producer and a primary consumer.
> **b** Why are plants so important in food webs and food chains?
> **c*** What is likely to be the difference between the number and size of organisms at different levels along a food chain? Explain your answer.
> **d*** Explain why animals at the end of a food chain are most at risk if the environment changes.

Fig. 4.6 (below left) Relationship between climate and different ecosystems.

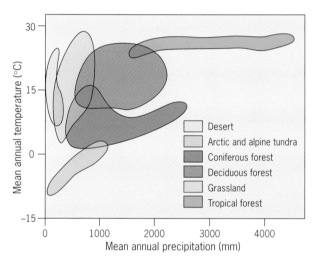

Food webs and nutrient cycles give ecosystems one of their key features: interdependence. What this means is that any change in one component in an ecosystem has a 'knock on' effect, causing change to occur elsewhere. Often, these changes result from human interference. Invariably, their impact is both unpredictable and damaging.

Fig. 4.7 (above right) Heather moor in Swaledale, Yorkshire.

Fig 4.8 (below left) A moorland food web.

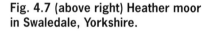

> **EXERCISES**
>
> **3** Study the moorland ecosystem in Figure 4.5.
> **a** How does energy enter the ecosystem?
> **b** How does energy leave the system?
> **c** What is the source of mineral nutrients?
> **d*** Suggest how mineral nutrients could leave the system.

Fig. 4.9 The rainforest canopy, Guatemala.

4.3 Global ecosystems: tropical rainforests

The equatorial lowlands are home to the most productive and most diverse ecosystem on the planet: tropical rainforest. Tall forest trees dominate the rainforest. They absorb and use the sun's energy and control the environment for all other life forms.

FACTFILE

- The rainforest covers nearly 17 million sq km in South America (Amazonia), Africa (Congo Basin) and South-east Asia, (Indo-Malaysia) (Fig. 4.2).
- The trees are evergreen. High temperatures mean that there is no temperature limit to growth, which continues throughout the year.
- Annual rainfall is high, ranging from 1500 to 4000 mm, and temperatures are constant between 25°C and 30°C all year round (Fig. 4.10).
- Temperature and humidity are ideal for plant growth and help to explain the huge **biomass** (mass of living matter) and **biodiversity** (variety of life) of the rainforest.
- Tall trees often have thick, leathery leaves for protection against the intense sunlight.
- Leaves have drip tips to shed moisture quickly after regular downpours.
- Many trees are tall and shallow-rooted, and need the extra support of buttress roots (Fig. 4.14).
- High temperatures and high humidity lead to the rapid breakdown of dead plants and animals. Thus the cycling of nutrients takes place very quickly.

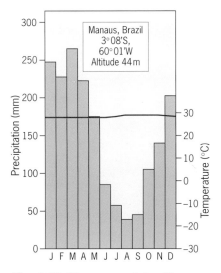

Fig. 4.10 Climate graph for Manaus, Brazil.

Manaus, Brazil
3°08'S,
60°01'W
Altitude 44 m

EXERCISES

4 Explain why temperatures at Manaus (Fig. 4.10) are so constant throughout the year. Use Figure 3.8 to help you.

REMEMBER
The tropical rainforest is the world's most productive terrestrial ecosystem. This is because high temperatures and abundant rainfall allow plants to grow continuously and rapidly.

Fig. 4.11 The structure of a tropical rainforest.

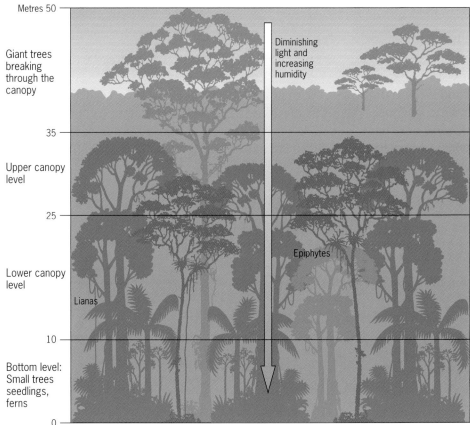

Metres 50

Giant trees breaking through the canopy

Diminishing light and increasing humidity

35

Upper canopy level

25

Epiphytes

Lower canopy level

Lianas

10

Bottom level: Small trees seedlings, ferns

0

Forest layers

Like a city with street-level activities, two- and three-storey apartment buildings and soaring office towers, the rainforest has its own vertical structure (Fig. 4.11).

◆ The top layer is the canopy (Fig. 4.9). Sunlight streaming down on the canopy is converted into plant growth. This food source attracts huge numbers of animals. Epiphytes, lianas and other climbing plants festoon the trees. Many have aerial roots and obtain their nutrients from rainwater.

◆ Beneath the canopy, life is a struggle. The trees cast a dense shade, and ground vegetation is sparse. Saplings may wait for years until a forest giant dies and leaves a gap in the canopy. Then, with a sudden burst of growth, they push towards the light.

◆ Fungi and micro-organisms on the forest floor decompose and recycle the dead organic material. In the warm and humid environment, they are so efficient that there is no thick layer of leaves on the forest floor.

Soils

Soils are a mixture of mineral and organic matter. The typical soils of the rainforest are deep and acidic (Fig. 4.12). Their distinctive red colour comes from iron oxides. These build up in the topmost layers (horizons) of the soil.

Soil fertility

It would seem logical that soils that support a dense vegetation would be highly fertile. In fact the reverse is true. Because the soils are old and have been weathered over long periods, they are low in essential nutrients like phosphate, potash and nitrate. Also, heavy rainfall quickly washes away any nutrients not taken up by the trees.

Poor soils: rich vegetation

With poor soils, how does the rainforest survive? The secret is the rapid nutrient cycle. Dead plant and animal remains that reach the forest floor are quickly broken down, and the nutrients are absorbed immediately by the trees. Thus, nutrients are mainly locked up in the trees, and the soil contains only a limited store. This has a lesson for farming. Destroy the trees and you remove the nutrients from the system, causing permanent cultivation to fail.

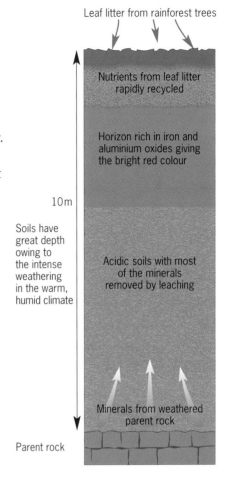

Leaf litter from rainforest trees

Nutrients from leaf litter rapidly recycled

Horizon rich in iron and aluminium oxides giving the bright red colour

10 m

Soils have great depth owing to the intense weathering in the warm, humid climate

Acidic soils with most of the minerals removed by leaching

Minerals from weathered parent rock

Parent rock

Fig. 4.12 Rainforest soil profile.

Fig. 4.13 (below left) The relationship between climate and diversity of vegetation in the northern hemisphere.

Fig. 4.14 (below right) Buttress roots on a rainforest tree.

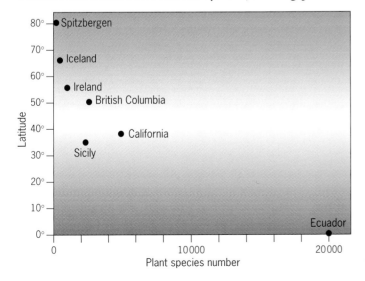

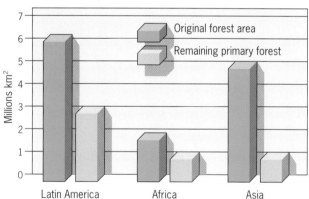

Fig. 4.15 (top) South America from space showing the River Amazon and the area of rainforest.

Fig. 4.16 (above) Destruction of the tropical rainforest.

EXERCISES

Study Figure 4.16.
5a Which continent has the largest area of rainforest?
b Which continent has suffered the most deforestation?
c* Suggest reasons for the differences in rates of deforestation in Latin America, Africa and Asia.

4.4 Amazonia

FACTFILE

- Amazonia is the largest area of rainforest on the planet (Fig. 4.15).
- The rainforest still occupies an area eight times greater than the British Isles.
- Deforestation reduces it by about 15 000 sq km a year.
- On average, one hectare of rainforest supports up to 5000 trees and a mass of living matter (biomass) weighing more than 11 000 tonnes. So large is the forest's biodiversity that scientists believe that nearly 90 per cent of all species are found there.
- The rainforest also influences the climate in Amazonia (Fig. 3.7). The trees act like giant pumps, taking water from the soil, and transpiring it through their leaves. Transpiration through forest trees causes the heavy convectional rainfall.
- Deforestation threatens Amazonia's water cycle and could make the region's climate much drier.

Deforestation: the crisis in Amazonia

The Amazonia rainforest, like those in Africa and Asia, is under threat (Fig. 4.16) because of deforestation. In Brazil, which covers the greatest part of Amazonia, only 60 per cent of the original forest remains. In Bolivia, less than half remains. In total, an area of rainforest nearly twice the size of the British Isles has been destroyed since 1960. What is the cause of this?

The causes of deforestation

Colonization of Amazonia

The main causes of deforestation in Brazil are population pressure and land hunger. Population growth has outstripped the government's ability to provide jobs for the people. Amazonia, with its vast empty spaces and huge timber and mineral resources, seemed to offer a solution to Brazil's economic problems.

Encouraged by the government and a major road-building programme (Figs. 4.18 and 4.19), migrants flooded into Amazonia, increasing its population from 2 million to 20 million between 1960 and 1992. Most of the migrants were peasant farmers who were given small plots of rainforest by the government. The farmers tried to cultivate the land but this proved disastrous. They had to cope with poor soils, soil erosion, disease and insect pests. All this meant that most farmers were forced to abandon their plots after just three or four years of cultivation. Often their land was bought up by commercial cattle ranchers, and the richest ecosystem on Earth was converted into poor grazing land.

Before deforestation

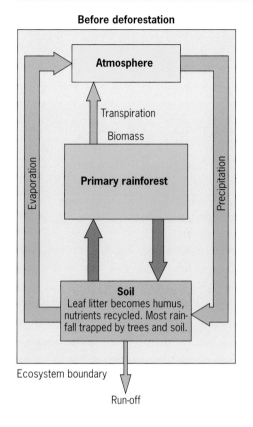

Ecosystem boundary

After deforestation

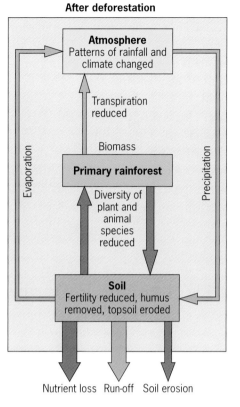

Fig. 4.18 A new road through the Amazon rainforest, Brazil.

Fig. 4.17 (above) The effect of deforestation on the ecosystem of the rainforest.

Fig. 4.19 (below) Roads and mineral reserves in the Brazilian Amazon.

Fig. 4.20 (below inset) Poor grazing land in the Amazon following deforestation.

EXERCISES

6 Study the changes to the rainforest ecosystem after deforestation (Fig. 4.17).
a Describe the changes.
b* Explain the changes.

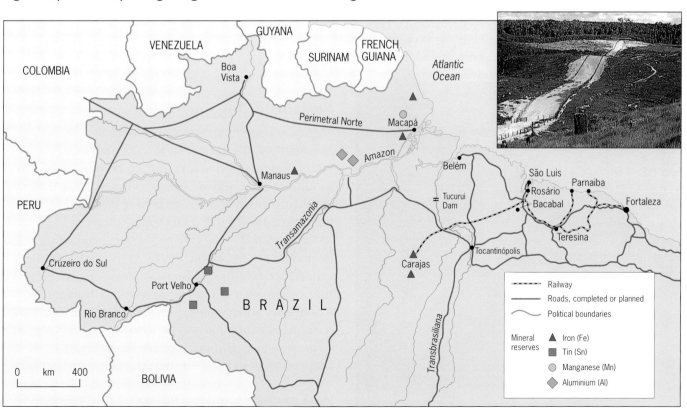

Fig. 4.21 Mining iron ore at Carajas.

Exploitation of minerals and energy

As well as the problem of population growth, Brazil also has a huge foreign debt. In order to pay off its debt, the government developed Amazonia's mineral wealth. Its most ambitious scheme was at Carajas (Fig. 4.19) in central-eastern Amazonia. This area has rich mineral reserves of bauxite, gold, nickel and manganese, as well as the world's largest deposit of iron ore. Ore is sent by rail to the Atlantic coast for export. The development of Carajas, the railway and an iron smelting industry based on charcoal, meant that large areas of forest were destroyed. The harnessing of Amazonia's hydro-electric power (HEP) potential also caused forest destruction. When the huge dam at Tucurui was built to provide HEP for the aluminium smelting industry, thousands of square kilometres of rainforest were flooded.

CASE STUDY

Fig. 4.22 (above) The location of Sarawak.

4.5 Logging in Sarawak: a chainsaw massacre

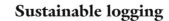

FACTFILE

- *Sarawak is in the north of the island of Borneo in South-east Asia (Fig. 4.22).*
- *It is about the same size as England, but with a population of only 1.5 million.*
- *70 per cent of Sarawak is still covered with primary rainforest.*
- *The timber industry is the biggest employer.*
- *Japan, North Korea and Taiwan are the main customers for its timber.*

Sarawak's rainforest (Fig. 4.23) supports a great diversity of trees. But, on average, there are fewer than six commercially valuable hardwood trees per hectare. For every tree that is extracted, five are badly damaged. Further damage results from road-building and dragging timber along skid trails. Heavy machines churn up the soil, ruining the land and causing erosion, which silts up rivers.

Sustainable logging

Ideally, any logging operation should be sustainable. For example, if a hectare of forest grows one cubic metre of new wood in a year, then no more than this should be harvested annually. Today, Sarawak is felling more than twice as many trees as it should. At this rate, its rainforest will disappear by the year 2020.

If Sarawak's forests are to survive, production must be limited to sustainable levels. At the moment, most exports are raw logs. If Sarawak could process its timber, e.g. into veneers and plywood, its exports would have added value, jobs would be created, and fewer trees would have to be felled. Using helicopters to move logs would help to reduce damage to non-commercial trees, though this is more expensive.

Fig. 4.23 Forest destruction through logging, Sarawak.

Table 4.1 Importers and exporters of tropical hardwood logs in 1998 (% total volume)

Importers Country	% of total volume	Exporters Country	% of total volume
Japan	27.0	Malaysia	49.0
China	20.0	Ivory Coast	14.5
Taiwan	12.5	Brazil	7.0
N. Korea	6.5	Ghana	5.5
India	7.0	Cambodia	5.5
Others	27.0	Others	18.5

EXERCISES

7a Plot the information in Table 4.1 as bar charts, using Excel if possible.
b Write a short paragraph describing the pattern of world trade in tropical hardwoods. (If you have used Excel in 7a, write your paragraph as a word-processed document.)

4.6 The future of the rainforest: conservation or development?

Deforestation raises the important issue of conservation versus economic development. We have seen that deforestation causes serious environmental problems, but equally the tropical forests represent valuable resources for countries in the developing world. Can they afford not to exploit them? Should the rich countries, who are the main importers of tropical hardwoods, give economic aid to the poor countries to help them conserve their forests? The arguments for and against deforestation are set out in Table 4.2.

Table 4.2 The rainforest debate: conservation versus economic development

Environmentalists	Economists
• Permanent cultivation by peasant farmers, or commercial ranching, is not sustainable. Agriculture destroys the forest and its wildlife, and ruins the environment.	• Countries in the economically developing world are poor. They need to develop their resources if standards of living are to improve.
• Scientists estimate that at least a quarter of all pharmaceutical products come from rainforest plants. Many plants have properties that could help to treat human diseases such as cancer. We cannot afford to lose such a valuable resource.	• MEDCs destroyed most of their forests in the process of development. It is hypocritical of these countries to tell the LEDCs that they must conserve theirs.
• The rainforest is a beautiful and diverse natural system. We should preserve it for future generations to enjoy.	• Seventy per cent of CO_2 emissions, which contribute to global warming, come from the burning of oil, coal and gas in MEDCs.
• Rainforest trees play a vital role in the global ecosystem. They absorb carbon dioxide from the atmosphere and release oxygen. The destruction of the rainforests will release more CO_2 into the atmosphere, and reduce the ability of the biosphere to absorb CO_2 by photosynthesis. Deforestation adds to global warming.	• Deforestation in countries like Brazil is partly driven by debts owed to banks and governments in the developed world. If the rich countries want to conserve the rainforests, they should reduce interest payments on debts or even 'forgive' debts.
• Most tropical hardwoods, minerals and beef produced in the rainforests are exported to the developed world. It is the demand for rainforest products in the MEDCs that is helping to cause deforestation.

EXERCISES

8a Read through the arguments in Table 4.2 and work out your own views on the issue of deforestation in the tropics. You will need to consider your own priorities (conservation or development) and beliefs (what you think is true) before arriving at an opinion.
b Would you recommend that countries should either conserve their rainforests, or cut them down for a profit? Write a lively article that might be published in your school magazine.

REMEMBER
The destruction of the tropical rainforest reflects the increase in global interdependence. The demand for hardwoods in MEDCs is the major cause of deforestation in the tropics.

Fig. 4.24 Savannah grassland, Brazil.

4.7 Savanna grassland

FACTFILE

- *The savannas are found between the equatorial rainforests and the hot deserts in Africa, South America and Australia (Fig. 4.2).*
- *Grasses dominate the savanna vegetation (Fig. 4.24) and can grow up to 2 metres high.*
- *Deciduous and evergreen trees, such as acacia and bottle-shaped baobab in Africa, dot the savanna.*
- *The savanna's climate is strongly seasonal with a wet season and a dry season (Fig. 4.25).*
- *Wet season thunderstorms produce torrential downpours; the rest of the year is dry.*
- *Because the savannas lie within the tropics, monthly temperatures rarely fall below 20–25°C.*

EXERCISES

9 Study the climate graph for Dakar, Senegal (Fig. 4.25).
a How long is (1) the wet season (2) the dry season at Dakar?
b In what ways does the savanna share the climatic characteristics of both tropical rainforests and hot deserts?
c* From the length of the wet season, what can you tell about the location of Dakar in relation to the tropical rainforest and hot desert?
d* Explain why August and September are the wettest months at Dakar.

Adaptation of vegetation to climate

Rainfall sets limits to plant growth in the savannas. Hence the productivity of vegetation, even in the wettest areas, is only half that of tropical rainforests. Many plants either die down or remain dormant during the long dry season. Others have a number of drought-resistant features:

- seasonal loss of leaves;
- small, hard leaves to reduce moisture loss;
- thick bark to protect against wildfires.

However, climate is not the only influence on savanna vegetation. Wildfires (caused by lightning strikes) and the deliberate firing of the vegetation by livestock farmers to improve the pasture, favour grasses at the expense of trees. In Africa, grazing animals (e.g. buffalo, antelope, zebra), and browsers (e.g. elephants and giraffe) also contribute to the dominance of grasses.

Soils

Soils in the savannas owe their main characteristics to climate. Seasonal wetting and drying removes silica and causes iron oxides to form a hard concrete layer known as laterite (Fig. 4.26). Over large areas of Africa, savanna soils have only limited potential for farming.

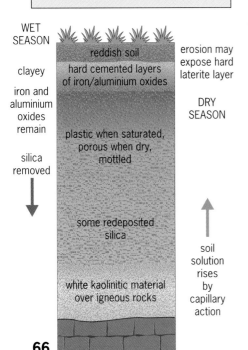

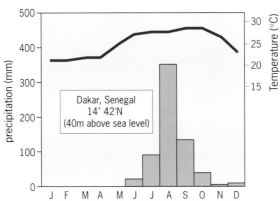

Fig. 4.25 (right) Climate graph for Dakar, Senegal.

Fig. 4.26 (left) Savanna soil profile.

4.8 Farming in the savannas

Farming is the most important human activity in the savannas. In Africa, both peasant cultivation and livestock herding (e.g. cattle and goats) for subsistence are important. However, the vegetation and soil resources for farming are both fragile and limited. A balance between environmental resources and the intensity of use is essential for sustainable agriculture in the savannas.

Farming and sustainability

Farming is sustainable when grazing and cultivation cause no long-term damage to vegetation, soil and water resources. Sustainable farming can be continued indefinitely. But over large areas of African savanna, there is mounting evidence that current farming practices are unsustainable. Rapid population growth is partly to blame. It has led to:

◆ increases in the number of livestock with subsequent overgrazing, permanent damage to vegetation, and soil erosion;

◆ an intensification of farming, which exhausts soil fertility and increases the risk of soil erosion;

◆ an extension of farming into unsuitable areas (e.g. where slopes are steep), which makes soils vulnerable to erosion by run-off;

◆ increases in the demand for firewood for fuel, which has encouraged deforestation.

In the Sahel region of Africa, drought has added to problems of population and poor resource management. The reduction in the natural resources of a region (e.g. soil, vegetation, water), which results from drought and mismanagement, is known as **desertification**. Worldwide, desertification makes 12 million hectares of cultivated land useless every year.

REMEMBER
Desertification rarely leads to full desert conditions. Desertification is part of the wider problem of land degradation, which also includes deforestation, soil erosion, salinisation and a reduction in biodiversity.

4.9 Desertification control: the Louga region of northern Senegal

FACTFILE

• *The mean annual precipitation in the Louga region is 600–800 mm.*

• *The Louga region is located on the northern edge of the savanna, in the Sahel zone, where precipitation is unreliable.*

• *Population grew from 503 000 in 1960 to 1 109 000 in 1998.*

• *Most people are farmers and herders from the two main ethnic groups – the Wolof and the Peulh.*

• *Traditional – and sustainable – cultivation is based on tockeur plots – small fields protected from wind erosion and livestock by hedges of local trees and shrubs.*

• *The tockeur plots grow a diverse range of crops, which help to maintain soil fertility.*

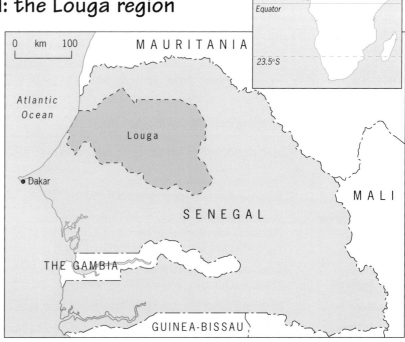

Fig 4.27 Location of the Louga region in Senegal.

Fig 4.28 Desertified landscape in northern Senegal.

The problem of desertification

The Louga region in northern Senegal (Fig. 4.27) suffered extensive desertification following a prolonged drought in 1973. Farmers' incomes declined as cattle died and crop yields fell. The farmers responded by converting their tockeur plots to monocultures of peanuts and millet. Although these crops required less fertiliser, they produced very low returns. Thus, farmers were forced to clear more woodland for cultivation, which in turn led to accelerated soil erosion and desertification (Fig. 4.28).

Restoring sustainable agriculture in Louga

World Vision International, a non-governmental organisation (NGO) began a programme to combat desertification in Louga in 1985. The programme had two main aims. The first was to restore and conserve soil fertility, and the second to achieve sustainable management of the other natural resources, such as water and forestry.

◆ Water: 458 boreholes were drilled providing water to supplement direct rainfall. Water use was monitored to ensure that rates of extraction were sustainable.
◆ Farming methods: the tockeur system was restored. Hedges were replanted to give protection from trampling and wind erosion, and to provide livestock with fodder, so reducing grazing pressure in other areas. Soil fertility was improved by growing a combination of manioc, potatoes and cow peas.
◆ Soil conservation: reafforestation, the introduction of nitrogen-fixing crops such as cow peas, the planting of hedges and the re-establishment of tockeur cultivation have protected soils. Some native tree species (e.g. baobab, ber etc.) have begun to recolonise the region.

The restoration programme has been so successful that cultivation is now possible outside the tockeurs. Many different crops are produced, output has increased, and food security and incomes have improved. The programme drew heavily on the knowledge and skills of local people. It demonstrated how, at fairly low cost, soil, water and timber resources can be managed for sustainable use.

> ### EXERCISES
>
> **10** Draw a flow diagram to show the links between population growth, drought and desertification in Louga.

> ### EXERCISES
>
> **11*** World Vision International's restoration programme did not address the problem of population growth in Louga. Explain how continued population growth in Louga could threaten the sustainability of agriculture in the region in the future.

Table 4.3 Approaches to solving desertification problems.

Soil conservation	Maintain soil fertility and humus content (avoid overcultivation, monoculture), use animal manure on the soil rather than as fuel. Retain soil moisture by mulching. Build terraces on sloping farmland to prevent loss of soil through run-off.
Vegetation cover	Reduce the density of livestock to sustainable levels. Substitute other fuels (e.g. kerosene) for firewood to avoid deforestation. Plant trees and protect from livestock by fencing.
Alternative water sources	Construct wells and boreholes to prevent overcrowding around waterholes, which destroys the vegetation cover. Soil trampling by livestock in these areas also compacts the soil, increasing run-off and soil erosion.
Education	Develop education programmes to increase awareness of desertification and teach skills needed to tackle it.
Family planning	Develop family planning programmes to reduce long-term population growth and restore the balance between population and resources, thus making farming sustainable.

4.10 Northern coniferous forest

North of the temperate deciduous forest lies a huge area of evergreen forest. This is the northern coniferous forest, which stretches in a great belt from Scandinavia, through Siberia and across the Bering Straits into Alaska, Canada and the USA (Fig. 4.2). A few tree species – mainly conifers (trees that bear cones, such as pine, spruce, fir and larch) – dominate the forest. The coniferous forest has not been greatly affected by human activity.

The coniferous forests are the world's main source of softwood timber and wood pulp (Fig.4.29). In Canada and Scandinavia, exports of timber products are high, and forests are largely managed on a sustainable basis.

Fig. 4.29 Forestry work in a coniferous forest.

Climate

The climate in these northerly latitudes is harsh. Continentality (Section 3.7) means that temperatures are below freezing for several months. However, the short summer and low temperatures are offset by long hours of daylight, which extend the growing season. Precipitation is low in the dry continental interiors and mainly falls in the summer.

Forest and climate

Compared to the rainforest, the coniferous forest (Fig. 4.31) has little variety. It contains fewer plant and animal species, and has a much smaller biomass.

In part, this is due to the severe climate. Few species can adapt to the freezing temperatures and short growing season. Some broad-leaved trees, such as birch and aspen, grow in these high latitudes but conifers, such as pine and spruce, are the most successful. Why is this?

Fig. 4.30 Climate graph for Churchill, Manitoba.

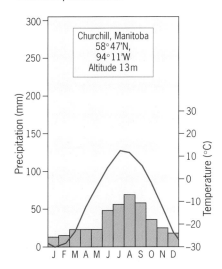

Fig. 4.31 Coniferous forest, Rocky Mountains, Alberta, Canada.

EXERCISES

14a Draw three simple food chains for the coniferous forest with two, three and four levels in the chain.
b Study Figure 4.13 and describe how the number of plant species varies with latitude.
c* Suggest two reasons for this pattern.

EXERCISES

15* Make a table to compare the main features of rainforest, savanna and podsol soils. Compare the soils under the following headings: depth, acidity, nutrient content, nutrient cycle, suitability for farming.

Fig. 4.32 Podsol soil profile.

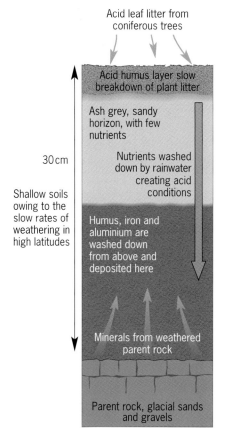

Acid leaf litter from coniferous trees

Acid humus layer slow breakdown of plant litter

Ash grey, sandy horizon, with few nutrients

Nutrients washed down by rainwater creating acid conditions

30 cm

Shallow soils owing to the slow rates of weathering in high latitudes

Humus, iron and aluminium are washed down from above and deposited here

Minerals from weathered parent rock

Parent rock, glacial sands and gravels

Adaptation of forest trees to climate

Most conifers are evergreens, and like rainforest trees retain their leaves all year. Given the severe winters in the coniferous forest, this may surprise you. Yet there is a clear advantage for evergreens. They can begin to grow as soon as air temperatures rise above a daily average of 6°C. This gives them a head start over other species, which use time growing new leaves every spring.

A second adaptation to climate is the conifers' needle-shaped leaves. These leaves have a thick outer skin and not many pores for transpiration. This reduces moisture loss, which is essential because for much of the year water is frozen and is not available to plants. A third adaptation is the conical shape of conifers, which helps them to shed snow easily in winter.

Ground vegetation

Beneath the canopy of forest trees there is a layer of low-growing plants, such as bilberry and cowberry, while lichens and mosses carpet the forest floor. Typical forest herbivores include insects, moose, beaver, squirrels and a variety of seed-eating birds. Carnivores include lynx, wolves, owls, pine martens and bears (which also eat plants).

Soils

The coniferous forest is based on shallow, acidic soils known as **podsols** (Fig. 4.32). These soils are so infertile that cultivation is impossible. Conifer needles contain few nutrients. In the low temperatures they break down slowly and produce an acid humus. Rainwater filtering through the humus becomes highly acidic and washes nutrients from the soil's upper layer. This horizon becomes sandy and bleached. It is a distinctive feature of podsols. Some minerals and humus are deposited beneath this layer. Because podsols are so acid, they contain few earthworms, which would normally mix the soil layers together. As a result, these soils have very well developed and contrasting horizons. Podsol soils are also shallow due to the cold climate, which slows down weathering processes as well as plant growth.

4.11 Caledon: the lost forest

Until the 18th century, large parts of the Highlands of Scotland were covered by a coniferous forest dominated by Scots pine. This was the ancient Caledonian forest: the western edge of the great coniferous forest that stretches across Eurasia. Today, the Highlands are largely treeless. As the forest disappeared, most of the larger forest animals – beaver, moose, lynx, bear, wolf – disappeared too.

Human activity is responsible for the appearance of the Highlands today. Although deforestation has occurred since prehistoric times, the main period of destruction was between about 1400 and 1800. Producing charcoal for iron making, clearing land for farming, and warfare between the English and Scottish, completed the destruction of the forest. Since the 18th century, grazing by sheep and red deer has prevented the forest from regenerating.

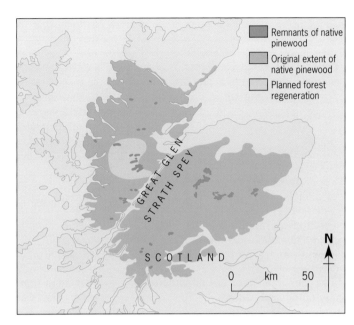

Fig. 4.33 The Caledonian forest.

Fig. 4.34 Scots pines in Strathspey.

Today only a few tiny pockets of original forest survive in the Highlands (Fig. 4.33). However, conservationists plan to re-establish large areas of the old Caledonian forest in the Highlands. Seeds taken from ancient pines (Fig. 4.34) are used to raise saplings, which are planted in specially fenced areas to protect them from deer. Meanwhile, foreign conifers are removed and replaced by native Scots pine and birch. The aim is to create a block of 1500 sq km of natural forest. Once the forest is mature, it may be possible to re-introduce extinct forest animals, including bears and wolves, but this would be controversial.

EXERCISES

16 Imagine a public debate on a proposal to re-afforest 1500 sq km of mountain, moorland and rough pasture, and re-establish the original food web. The following people are represented in the debate: a conservationist, a landowner with shooting rights to deer and grouse, a hill sheep farmer, a representative of the Ramblers' Association, a local hotelier, and a member of the Scottish Tourist Board.

a In your role as one of these people, set out your attitude to the proposal, supporting your view with arguments. Be prepared to speak in a class debate.

b Summarise the viewpoints and arguments of the other interested parties in the debate.

c What is your opinion on the issue? What values and beliefs led you to form this opinion?

4.12 Summary: Ecosystems

KEY SKILLS OPPORTUNITIES
C1.1: Ex. 16a; **C1.2**: Ex. 1b, 2, 3, 5, 6, 9, 12a, 14; **C1/2.3**: Ex. 1a, 13a, 16; **C2.1**: Ex. 16a; **C2.2**: Ex. 11, 16b; **IT1.2**: Ex. 7a; **IT2.3**: Ex. 7b

Key ideas	Generalisations and detail
Ecosystems comprise plants, animals, decomposers and the physical environment.	• The living and non-living parts of ecosystems are linked together by a complex web of relationships. • Ecosystems are powered by sunlight. They have flows of nutrients. • Sunlight is trapped by plant leaves and converted to sugar and starch by photosynthesis. • Energy 'flows' through ecosystems along food chains and food webs.
Ecosystems vary in scale from local to global.	• Moorland is an example of a local ecosystem. The tropical rainforest, savanna grasslands and northern coniferous forest are global ecosystems.
The tropical rainforest is the most productive and most diverse ecosystem.	• The tropical rainforest is found in lowland areas within 10 degrees of the Equator and contains 90 per cent of all living species. • The rainforest climate is warm and humid. These conditions are ideal for plant growth.
The rainforest trees are adapted to the equatorial climate.	• Trees are evergreen (they don't lose their leaves once a year). Some trees have leathery leaves with driptips, and buttress roots.
Rainforest soils have little fertility.	• Forest soils are acidic and contain few nutrients. • The forest is sustained by the rapid cycling of nutrients. • Permanent agriculture is not sustainable in the rainforest.
Exploitation of forest resources is rapidly destroying the rainforest.	• Deforestation is caused by agriculture, settlement, road building, mineral extraction, logging and HEP projects. • Most logging in the rainforest is not sustainable.
There are arguments for and against the destruction of the rainforest.	• Arguments centre on the conflict between environmentalists who want to conserve the rainforest, and economists who want to develop its resources.
Savanna vegetation is adapted to climate.	• Rainfall rather than temperature determines the seasons in the savanna. Plants are adapted to the long dry season. Perennial plants, e.g. trees, are often deciduous, fireproof and have leaves modified to reduce moisture loss.
The recent exploitation of agricultural resources in the savanna has often been unsustainable.	• Overstocking of pastures and overcultivation of arable land (both caused by rapid population growth), and the effects of prolonged drought, have led to widespread land degradation (desertification) in the savannas.
Degraded land in the savannas can be restored to achieve future sustainability.	• Restoration of degraded savannas can be achieved by: afforestation, enclosure of farmland, diversification of crops, drilling of boreholes to increase water security, education of farmers etc.
The coniferous forest is found between the temperate deciduous forest and the Arctic.	• Climatic conditions set severe limits on plant growth in the coniferous forest. • Productivity and biodiversity in this type of forest are low.
Coniferous trees are adapted to the severe continental climate.	• Trees are evergreen and have needle-shaped leaves. • Trees have conical shapes.
The coniferous forest is the world's main source of softwood and pulp.	• Canada, Sweden, Finland, Norway and Russia are the leading exporters of softwood timber and pulp.
Coniferous forest once covered the Highlands of Scotland.	• Attempts are being made to re-establish the ancient Caledonian forest in Scotland using seed from the trees in the remaining fragment of the original forest.

5 Settlement patterns

5.1 Introduction

In this chapter we try to answer basic questions about the location, size, shape and purpose of settlements. We all know a lot about settlements. Whether sprawling cities or neat hamlets, settlements are where we live and where we spend most of our time. Settlements have many different purposes: they are places to work in, places to shop in, places to visit, and for all of us they are simply home. Most settlements have a long history – for instance, it is likely that people have occupied the settlement where you live for many centuries. The past is all around us – a village green laid out in Anglo-Saxon times; a street pattern that was planned in the Middle Ages; a town hall built by the Victorians and so on. Without our realising it, our lives are influenced by settlements that have often been designed to meet the needs of an earlier age.

EXERCISES

1a Study Figure 5.1. Draw a labelled sketch of Whalton to show the following features: buildings, roads, services (e.g. church) and open spaces.
b List the main purposes of Whalton. Give the evidence for each purpose from Fig. 5.1.

Fig. 5.1 An aerial photograph of Whalton, Northumberland.

EXERCISES

2a How old is the settlement in which you live? Find out by looking in a dictionary of place names in your school or local library and at old maps.
b* 'The past is all around us.' How well does this statement describe your journey to school? Your answer should take the form of a short essay.

EXERCISES

3a How does Whalton (Fig. 5.1) compare with the settlement in which you live (size, density of building, layout, range of services)?
b Would you say that Whalton was a rural or urban settlement? Give reasons for your choice.

Fig. 5.2 (right) Settlement types and patterns.

Fig.5.3 (below) A nucleated village.

5.2 Rural and urban settlements

We divide settlements into two basic types – rural and urban (Fig. 5.2). Unfortunately, it is not always easy to distinguish rural from urban settlements. This is partly because there is no one definition of an urban (or rural) place agreed by everyone. For example, some countries measure the population size, some use the proportion of the population working in non-rural activities, and some the density of buildings. Some even use all three measures!

However, we can be sure that settlements whose inhabitants are involved mainly in agriculture are rural. We recognise three types of rural settlement: isolated farms, hamlets and villages.

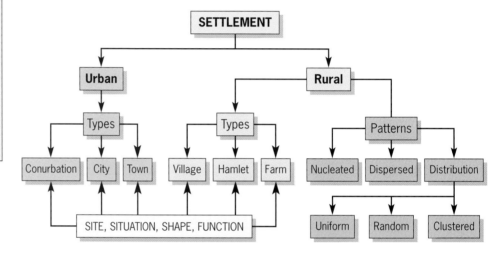

5.3 Rural settlement patterns

The distribution of farms, hamlets and villages in an area is called the **rural settlement pattern**. Here we look at two aspects of rural settlement patterns: nucleation and dispersion, and distribution.

Nucleated and dispersed patterns

The basic unit of all rural settlement patterns is the farm. A farm is an agricultural workshop and tied to the land it uses. In some areas, farms cluster together to form villages and hamlets. This is a **nucleated** settlement pattern (Figs. 5.3, 5.4). Such patterns are widespread in lowland Britain, where:

◆ in the Middle Ages, peasants farmed the land co-operatively;
◆ water is available only in a few places – for example at springs or wells. Because water is so vital, settlements group together at these **wet-point** sites. Good examples of settlements at wet-point sites are the spring-line villages of Abbotsbury and Portesham at the foot of the chalk escarpment in South Dorset (Figs. 5.6, 5.10).

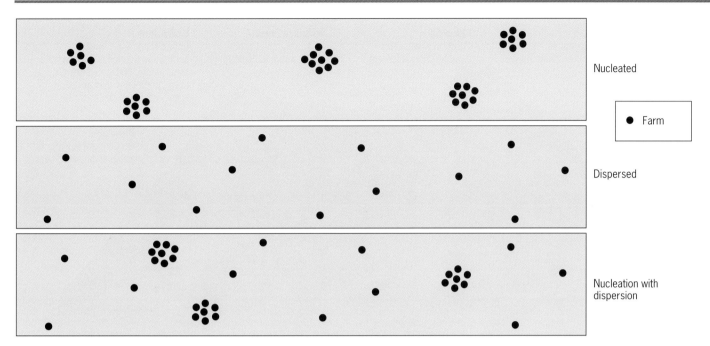

Fig. 5.4 (above) Nucleated and dispersed settlement patterns.

Fig. 5.5 (below) Dispersed settlement:: isolated farms in Upper Teesdale.

In highland Britain, isolated farms are the most common settlement pattern. **Dispersed** settlement patterns are typical of regions where the agricultural land is poor (Fig. 5.5). Here each farm needs a large area of land to be self sufficient. As a result, individual farms are widely scattered and population densities are low. But nucleated and dispersed patterns are the extremes. In reality, most settlement patterns are a mixture of isolated farms, hamlets and villages (Fig. 5.4).

Table 5.1 Causes of nucleation and dispersion

Land quality	In highland Britain, a cold damp climate and poor soils mean that each farm needs a large area to produce enough food. This gives a dispersed pattern.
Social traditions	A long tradition of individual land ownership, as in Cumbria, leads to a dispersed pattern. Communal land ownership in lowland Britain in the Middle Ages produced villages and nucleated settlement patterns. In the 18th century, enclosure of medieval open fields in lowland Britain led to the dispersal of farms from villages into the surrounding fields.
Localised resources	Small 'islands' of dry land in marshy areas (e.g. The Fens or the Somerset Levels) leads to the clustering of farms. Springs and wells in chalk areas, where there are few surface streams, cause nucleation.

Distribution of settlement

The distribution of settlements may be uniform, random or clustered.

◆ A uniform settlement pattern is where settlements are fairly evenly spaced. Usually, this is because there is an even spread of resources for farming or, in some cases, mining. Thus a plain where water and fertile soils are available everywhere is likely to develop a uniform settlement pattern.

◆ In most regions, resources are unevenly distributed, so that settlements are absent in some areas, and concentrated in others. We refer to these patterns as either random or clustered.

REMEMBER
The term 'rural settlement patterns' refers to types of rural settlement and their distribution across an area. It does not refer to an individual settlement, such as a village or hamlet.

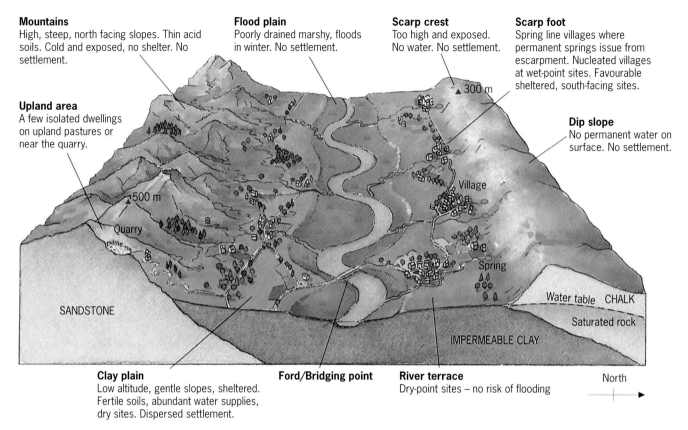

Mountains
High, steep, north facing slopes. Thin acid soils. Cold and exposed, no shelter. No settlement.

Upland area
A few isolated dwellings on upland pastures or near the quarry.

Flood plain
Poorly drained marshy, floods in winter. No settlement.

Scarp crest
Too high and exposed. No water. No settlement.

Scarp foot
Spring line villages where permanent springs issue from escarpment. Nucleated villages at wet-point sites. Favourable sheltered, south-facing sites.

Dip slope
No permanent water on surface. No settlement.

Village

300 m

500 m

Quarry

Spring

Water table   CHALK

Saturated rock

SANDSTONE

IMPERMEABLE CLAY

Clay plain
Low altitude, gentle slopes, sheltered. Fertile soils, abundant water supplies, dry sites. Dispersed settlement.

Ford/Bridging point

River terrace
Dry-point sites – no risk of flooding

North

Fig. 5.6 (above) Factors influencing the sites and distribution of settlement.

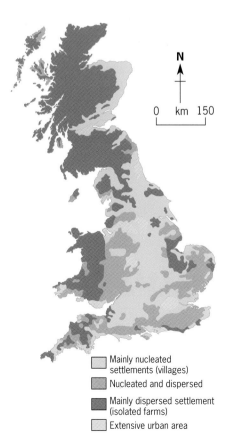

N

0   km   150

☐ Mainly nucleated settlements (villages)

☐ Nucleated and dispersed

☐ Mainly dispersed settlement (isolated farms)

☐ Extensive urban area

5.4 Rural settlement patterns in Britain

We saw in Chapter 2 that the Tees-Exe line divides Britain into two contrasting regions of geology and relief: the Highland Zone to the north and west, and the Lowland Zone to the south and east. Because physical geography has a strong influence on settlements, rural settlement patterns in north and west Britain are very different to those in the south and east (Fig. 5.7).

In the Highland Zone, rural settlement is sparse and widely scattered. Isolated farms and small hamlets are more common than villages (Fig. 5.5). The reasons for this are both physical and economic.

◆ Poor soils and a cool damp climate have led to extensive livestock farming in the uplands (see Chapter 8).

◆ Because of the limited resources, a large area of land is needed to support each family.

◆ There is a long tradition of independence. Farmers owned their own livestock and land, and so there was less need to co-operate and live in villages.

In the lowlands, where there is a warmer, drier climate and more-fertile soils, cultivation is usually more important than livestock farming. This has meant that farming is more intensive (Chapter 8). Land can be cultivated successfully even if farms are clustered in villages. Social factors have also played a part. In the Middle Ages, under the feudal system, peasant farmers did not own their own land, but shared the cultivation of large open fields. This led to a nucleated settlement pattern.

Fig. 5.7 Settlement patterns in Britain.

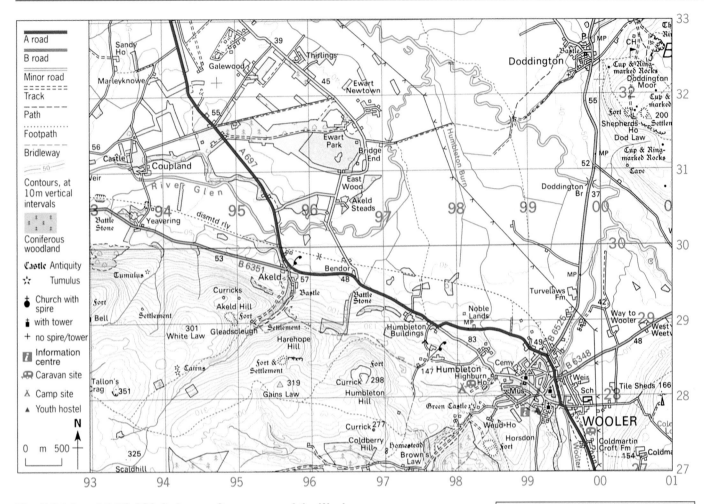

Fig. 5.8 (above) 1:50 000 Ordnance Survey map of the Wooler area.

Fig 5.9 (below) Sketch map of the Wooler area, Northumberland.

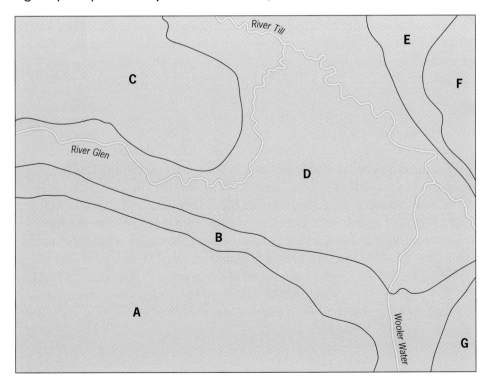

EXERCISES

4 Study Figure 5.8.

a What evidence is there that this area has been settled for hundreds of years?

b Name and give grid references for one of each of the following types of settlement: isolated farm, hamlet, village, market town.

c Copy Figure 5.9. Shade the areas A to G according to their density of settlement. Use the following divisions: fairly densely settled; sparsely settled; little or no settlement.

d Using evidence from Figure 5.8 give two possible reasons for:
• the absence of settlement in (1) areas A, F and G, (2) area D.
• the concentration of settlement in B, C and E.

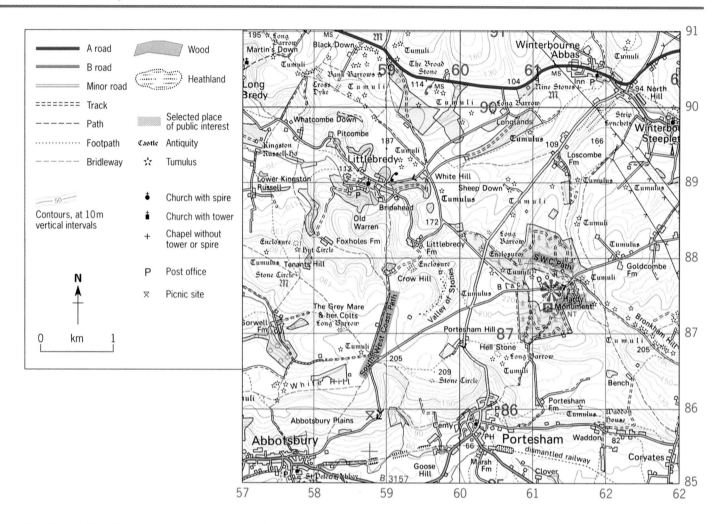

Fig. 5.10 1:50 000 Ordnance Survey map of the Abbotsbury area.

EXERCISES

5 Study Figure 5.10.
a What evidence is there that this area has been settled for hundreds of years?
b Draw a sketch (similar to Fig. 5.9) of the area covered by Figure 5.10. Mark on it the main areas of settlement.
c* Explain for the area covered by the map extract: (1) the distribution and density of settlement; (2) the strongly nucleated pattern of settlement.
d* What other factors (not evident in Figs. 5.8 and 5.10) might explain differences in the settlement patterns of Northumberland and Dorset?

5.5 Setlement location

We have been studying groups of settlements that, on a regional scale, form settlement patterns. In this section we turn our attention to a smaller scale and investigate individual settlements. In particular, we shall look at the characteristics of their site, situation, form (shape) and function.

Site

Site is the land on which a settlement is built (Fig. 5.12). The original choice of location for a settlement was usually determined by the characteristics of the land on which it was built. Most settlements were established by groups of self-sufficient farmers, so that the site had to meet all the basic needs of the community. It had to provide land that was well drained and not at risk from flooding, shelter from storms, a permanent water supply, and arable land for cultivation. A community would also need pasture for livestock, and timber for building and fuel.

In the British Isles most settlements are at least one thousand years old. The fact that they have survived for so long suggests that they were chosen by people who understood their physical environment.

Fig. 5.11 Warkworth, Northumberland, from the air.

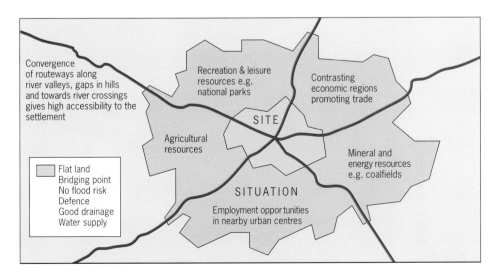

Convergence of routeways along river valleys, gaps in hills and towards river crossings gives high accessibility to the settlement

Recreation & leisure resources e.g. national parks

Contrasting economic regions promoting trade

SITE

Agricultural resources

Mineral and energy resources e.g. coalfields

SITUATION

Employment opportunities in nearby urban centres

Flat land
Bridging point
No flood risk
Defence
Good drainage
Water supply

Fig. 5.12 (left) The site and situation of settlements.

EXERCISES

6 Study Figure 5.11.
a Draw a labelled sketch map to show the main features of Warkworth's site.
b Where was the main defensive weakness in the site of Warkworth? How was this strengthened in the Middle Ages?
7* Using Figure 5.8 write an account of the advantages of Wooler's site.

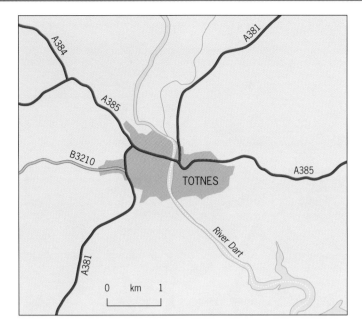

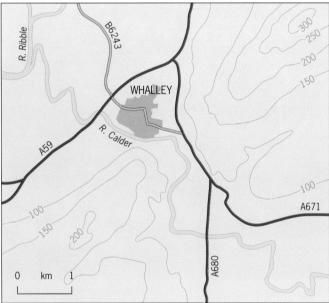

The physical factors that influence site are the same as those affecting settlement patterns (Table 5.2). However, some sites were chosen not just because they provided shelter, fuel, food and water. These sites often had strategic importance. For example, Paris and London controlled river crossings. Others had natural advantages, such as a commanding position raised above the surrounding countryside, or protection from attack given by steep slopes (e.g. Lincoln), river meanders (e.g. Durham) and the sea (e.g. Berwick-upon-Tweed).

Situation

Situation describes the location of a settlement in relation to its surrounding region (Fig. 5.12). For example, a settlement situated between an upland region devoted to livestock farming, and a lowland region specialising in cereal crops might develop as a market centre. Trade between upland and lowland farmers could be conveniently carried out at a midpoint between the two contrasting regions.

Sometimes physical geography is responsible for a favourable situation. Examples include:

◆ the lowest bridging point before a river widens out into its estuary (Fig. 5.13);
◆ the convergence of several valleys;
◆ a gap in a range of hills (Fig. 5.14).

As a result of these physical advantages, transport routes will focus on a settlement, increasing its accessibility (**nodality**) and often making it a hub for trade and industry.

Fig. 5.13 (top) Totnes, at the lowest bridging point on the River Dart.

Fig. 5.14 (above) Whalley, a gap town situated between the Ribble and Calder valleys.

Fig. 5.15 (right) Favourable locations for settlements.

● **REMEMBER**
Site is the immediate area on which a settlement is built. Situation is the wider area, including features that have favoured settlement growth e.g. resources for farming, industry, tourism and trade.

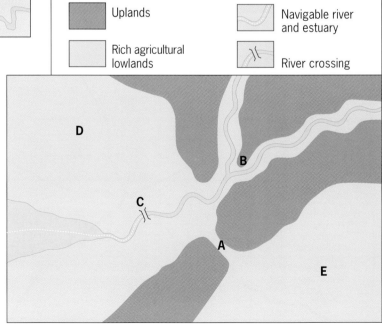

5.6 Settlement shape

What is the shape of the settlement in which you live? Is it linear (ribbon-like), rectangular, circular or even star-shaped? Settlements have all kinds of shapes, and shape tells us a lot about how a settlement has grown.

There are two types of factor that influence the shape of any settlement:
◆ positive factors, such as transport routes and flat land, which encourage growth;
◆ negative factors, such as planning controls and flood-prone valleys, which stop growth.

You can see the influence of some of these on Ordnance Survey maps.

Table 5.2 Explaining settlement shape

Factors	Description
Physical	
Steep slopes	Steep slopes make building difficult and expensive. Unless land is in short supply, building avoids steep slopes.
Flood plains	Rivers spill onto flood plains during times of high flow. Settlements may avoid flood plains altogether, cluster on high points, or ignore the danger of flooding because of the attractions of flat land, accessibility and bridging points e.g. Tewkesbury.
Coastlines	Resorts often have a linear shape as they follow the coastline (e.g. Blackpool). This is because the coastline is an attraction both for tourists and residents. A linear shape maximises access.
Human	
Transport routes	Major roads and railways encourage development owing to the improved access they provide. Infrastructures, including water, gas, electricity and telephone, also follow roads. The effect is to give settlements a linear shape (ribbon development).
Planning policies	Green belts around British cities (Chapter 7) place strict controls on urban growth and may cause an abrupt boundary to the built-up area. Some new towns have been planned from scratch.
Land ownership	Land ownership may prevent urban growth and influence the shape of a settlement e.g. the Town Moor in Newcastle, which is common land, and Central Park in New York, USA.

EXERCISES

8a Describe the advantages of the situation of each location, A to E, in Figure 5.15.
b Suggest reasons why so many roads converge on Wooler (Fig. 5.8). What does this tell you about the settlement's situation?

EXERCISES

9 Figure 5.16 shows the location and extent of two imaginary towns 150 years ago.
a Copy Figure 5.16.
b Assuming that the area of each town has increased five-fold, draw the likely shape of the towns today.
c Add labels to explain the factors that have influenced the shapes of the towns.
10 Study Figure 6.14.
a* Suggest a reason for the abrupt edge to the built-up area on the eastern side.
b* Give a possible reason why only half of grid square 5702 is built-up.
11a Study Table 5.2 and describe and explain the shape of Whalton (Fig. 5.1).
b* Using the evidence of Figure 5.8 and Figure 5.17 draw a labelled sketch map to explain the shape of Wooler.

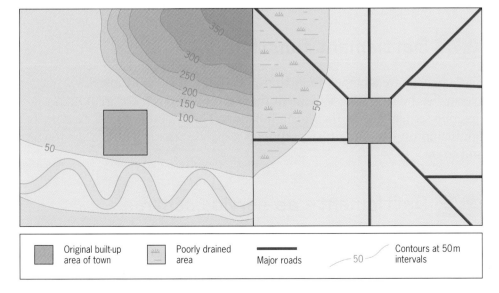

| | Original built-up area of town | | Poorly drained area | ▬▬▬ Major roads | ⌐50⌐ Contours at 50 m intervals |

Fig. 5.16 Influences on settlement growth and shape.

Fig. 5.17 The town of Wooler from the air.

EXERCISES

12a Study Figure 6.14 and make a list of the different functions in Leicester. Sort your list into a table like Table 5.3.
b Make similar tables for Wooler (Fig. 5.8) and Abbotsbury (Fig. 5.10). Write a paragraph to describe how the number of functions varies with settlement size.
c Make a list of functions in Wooler based on Figure 5.17. How does your list compare with the one above (Exercise 12a) based on an Ordnance Survey map?

5.7 Settlement function

Settlements have a range of functions, i.e. things they do (Table 5.3). Normally, the larger the settlement the more functions there are. Often we describe settlements by their main function. Thus Edinburgh is a capital city, Southampton is a port city, Blackpool is a seaside resort, Bath is a spa town, and so on.

5.8 Settlements as service centres

Figure 5.18 shows an idealised settlement pattern. Each settlement is a service centre or **central place**, supplying goods and services to its own population and to people living in its surrounding trade area.

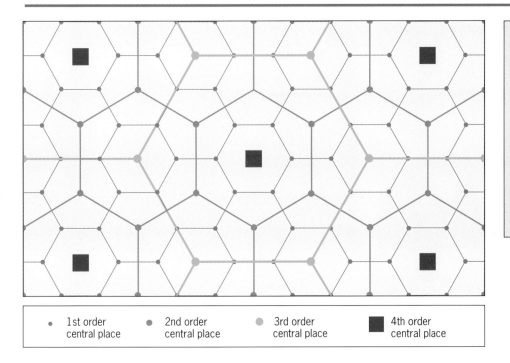

- ● 1st order central place
- ● 2nd order central place
- ● 3rd order central place
- ■ 4th order central place

EXERCISES

13 Study Figure 5.18.
a How many settlements are there of 1st, 2nd, 3rd and 4th orders?
b Describe the main features of the size distribution of the settlements.
c What shape are the trade areas of the central places? What advantage does this shape have over circular trade areas?

Fig 5.18 (above) Idealised patterns of settlement according to central place theory.

Table 5.3 Large urban settlements: functions shown on Ordnance Survey maps

Residential	Housing – house types and ages can be worked out from their location relative to the town centre and by the layout of buildings and street patterns. (Section 6.6)
Industrial	Manufacturing industry – mills, factories, works etc. Sometimes large complexes, such as oil refineries and steelworks, are individually named.
Commercial	Shops, wholesaling, warehousing etc., are found in all large settlements, often concentrated near the town centre. They are not specifically named on maps; new edge-of-town shopping centres are more obvious.
Administrative	County, district, local council offices, courts and prisons are sometimes named. Town halls are marked on 1: 50 000 maps.
Social services	Hospitals, schools, colleges, churches, cemeteries, crematoria, water and sewage works.
Recreational	Golf courses, sports centres, tourist information offices and attractions. Sometimes, theatres and public houses are shown.
Transport	Airports, train and bus stations, ports, ferries, harbours, roads, railways, footpaths, canals.

To create such an orderly pattern of settlement we have to simplify the situation in the real world. In this case we have assumed that the area of settlement is a plain; climate and soils are everywhere the same; the population is evenly distributed; and all areas are equally accessible. We have also assumed that people will travel only to the nearest centre, which can provide them with the goods and services they need. Given these assumptions, a settlement pattern similar to the one in Figure 5.18 should develop.

Hierarchy

As settlement **order** (size) increases, the number of settlements of each order decreases. We call this a settlement **hierarchy**. Why do settlements form hierarchies? To find out we must consider two important ideas: **threshold** and **range**.

Threshold

Each service in a settlement requires a minimum number of customers to make it profitable. This is known as the service's threshold population.

Convenience stores

Some services, such as small food shops, have low thresholds. These shops sell **convenience goods** (or services) (Fig. 5.19). These are goods (or services) that people buy often. They spend a lot of money on them. This means that convenience stores can make a profit by serving just a few hundred people.

Fig. 5.19 (above left) A convenience store in Leicester.

Fig. 5.20 (above right) The village stores, Stamfordham, Northumberland.

Table 5.4 Threshold populations of selected services

Pub	250
Post office	500
General store	500
Hairdresser	750
Chemist	1000
Small supermarket	2500
Garage (filling station)	2500
Video rental	5000
Clothes shop	7500
Shoe shop	7500
Travel agent	10 000
Large supermarket	25 000
Variety store (e.g. M&S)	100 000

EXERCISES

14a Divide the services in Table 5.4 into convenience and comparison types.
b* Assuming that only the limited range of services in Table 5.4 is available in the settlements in Table 5.5, calculate for each settlement:
(1) the number of different services;
(2) the total number of services.
c* How do the number of services, and number of different services, vary in the four settlement types in Table 5.4? Try to explain why they vary.

Comparison stores

Electrical goods stores like Dixons or Comet sell **comparison goods**. People don't buy comparison goods, such as computers and video cameras, very often. Their total spending on these items in a year is likely to be small compared to their spending on food. Thus, a Dixons or a Comet will need a higher threshold population than a food shop. As a result, it will have to locate in a larger settlement.

There are not very many services that can survive on low thresholds. Thus, small settlements like hamlets and villages will support only a few low-order services (Fig. 5.20). But large centres of population can support a wide range and large number of services. In this way, a hierarchy of central places is built up in a region, with lots of small places, fewer medium-sized places, and just a handful of big ones.

Table 5.5 Settlement hierarchies

Settlement order	Population served	Total number of services	Number of different services
1. Hamlet	250	?	?
2. Village	2500	?	?
3. Town	25 000	?	?
4. City	250 000	?	?

Range

The distance people are prepared to travel to buy a particular item or service is known as the range. Range, together with threshold, explains the spacing of service centres in an area. Normally, we expect people to travel only short distances to purchase low-cost items or convenience goods and services that they need frequently. This means that these goods and services must be available locally. Thus, service centres supplying convenience goods and services will be closely spaced. In addition, because convenience goods have low thresholds, the required threshold population can usually be found within a small trade area. This also helps to explain the close spacing of low-order centres.

5.9 Service centres in Dorset

Dorset, in southern England, is a mainly rural county (Fig. 5.21). The central and western areas of the county have few manufacturing industries, and most of the larger settlements, such as Dorchester and Blandford Forum, are market centres.

Table 5.6 Hierarchy of service centres

Order	Number of centres
1	14 (other service centres)
2	?
3	?
4	1 (Weymouth)

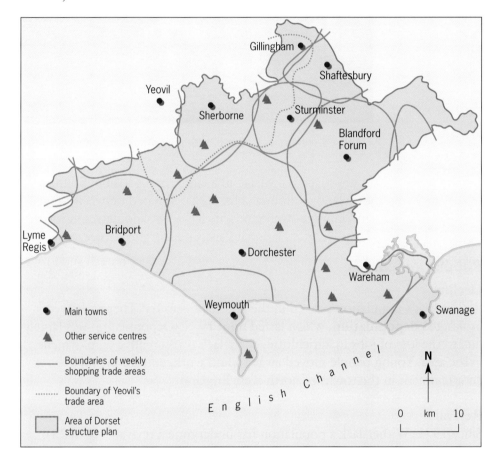

EXERCISES

15 Study Fig. 5.21 and Table 5.6.
a Which settlement in Figure 5.21 is likely to be the highest order service centre? Explain your choice.
b Define your own hierarchy of service centres in Dorset by completing Table 5.6.
c* How does the spacing of the main towns differ from the other service centres in Dorset (Fig. 5.21)? Try to explain why.

Fig. 5.21 Distribution of service centres in Dorset.

EXERCISES

16a* Using the information in Table 5.7 draw a scattergraph, either manually or by using Excel, by plotting the population (y axis) of each centre's trade area against retail floorspace (x axis). Draw in a best-fit trend line.
b* Describe and explain the relationship shown by the graph.
c* From the evidence of your graph, which centre's customers are most poorly served?
d* Figure 5.21 shows that Dorchester's trade area is more extensive than Weymouth's. Using the evidence of Table 5.7 can you suggest why this is unexpected? Try to suggest an explanation.

Table 5.7 Retail floorspace and population of trade areas in the main towns of Dorset.

Main towns	Retail floorspace (sq m)	Trade area population
Blandford	8260	26 164
Bridport	10 860	24 203
Dorchester	16 720	36 556
Gillingham	3810	8405
Lyme Regis	3620	3542
Shaftesbury	5290	10 975
Sherborne	7430	16 162
Sturminster	4180	12 314
Swanage	4920	12 009
Wareham	3250	19 946
Weymouth	18 580	70 988

5.10 Changing functions of settlements: Witherslack, South Lakeland

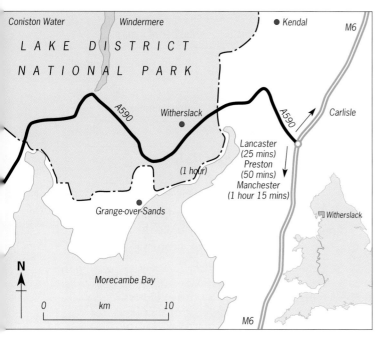

Fig.5.22 The location of Witherslack.

Fig. 5.23 Witherslack village, with post office and general store.

Witherslack is a village in a large rural parish in South Lakeland, Cumbria (Fig. 5.22). Situated between Kendal and Grange-over-Sands, its lies a few kilometres inside the Lake District National Park, and close to Morecambe Bay.

EXERCISES

17 Using the evidence of Figure 5.22 only, suggest reasons why Witherslack is an attractive place to live for (1) retired people and (2) commuters.

Population change

Decline

Witherslack's population peaked in the late 19th century. There followed prolonged **depopulation**, which lasted until 1971. Depopulation was largely due to the loss of jobs in agriculture, and a lack of alternative employment in the area. Young people moved away to find work, education and entertainment in the towns of north-west England.

Revival

Since 1971, Witherslack's population has undergone a revival (Fig. 5.25). Between 1971 and 1991, its population increased by nearly one third. The main reason for this was in-migration: more people moved into the parish than moved out. Most incomers were retired people or commuters to nearby towns, such as Kendal and Lancaster.

Second homes and holiday homes

In 1991, of the 191 households in Witherslack, only 148 were permanently occupied. The rest were mainly second homes, occupied only at weekends and holidays.

Service decline

In the past 50 years, the number of services in Witherslack has declined. Until 1971, this was due to falling demand caused by depopulation. Despite population growth in the last 30 years, Witherslack's services have continued to decline because of:
◆ in-migration of commuters who make use of the services in the towns where they work;

Fig. 5.24 The countryside around Witherslack, looking south-east across the Kent estuary.

- in-migration of retired people who do not require services such as primary schools;
- second-home owners who are not permanent residents and make little use of local services;
- the growth of superstores on the edge of towns such as Kendal.

Table. 5.8 Changing services in Witherslack

Services	Services 2001	Changes in the last 20 years
Retailing	General store and post office • Pub Garden centre • Restaurant	Closure of sweet shop and tobacconist
Church	Parish church	None
Village hall	Village hall	None
Education	Primary school (37 on roll)	Decline in school roll
Mobile services	Library	Withdrawal of mobile butchers, fishmongers
Public transport	None	Village services withdrawn
Health	GP surgery 2 days per week	None

Problems caused by service decline
- People who do not drive or own a car are severely disadvantaged. They must rely on the goodwill of neighbours or use taxis for weekly shopping trips to Kendal.
- Rural life is undermined. Many people are forced to move to the town.

Decline in rural banking and post offices
If rural life is to flourish, basic services have to be available locally. In the late 1990s, several high street banks closed their smaller rural branches. This caused hardship for many rural dwellers who faced lengthy journeys to market towns to use banking services.

Rural post offices are also under threat. By the end of the 1990s, more than 400 rural post offices were closing every year. Post offices provide essential services, such as paying social security benefits (e.g. pensions, child allowance, etc.), and are a focal point for village life. The government's decision to change the method of paying benefits to automatic credit transfer threatens thousands of rural post offices.

Government response
The British government plans to spend hundreds of millions of pounds to save rural post offices. The idea is to modernise the post office service, including e-commerce, one-stop shops for government, and a post office-based bank.

Table 5.9 Lack of services in English parishes

Service	% parishes in England without the service
No GP practices in the parish	83
No pharmacy	80
No schools for 5–8 year olds	51
No general store	72
No post office	43
No petrol station	66

EXERCISES
18 Study the age structure of Witherslack and Cumbria (Fig. 5.26).
a Describe the main differences between the population of Witherslack and Cumbria.
b Suggest reasons for 1) the lower proportion of children and young adults in Witherslack 2) the large proportion of older people in Witherslack.
c* Suggest ways in which the age structure of Witherslack could affect the provision of services in the village.

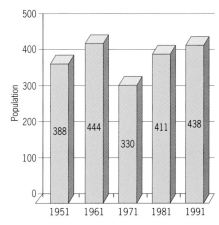

Fig. 5.25 (above) Population change 1951–1991 in Witherslack.

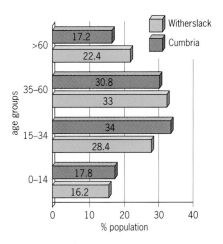

Fig. 5.26 Age structure of population in Witherslack and Cumbria 1991.

5.11 Summary: Settlement patterns

KEY SKILLS OPPORTUNITIES
C1.2: Ex. 1, 2a, 4, 5, 8, 9, 10, 11, 12a, 12c, 13, 15, 17, 18; **C1/2.3**: Ex. 2b, 6, 7, 12b, 18a; **N1/2.1**: Ex. 16b, 16c, 16d; **N1/2.3**: Ex. 14c; **IT1.2**: Ex. 16a

Key ideas	Generalisations and detail
Settlements can be divided into rural and urban types.	• We recognise farms, hamlets and villages as rural: towns and cities as urban. However, there is no clear division between rural and urban types. Population size, employment in non-rural activities, population density and function are all used to distinguish urban from rural settlements.
Rural settlement patterns may be nucleated or dispersed.	• Nucleated patterns are dominated by villages. They are often associated with localised resources e.g. water, and a communal system of agriculture e.g. open field agriculture in medieval Europe. • Dispersed patterns consist of scattered isolated farms and hamlets. They are associated with pastoral farming, poor resources for farming, and a tradition of individuality. • In Britain, nucleated patterns are more common in the Lowland Zone; dispersed patterns are typical of the Highland Zone.
Rural settlement may have uniform, random or clustered distributions.	• Clustered distributions are most common. They result primarily from the influence of physical factors such as relief, climate, soils, water supply etc. These factors can either attract or repel settlement. • Uniform distributions often indicate an even spread of resources e.g. on a lowland plain.
The characteristics of site, situation, shape and function are important features of individual settlements.	• Site refers to the land on which a settlement is built. In the past, sites were chosen to provide resources (e.g. water, soil etc.) that would satisfy the basic needs of farming communities. • Situation is the location of a settlement in relation to the surrounding region. • Settlement shape is influenced by both physical factors (e.g. relief, drainage) and human factors (e.g. roads, planning). • Settlements have a variety of functions, which increase with settlement size. The most important functions are residential, industrial and commercial.
Large settlements are central places or service centres.	• Settlements form hierarchies based on their importance as central places. Large settlements have many functions and serve large trade areas. They support high order functions (comparison goods/services, theatres, hospitals etc.), which require high threshold populations and have a large range.
The functions of many rural settlements are undergoing change	• Car ownership (giving greater mobility) and new retail formats (e.g. edge-of-town superstores) are responsible for the decline of retailing in many market towns. Smaller places, such as villages, are losing shops (also schools, GPs etc.) to larger centres. • There is a general decline of services in rural areas in the British Isles. This decline is due to a reduction in local demand caused by a) depopulation, b) rural commuters, c) retired people and d) second homes.

Witherslack

Lake District mountains

Kent estuary

Fig. 5.27 The landscape around Witherslack, looking north across the Kent estuary.

6 Urbanisation and urban structure

6.1 Introduction

People first began living in urban settlements about 5500 years ago. These early towns and cities emerged in the fertile river valleys of the Tigris and Euphrates in modern Iraq, and the Nile in Egypt. This was no coincidence. A productive local agriculture was essential to create the food surpluses needed to support urban life. In these early examples, agriculture was based on irrigation of the fertile valley soils (Fig. 6.1).

Towns and cities appeared much later in Britain. The first recognisable towns were built by the Romans, and by AD 140 the total urban area in Britain was little more than 10 sq km. Compare this with 2000, when towns and cities covered 28 000 sq km, or 11 per cent of the land area of the UK!

The process of urbanisation

As towns and cities expand, an increasing proportion of the population lives in urban areas. This process, called **urbanisation,** has increased dramatically in the last 200 years. In 1800, only one in ten people in the world were city dwellers, but by 2000 the proportion was almost one in two.

Globally, the spread of urbanisation has been very uneven (Fig. 6.4). The most highly urbanised countries are in the economically developed world. In the UK, more than 90 per cent of the population live in towns and cities. In the poorest countries, the proportion of city dwellers is often less than 30 per cent, although it is rising rapidly. Even so, two out of every three urban dwellers live in the economically developing world today (Fig. 6.2).

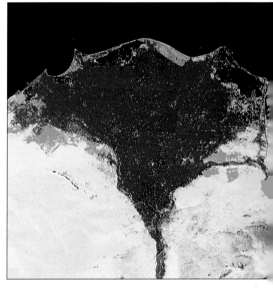

Fig. 6.1 Satellite image of the Nile delta. Irrigated land shown in red.

EXERCISES

Study Figure 6.2.
1a In 2000, the world's population was estimated to be 6100 million. Calculate the percentage that was urban.
b Describe the global distribution of urbanisation in Figure 6.4.
c Describe the main changes to the world's urban population that are likely to occur between 1997 and 2030 (Fig. 6.3).
d Log on to the website www.worldpop.org/prbdata.htm and source the following data on the world population: •total •doubling time •birth rate •death rate.

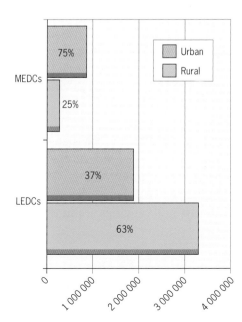

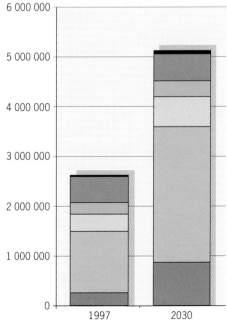

Fig. 6.2 (far left) Urban and rural populations in MEDCs and LEDCs (in thousands) in 1997.

Fig. 6.3 (left) The world's changing urban population, (in thousands), 1997–2030.

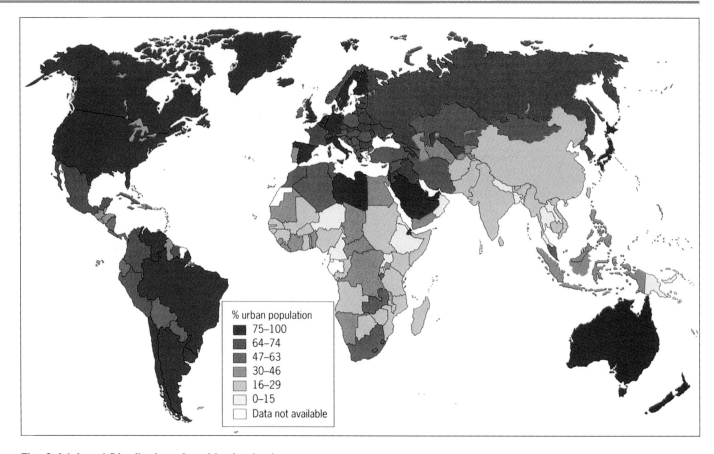

Fig. 6.4 (above) Distribution of world urbanisation.

Fig. 6.5 (below) Growth of the largest cities, 1994–2015

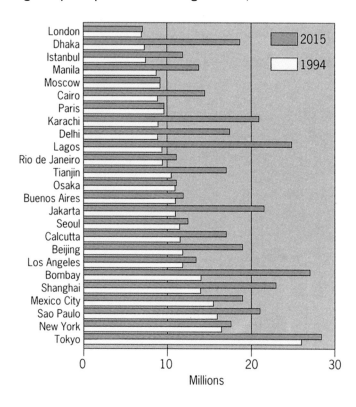

6.2 Urbanisation today

Urbanisation today is largely confined to the economically developing world. In the rich countries of Europe and North America, rapid urbanisation took place in the 19th century linked with industrial development. By the mid-20th century, urbanisation had almost come to an end.

'Million cities'

One of the most striking features of today's urban growth is the increase in the number of large cities with a million or more people (Fig. 6.6). These 'million cities' are overshadowed by the mega cities, such as Tokyo, Mexico City and Shanghai, which contain more than 10 million people. (Fig. 6.5).

In 1950, there were 70 cities with more than one million inhabitants, mostly in the economically developed world. By 1982, the number had grown to 154, and by the end of the century there were an estimated 270. Today, most million cities are in the economically developing world.

The growth of million cities in LEDCs

Many million cities in Africa and Latin America began as administrative centres and ports in former colonies.

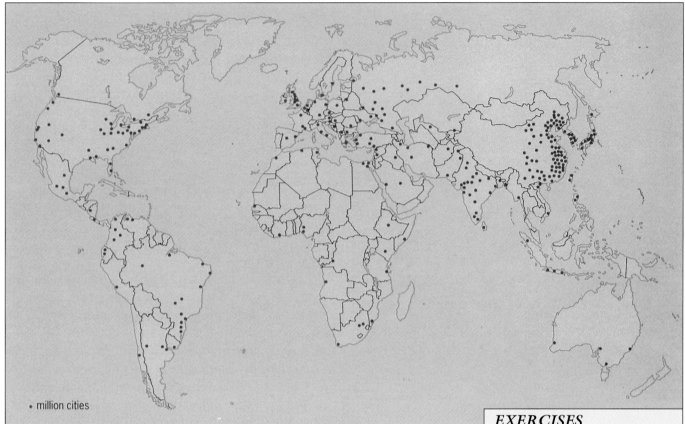

Fig. 6.6 The 'million cities'.

They served as gateway cities, exporting minerals and agricultural products to the 'mother country' and importing manufactured goods. The cities were the means by which colonial powers controlled the colonies and exploited their resources.

Once the colonies had gained independence, these large cities became the obvious place for overseas investment. Large trans-national corporations (TNCs) and foreign banks were attracted to these cities, which, compared to the rest of the country, often had well educated workforces, good roads, a water supply, electricity and so on. Some of these cities became large and wealthy and were important markets for manufactured goods. Foreign investment has created jobs, which in turn has encouraged in-migration and rapid population growth. Some cities have been so successful that they have grown to be several times bigger than their nearest rivals. There is a special name for these cities: **primate** cities.

Table 6.1 Per cent of urban population living in the largest city: South America

as % of urban population		as % of urban population	
Argentina	38.5	Guyana	86.3
Bolivia	24.1	Paraguay	42.7
Brazil	13.3	Peru	40.0
Chile	41.0	Surinam	53.4
Colombia	23.4	Uruguay	46.1
Ecuador	27.1	Venezuela	16.0
French Guiana	40.1		

EXERCISES

2 Study Figure 6.6.
a How many million cities are there in: Europe, North America, Latin America, Africa, Asia and Oceania?
b Draw a pie chart to show the distribution of million cities by continent.
c What proportion of these cities are in the economically developing world?
3 Study Figure 6.5.
a Which was the largest city in the world in 1994?
b Which city will be the largest in 2015?
c Which city is likely to have the largest population increase between 1994 and 2015?
d* Plot the distribution of the world's 25 largest cities (in 1994) on a world map. Comment on their distribution.
e* Compare the growth of mega cities in the developed and developing worlds between 1994 and 2015.

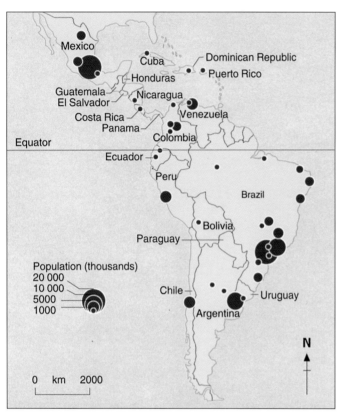

Fig. 6.7 Latin America's largest cities.

6.3 Causes of urbanisation

Migration and natural increase

The population of a town or city can grow in two ways: either through natural increase, where the number of births exceeds the number of deaths, or through **migration** (people moving from one place to another). In practice, urban growth usually combines both processes. About one-third of the urban population increase in Africa and Asia comes from migration. In Latin America, the proportion is somewhat higher – about 60 per cent.

Rural poverty

Why do people move in such large numbers from the countryside into towns and cities? If we take Latin America as being typical, then there is one simple answer: despite the massive urban slums (*favelas*), city dwellers are better off. For example, in Sao Paulo state in Brazil, 15 per cent of the population lives in rural areas, and 26 per cent of the poor are rural dwellers.

Among other things, rural poverty leads to higher infant mortality in the countryside. Poor families cannot feed their children a balanced diet, causing malnutrition. There is also a lack of safe water, fewer medical facilities, and poorer housing, all of which lead to higher infant deaths. Poverty creates the conditions for **rural-urban migration** (the movement of people from the countryside to the towns).

Natural disasters and political unrest

Natural disasters and political unrest also contribute to urbanisation. In Latin America, drought (in areas like north-east Brazil) and floods and hurricanes along the Caribbean coast, have promoted rural-urban migration. Meanwhile, guerrilla and drug wars have given added impetus to population movements in several Latin American countries.

EXERCISES

4a Which countries in Table 6.1 are likely to have primate cities? Use an atlas to find the names of these primate cities.
b Study Figure 6.7
• Refer to an atlas and name the cities with more than 5 million people.
• Describe the distribution of the cities in Figure 6.7.
c What proportion of the cities is located on the coast?

CASE STUDY

6.4 Rural poverty in Ceara

FACTFILE

• *Ceara state in north-east Brazil has a population of nearly 7 million.*
• *It is one of the poorest regions in the country (Fig. 6.8), with a GDP per capita that is 60 per cent less than the national average.*

• *More than one-third of the population lives in the state capital, Fortaleza, and 30 per cent in the countryside.*
• *The region is hot and dry, and land degradation is widespread.*
• *Although poverty is common in the cities, the poor are concentrated more in rural than in urban areas.*

Social conditions

Malnutrition, especially among children, is high in rural areas. In spite of recent improvements, infant mortality rates in Ceara are nearly three times higher than in Sao Paulo, Brazil's largest city. Levels of education and literacy are low throughout the north-east region, with illiteracy highest in rural areas. Lack of education, particularly among women, contributes to high infant mortality. Often children die because mothers lack knowledge of simple child care.

Economic conditions

Agriculture is the main employment in rural areas, and compared to industry its productivity and wages are low. Cotton is a staple crop, but was badly affected by pests in the 1980s and a severe drought in 1993. Irrigation is limited because there are few permanent rivers. One-sixth of Ceara's farmers have no legal title to the land they cultivate. Land ownership is very unequal. On the one hand hundreds of huge estates; on the other thousands of landless peasants.

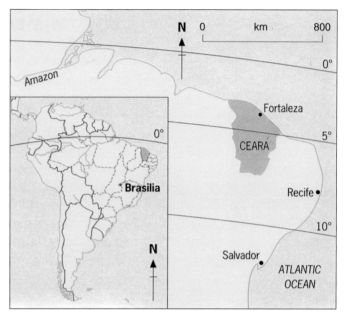

Fig. 6.8 (above) Ceara state in north-east Brazil.

Table 6.2 Ceara: population changes 1980–96 (millions)

	1980	1996
Urban	2.81	4.72
Rural	2.48	2.09

Fig. 6.9 (left) Peasant house, Brazil.

The urban environment

Given conditions in the countryside, it is hardly surprising that Fortaleza attracts large numbers of migrants. Free sites with roads, water and power have been made available for migrants to build their own houses. Industry is growing, with investment from large firms from the south. There are plans for an oil refinery and a new deep-water harbour for the port. Tourism is being developed – beachside hotels and tall apartment blocks are springing up. With just 36 per cent of Ceara's population, Fortaleza generates 78 per cent of the state's GDP. Yet there is also acute poverty in the slums, where one-quarter of the families have no father; one man in three has no regular employment; and about 6000 children work or live on the streets.

EXERCISES

5a Calculate the proportions of urban and rural population in Ceara in 1980 and 1996 (Table 6.2).
b Explain the evidence for urbanisation from the figures in Table 6.2.
c We can divide the reasons for rural-urban migration into push and pull factors. Push factors are the negative reasons, such as poverty, which cause people to leave rural areas. Pull factors are the things that attract people to urban areas, such as jobs and educational opportunities. Read through the case study of Ceara state. Make a list of push and pull factors that might cause rural-urban migration.

6.5 Counter-urbanisation

In the economically developed world, urbanisation has largely ceased. Cities such as London, Paris and New York are unlikely to show much population growth in the future (Fig. 6.5). In richer countries, the balance of migration is now out of the city. Moreover, the people who move out are the better-off ones, leaving behind mainly the poor, unemployed and unskilled. This urban-rural shift is known as counter-urbanisation. It is common throughout the developed world.

CASE STUDY

6.6 Counter-urbanisation in the UK

In the UK, most large urban areas have experienced a decline in their populations since 1971. This decline was most rapid between 1971 and 1981, but it continued throughout the 1980s (Fig. 6.10). The areas losing population are the largest conurbations and cities. For example, between 1981 and 1991, Glasgow's population fell by 15.5 per cent, Liverpool's by 13.5 per cent, and Birmingham's by 7.3 per cent. In contrast, there was rapid population growth in many of the rural counties of southern England: Buckinghamshire grew by 10 per cent; Cambridgeshire by 10.1 per cent; Norfolk by 6.3 per cent, and so on. Even some remote rural counties had a population revival. Thus Powys in central Wales grew by 6.1 per cent and Skye in North-west Scotland by 14.9 per cent.

The reasons for counter-urbanisation are complex. However, the essential causes are growing mobility, wealth, and the technological revolution, which have enabled the better-off to leave the city for small towns, commuter villages and rural areas (Table 6.3).

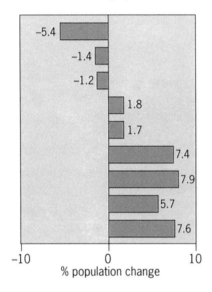

Fig. 6.10 Population change in Britain, 1981–1991.

Table 6.3 Causes of counter-urbanisation in the UK

Retirement	Retired people, with generous occupation pensions, move to the environmentally attractive areas. This accounts for some of the rapid growth in coastal counties in southern England, such as Cornwall, Devon and Dorset.
Commuting	Higher-income workers move out from the city to nearby smaller towns and dormitory villages where the quality of life (environment, education, crime) is seen to be better. Car ownership and motorways allow long-distance commuting. Thus, the population in rural counties close to major cities and conurbations (e.g. Berkshire, Cheshire, North Yorkshire) has grown rapidly. Other workers move even further away and rely on fast train services to commute (e.g. from Lincolnshire to London).
Decentralisation of employment	Many offices have moved out of large towns and cities. Thanks to modern telecommunications (computers, faxes etc.), they can choose market towns, seaside resorts etc. Some employees can work from home using computer technology. There has been a similar rural movement by some industries, and the workforce has followed. Many high-tech firms have preferred locations in rural counties with good access to scenic areas like the Lake District, Scottish Highlands and Norfolk Broads.

6.7 Inside the city

When we look inside cities, our first impression is frequently one of disorder. The layout of buildings, the network of streets and types of land use often seem quite haphazard. However, on closer inspection, order does appear. For example, all cities have a clearly defined core – the **central business district** – dominated by shops and offices (Fig. 6.12). Some areas are devoted exclusively to manufacturing industry. Others are residential, with distinctive housing types reflecting the wealth and social standing of their inhabitants. But do these areas have a spatial pattern? Geographers think so, and they have developed a number of simple models to describe the spatial pattern of cities (Fig. 6.11). However, no one city will exactly fit any model.

REMEMBER
No single city corresponds exactly with the models in Figure 6.11. However, we might expect to find some examples of zones, sectors and areas of land use in most cities.

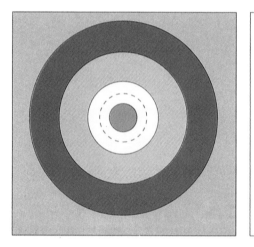

- ▨ Central business district
- ☐ Factory zone
- -- Zone of transition
- ▨ Zone of working men's homes
- ▨ Residential zone
- ▨ Commuter's zone

Zonal model
Land use is arranged in a series of concentric rings or zones around the city centre. The idea is that the city has grown outwards in all directions from its centre, adding new building around the edges. This process is rather like the annular growth rings of trees. It means that the urban fabric should get older towards the centre. The width of the zones varies according to the density of building

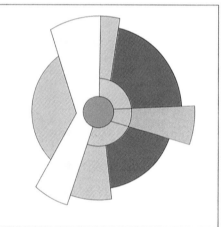

- ▨ Central business district
- ☐ Wholesale light manufacturing
- ▨ Low class residential
- ▨ Medium class residential
- ▨ High class residential

Sector model
Land use is arranged in wedges or sectors which radiate from the city centre. Growth follows a linear pattern along major transport routes or physical features such as river valleys. We assume that once a particular type of land use establishes itself in an area it attracts similar activities (e.g. industry) and repels dissimilar ones (e.g. high status housing).

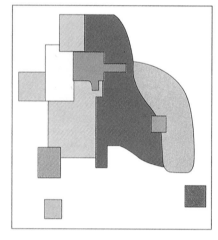

- ▨ Central business district
- ☐ Wholesale light manufacturing
- ▨ Low class residential
- ▨ Medium class residential
- ▨ High class residential
- ▨ Heavy manufacturing
- ▨ Outlying business district
- ▨ Residential suburb
- ▨ Industrial suburb

Nuclei model
Distinctive land uses form small areas or nuclei such as the central business district, housing estates, industrial estates, office and retail parks etc. Often similar activities/types of land use benefit from being clustered together.

Fig. 6.11 Models of city structure.

6.8 How do cities grow?

Transport, more than anything else, influences the size and shape of cities.
- ◆ Before 1850, urban transport was slow and inefficient. People were forced to live close to their work and to services. This resulted in a densely populated city with a circular form.

Fig. 6.12 The central business district, Seattle.

◆ In MEDCs, city size and shape was transformed in the second half of the 19th century. A series of transport improvements freed the better-off from living close to their work place. First there were horse-drawn trams and buses, then suburban railways and finally electric trams. Higher income groups moved out of the city and settled along the transport routes so that they could commute to work. The effect on the city was immediate. It grew outwards, with great ribbons of housing following the lines of transport.

◆ In the late-20th century, this spreading process went even further. With the majority of households owning private cars, houses could be built anywhere provided that there were roads. So the areas between the ribbons were filled in and the city regained the circular form it had lost 150 years before.

CASE STUDY

Table 6.4 Population change in Leicester: 1801-1996

1801	17 000	1931	257 700
1851	60 600	1951	285 200
1871	95 100	1961	288 100
1881	122 400	1971*	284 200
1891	142 100	1981	280 300
1901*	211 600	1991	272 100
1911	227 200	1996	294 800
1921	234 200		

*major boundary changes

EXERCISES

6a Plot the growth of Leicester's population as a line graph, either manually or using Excel.

b Suggest reasons for the rapid growth of Leicester's population in the 19th century.

c What evidence suggests that Leicester is currently affected by counter-urbanisation?

6.9 Leicester

FACTFILE

- *Leicester is a medium-sized British city in the East Midlands.*
- *Its origins go back at least to the first century AD, when the Romans established a settlement there.*
- *In the 11th century, the Normans built a castle on the Roman ruins and by 1086 Leicester had an estimated population of 2000. During the Middle Ages, the town grew steadily as a market centre serving the surrounding agricultural region.*
- *Early industrialisation in the 18th century was based on hosiery and knitting.*
- *The building of the Grand Union canal and railways in the first half of the 19th century led to full-scale industrialisation.*
- *In the 20th century, many new industries developed including light engineering, shoe manufacture, machine tools, printing and electronics.*
- *Leicester remains important as a market centre for surrounding rural areas.*
- *Leicester is the administrative centre for Leicestershire, and also a major university town.*

Land-use patterns

Alongside population growth, there was rapid expansion of Leicester's built-up area. The result was a series of distinctive land-use **zones**, **sectors** and **nuclei** (Fig. 6.13).

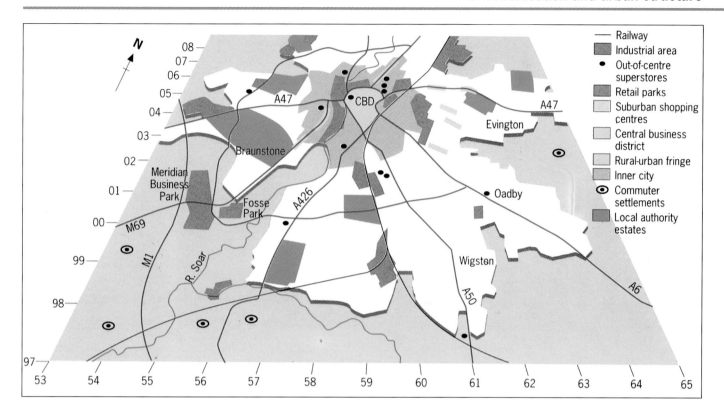

Table 6.5 Land-use patterns in a typical British city

Fig. 6.13 Land use in Leicester.

CBD	The city centre is known as the central business district (CBD). It is a zone of shops, offices and entertainment. There are also important public buildings, such as the town hall and cathedral. Land is scarce and in high demand. Thus multistorey buildings dominate the centre. Traffic and pedestrian flows are higher than in any other part of the city. Branches of national chainstores (e.g. Marks & Spencer, Boots) are found here. The advantage of a central location for shops is the access it gives to the largest number of shoppers. Roads and public transport converge on the centre giving unrivalled accessibility. With a large turnover, these shops can afford the high rents for central sites and thus out-bid other potential land users.
Inner city	In most British industrial cities, rapid population growth between 1850 and 1914 added a distinctive zone to the urban fabric. This zone, consisting of high-density housing interspersed with factories and workshops, is known today as the inner city. Before the development of efficient urban transport systems, people needed to live close to their work. The original 19th-century housing is terraced and is laid out in a simple grid pattern. Since 1960, the worst terraced housing has been replaced by modern terraces and high-rise flats, in a process called **urban renewal**.
Outer suburbs	Housing built since 1914 is generally of lower density and consists mainly of detached and semi-detached dwellings. These houses, either privately or council owned, are more spacious and have gardens. Often the built-up area is interrupted by open spaces, such as parks and school playing fields.
	Many manufacturing, service and distribution firms have located in edge-of-town sites on industrial estates and business parks. The advantages of edge-of-town sites are: better access by goods vehicles along dual-carriageway ring roads and motorways; large, purpose-built single-storey factories with space for production lines and parking; cheaper land. Retailing has also moved out of the centre, with **retail parks** and superstores often lining major routes.
Commuter zone	Many middle- and high-income families have moved out of cities into surrounding villages in the last 50 years. This is part of the counter-urbanisation process. Private car ownership gives people the mobility to commute from settlements, which often lack any public transport services.

EXERCISES

7a With reference to Figure 6.11, construct a simple land-use model for Leicester. Use three simple shapes: zones, sectors and areas.

b* Study Table 6.4 and Figure 6.13. Describe the differences between:
- the population growth in 1851–1911 and 1911–1996 in Leicester;
- the extent of Leicester's inner city and outer suburbs.

c* Account for the differences in timing between the most-rapid growth of population and the most-rapid growth of the built-up area in Leicester.

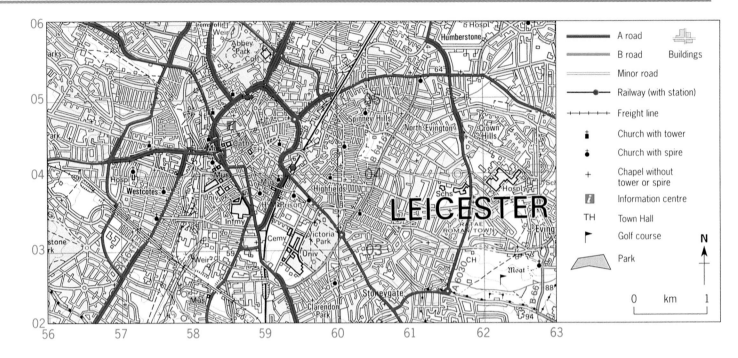

Fig. 6.14 Ordnance Survey 1:50 000 map of Leicester.

Population density

Population distribution is uneven in the city. In Leicester, population densities vary from more than 4000 per sq km in parts of the inner city, to about 300 per sq km in the outer suburbs.

◆ Few people live in the city centre. High rents in this area mean that housing cannot compete with shops and offices for space.

◆ The highest densities are in the inner city, with its cramped terraced housing and high-rise flats. This is the oldest part of the city. Most houses were built more than a century ago when living standards were much lower and people had to live close to their workplace.

◆ In the outer suburbs, densities drop steeply. There is more open space here. Most houses are detached or semi-detached and have large gardens.

Who lives where in the city?

Who lives where in the city depends on four factors: income; family status; ethnic group; and the distribution of housing types.

Income

Better-off people have the widest choice. Usually they opt for larger houses, with the benefits of a pleasant environment and good access to schools, shops and other services. In contrast, poorer people may have little choice but to live in sub-standard housing, where overcrowding, poor services, pollution and crime are often serious problems.

Family status

Family status refers to the composition of households. For instance, a household may consist of a single adult, a couple without children, a couple with young children and so on. Changes in family size are a common reason for people moving house. Usually this happens when a couple have children or when the children grow up and leave home.

Ethnic status

Many Western cities have large ethnic minority groups. Leicester is a good example: nearly one in three of the city's population belong to an ethnic minority group. Most of these people are of Indian origin. They first settled in Leicester in the 1960s and 70s to work in the hosiery and knitting industries. This Asian population is highly concentrated in the inner city (Fig. 6.16). We call this **segregation**, and it is typical of many ethnic minorities in UK cities.

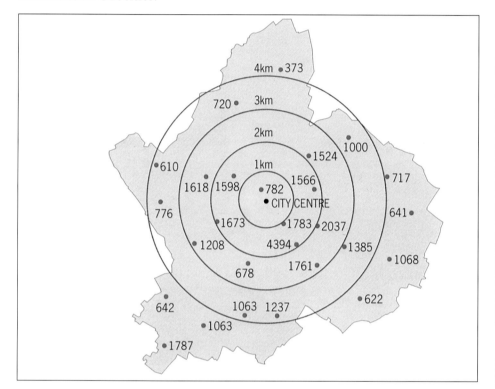

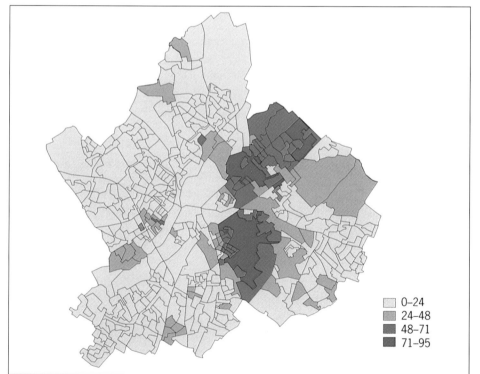

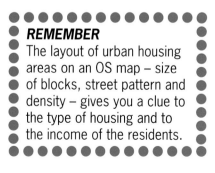

Fig. 6.15 Population density in Leicester, 1991.

Fig. 6.16 Percentage of non-white population in Leicester.

EXERCISES

9a Using the information in Fig.6.15 calculate the average population in the five zones (1 to 5 km). If possible, do your calculation using a spread sheet.
b Plot a line graph to show how the average density for each zone varies with distance from the city centre. If possible, use Excel.
c Describe and explain the density trend shown on your graph. If possible, present this as a word-processed document.
d Draw three smaller graphs to show how the trend line might be modified as a result of the following: urban renewal (slum clearance) in the inner city; **gentrification** (middle-income groups moving into refurbished terraced housing in the inner city); middle-income groups moving into the commuter belt.

REMEMBER
The layout of urban housing areas on an OS map – size of blocks, street pattern and density – gives you a clue to the type of housing and to the income of the residents.

Fig. 6.17 (centre) Who lives where in the city?

Fig. 6.18 (top left) Council estate.

Fig. 6.19 (top centre) Inner city terrace.

Fig. 6.20 (centre right) Detached houses, leafy suburb.

Fig. 6.21 (bottom left) Gentrification – private riverside apartments.

Fig. 6.22 (bottom right) Retirement bungalow.

Table 6.6 Typical families in Leicester

Family income (pa)		Marital status	Age	Ethnicity	Family status
A	£80 000	married	45 & 44	white	2 children (12 & 10)
B	£15 000	married	30 & 30	white	3 children (7, 5 & 2)
C	£10 000	widow	75	white	children left home
D	£50 000	married	32 & 30	white	no children
E	£20 000	married	35 & 34	Asian	3 children (10, 7 & 4)

Ethnic segregation

We can explain ethnic segregation in a number of ways.

◆ Positive reasons: people want to live close to those who share their culture, customs and language, and use local services, such as temples, mosques and ethnic food shops found in these areas.

◆ Negative reasons: many people do not feel safe living within a society that may be hostile to minority groups.

In Leicester and other cities with large Asian minorities, such as Bradford and Wolverhampton, Asians are often attracted to the inner city because of its affordable terrace housing. As a rule, they do not have a tradition of renting housing from the local authority.

EXERCISES

10 Allocate the families in Table 6.6 to the houses in Figures 6.18–22. In each case explain your choice.

6.10 Cities in LEDCs

The simple models of city structure in Fig. 6.11 describe urban land-use patterns in MEDCs. These models are not very helpful when we study cities in LEDCs. Here, history, traditions and economic conditions are very different, and there is a great variety of form. Indeed, the contrasts between cities in India and the Middle East, or Africa and South-east Asia, are just as great as between those in the economically developed and economically developing worlds.

Latin American cities

Latin American cities are examples of just one type of city in the economically developing world. Most large Latin American cities were founded in the 16th and 17th centuries by the Spanish and Portuguese. These cities often have a distinctive structure (Fig. 6.23).

◆ A historic core that was the original colonial settlement. Typically, the core includes a central square with a church or cathedral, office buildings and houses of the rich. The streets have a simple grid pattern. Alongside the historic core is the modern CBD with its shopping malls and multistorey office blocks.

◆ Extensive residential and commercial areas surround the core. They are the result of massive 20th-century urban growth. A spine of commercial land use (shops, restaurants, entertainment etc.) often extends outwards from the core. This spine is an extension of the CBD. The homes of the rich are found nearby, attracted by the services in the commercial spine.

◆ Housing declines in quality and permanence with distance from the city centre. The outermost zone is dominated by huge areas of slums and squatter settlements.

Bogota

Bogota is the capital of Colombia (Fig. 6.25). It is situated on a plateau at 2650 metres, and the Andes mountains rise steeply to the east. Like other large Latin American cities, it has undergone rapid growth this century. Between 1938 and 1997, its population increased from 350 000 to 6 100 000 – a seventeen-fold growth in only 60 years. Growth on this scale can happen only by migration. Migrants come to Bogota from all over the country.

Bogota is a city of contrasts. Its CBD is dominated by office blocks and skyscrapers. A grid-like pattern of streets runs north-south parallel to the mountains. A four-lane freeway leads into the centre and is lined with modern factories and the offices of major trans-national corporations. This

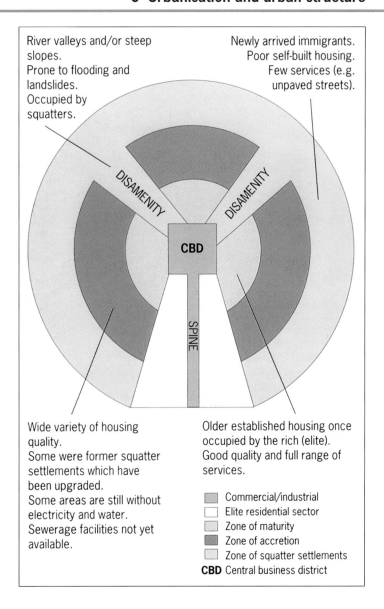

River valleys and/or steep slopes.
Prone to flooding and landslides.
Occupied by squatters.

Newly arrived immigrants.
Poor self-built housing.
Few services (e.g. unpaved streets).

Wide variety of housing quality.
Some were former squatter settlements which have been upgraded.
Some areas are still without electricity and water.
Sewerage facilities not yet available.

Older established housing once occupied by the rich (elite).
Good quality and full range of services.

■ Commercial/industrial
□ Elite residential sector
▨ Zone of maturity
▨ Zone of accretion
▨ Zone of squatter settlements
CBD Central business district

Fig.6.23 (above) Model of the structure of a Latin American city.

Fig. 6.24 (below) Squatter family living beside the railway, Bogota.

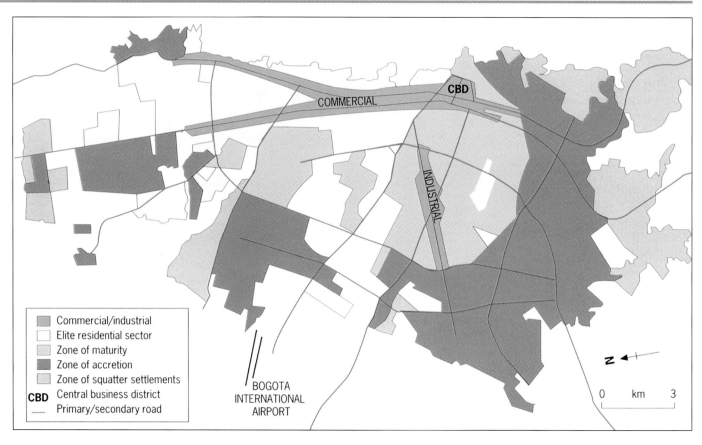

Fig. 6.25 Bogota: land use and housing quality.

11 Study Figures 6.23 and 6.25.

a How does the actual lay-out of Bogota (Fig. 6.25) differ from the model's structure (Fig. 6.23)? Suggest one possible reason for the differences.

b Describe, and suggest possible reasons for, the location of the elite residential areas and the zone of squatter settlements in Bogota.

c* Make a table and list the main differences in the distribution of high- and low-income groups in cities in MEDCs and in Latin America.

part of the city could be New York, Chicago or Los Angeles. The northern suburbs are modern. The residents are well off and have US suburban lifestyles with access to modern shopping malls, McDonald's and Kentucky Fried Chicken restaurants. However, the rich are a tiny minority. Most people are poor, and millions live in self-built housing around the edge of the city without basic services like water, electricity and sewerage.

'The north of Bogota is typical of the way that Latin American cities have managed to create areas of 'modernity' amidst vast surrounding expanses of poverty. Should the visitor move further north or travel to the segregated south of the city, a different world appears. The shops are smaller and offer a more limited range of goods. The housing gradually becomes more rudimentary, revealing the self-help nature of the building process. The plots are laid out in a regular pattern, but every house looks very different. Each family has built what it can afford. One plot has a well constructed two-storey home, the next a rickety shack.'

Alan Gilbert *The Latin American City*

6.11 Summary: Urbanisation and urban structure

KEY SKILLS OPPORTUNITIES

C1.2: Ex. 1a, 3, 4a, 5c, 8a, 10, 11a; **C1/2.3**: Ex. 4b, 5c, 6b, 7b, 7c, 8b, 8c, 11b, 11c; **N1/2.2**: Ex. 1a, 2a, 2b, 2c, 4c, 5a; **N1/2.3**: Ex. 5b; **IT1/2.1**: Ex. 1a, 6a; **IT 1.2**: Ex. 9c; **IT2.2**: Ex. 9a, 9b

Key ideas	Generalisations and detail
Cities first appeared about 5500 years ago	• The first cities were in the Middle East and Egypt. They were supported by food surpluses from irrigation agriculture in fertile river valleys
Urbanisation is an increase in the proportion of people living in towns and cities.	• Urbanisation has increased in the last 200 years. By 2000, nearly half the world's population lived in urban areas. • Rapid urbanisation occurred in Europe and North America in the 19th century. • Today, urbanisation is concentrated in the economically developing world.
Today, urbanisation in the economically developing world is leading to the growth of mega cities.	• Mega cities have populations of 5 million and above. Many of these cities are primate cities and dominate industry, commerce and investment in their respective countries.
Most urban dwellers live in LEDCs.	• Two out of three urban dwellers live in LEDCs. Most of them are poor.
Urbanisation results from natural population increase and rural-urban migration.	• Rural-urban migration is the principal cause of urbanisation. People in the countryside in LEDCs move to towns and cities because they think that living standards are better there.
Counter-urbanisation is an important trend in MEDCs.	• In many MEDCs the number of people living in conurbations and large cities is falling. Better-off people are moving out to the commuter belt and retiring to environmentally attractive areas. A few are moving to remoter rural areas,
Land-use patterns in cities are known as urban structure.	• Most cities have a central business district surrounded by distinctive zones, sectors and areas. There are clear differences in urban structure between cities in MEDCs and those in LEDCs.
In MEDCs, population density generally declines with distance from the centre to the edge of the city.	• Few people live in the CBD in MEDCs. Densities usually peak in the inner city, and then fall steadily towards the edge of the city. • Urban renewal and gentrification have led to an increase in the population of some central areas of cities.
Different social, economic and ethnic groups locate in different parts of the city.	• Different groups become segregated according to income and ethnicity. High-income groups are able to choose areas with most advantages. Low-income groups have little choice and often suffer many disadvantages. Ethnic minorities may cluster together out of choice.

Fig. 6.26 The central business district of Bogota.

7 Urban problems and planning

7.1 Introduction

As cities grow, their demand for space and resources for housing, transport and jobs increases. Often these demands cannot be met immediately and a range of urban problems (Fig. 7.1) such as homelessness, poverty, traffic congestion and air pollution develop.

In this chapter, we shall investigate some of these problems and the attempts of planners to solve them. Most of the urban problems of MEDCs are essentially the same as those of LEDCs. However, their impact is often very different. Whereas in the cities of Europe, North America and Japan these problems may reduce the quality of life of urban dwellers, in the cities of Asia, Africa and Latin America they often concern the very survival of their inhabitants.

7.2 Poverty and social exclusion

Poverty is widespread in cities in the UK and other MEDCs. Many poor people are unemployed, poorly educated, poorly housed, lack basic skills, and have only limited access to services. These people, who because of these disabilities are denied a meaningful place in society, suffer social exclusion.

Poverty and social exclusion are concentrated in two main areas: the inner city and edge-of-town estates.

Fig. 7.1 Urban problems in MEDCs.

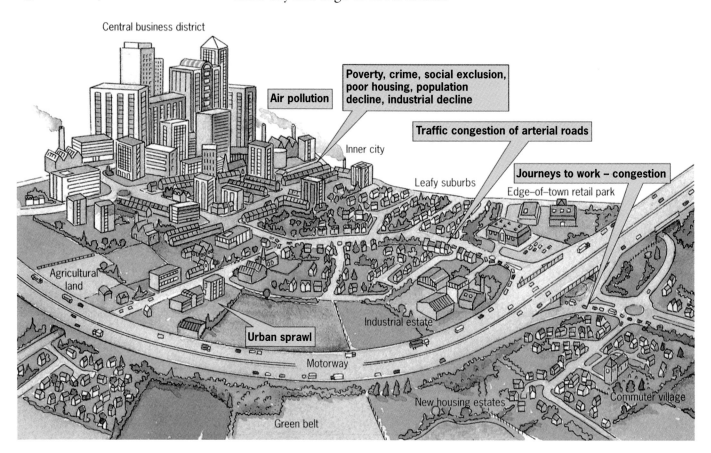

Central business district

Air pollution

Poverty, crime, social exclusion, poor housing, population decline, industrial decline

Traffic congestion of arterial roads

Inner city

Leafy suburbs

Journeys to work – congestion

Edge–of–town retail park

Agricultural land

Industrial estate

Urban sprawl

Motorway

New housing estates

Commuter village

Green belt

Table 7.1 Indicators of poverty in six Leicester wards

	% non-whites	% male unemployment	% families with no car	% council housing	% overcrowding
Belgrave	51.3	22.1	49.7	16.4	6.3
Latimer	70.8	23.9	0.6	21.0	7.5
North Braunstone	2.9	38.3	66.2	77.1	2.9
Saffron	5.3	30.8	51.3	52.2	5.3
Spinney Hill	82.5	31.7	52.6	8.3	12.0
Wycliffe	51.5	34.1	72.4	53.2	6.9
Leicester average	28.5	18.3	5.3	27.1	3.8

EXERCISES

1 Study Figure 7.2 and Table 7.1.

a Describe the distribution of the six poorest wards in Leicester.

b How does inner-city poverty in Leicester differ from that on edge-of-town council estates?

c* Explain how out-migration can lead to concentrations of poverty in inner city areas.

The inner city

In Leicester, as in other British cities, the inner city wards are among the poorest (Table 7.1 and Fig. 7.2). Jobs are hard to find, overcrowding is common, levels of crime and drug abuse are high, and two out of three households cannot afford a car. Over the years, the better-off have moved away, leaving behind an aged population, often on low incomes, and ethnic minority groups.

Edge-of-town estates

Urban poverty is not confined just to the inner city. In UK cities, some of the poorest neighbourhoods are large edge-of-town council estates. Although housing on these estates is often of better quality than in the inner city, unemployment and crime are high (Table 7.1).

Government policy

In 1998, the government introduced its New Deal for Communities programme. It targeted 17 of the most deprived neighbourhoods in the UK. Money was available in these areas for housing improvements, job creation, training and other schemes.

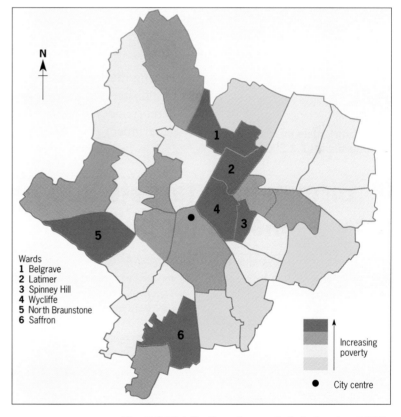

Wards
1 Belgrave
2 Latimer
3 Spinney Hill
4 Wycliffe
5 North Braunstone
6 Saffron

Fig. 7.2 Distribution of poverty in Leicester, 1991.

7.3 Housing – the high-rise solution

In the 1960s and 1970s, many British cities undertook huge **urban renewal** schemes. Vast areas of slums in the inner city were cleared and replaced by multistorey tower blocks (Fig. 7.3). Although these had amenities such as baths and central heating, which the slums lacked, they were soon unpopular with tenants.

◆ Re-housing broke up the tight-knit communities of the inner-city slums.

◆ The tower blocks were poorly built, expensive to heat and suffered from condensation and poor sound insulation.

Fig. 7.3 Multistorey flats at Nechells Green, Birmingham.

EXERCISES

2 Read Figure 7.4.

a Why has Birmingham city council decided to demolish up to 300 tower blocks?

b What type of housing will replace the tower blocks?

c What was the 'driving force' behind the building of tower blocks in the 1960s?

d* Suggest ways in which the residents of tower blocks are likely to have been dissatisfied with the 'quality of their environment'.

- They were unsuitable both for families with young children and for old people.
- Vandalism and crime became increasingly difficult to control.

So bad were the problems, that some local authorities decided it was cheaper to demolish their high-rise blocks and build conventional terrace and semi-detached housing instead (Fig. 7.4). Thus massive tower blocks (e.g. Hulme in Manchester and Hyde Park in Sheffield), which were barely 25 years old, were demolished in the early 1990s.

The large-scale urban renewal of the 1960s and 1970s was very expensive. It was abandoned in the 1980s and replaced by a policy of upgrading older housing – urban renovation. Improvement grants were given to householders. This proved cheaper, more effective and more popular than complete urban renewal.

7.4 Dereliction and urban decay

During the 1960s and 1970s, Britain's inner cities were hit by the decline of industry and other economic activities. As a result, huge areas became derelict and job prospects for inner-city residents were bleak. The government responded with two initiatives: Enterprise Zones (EZs) and Urban Development Corporations (UDCs) (Fig. 7.5).

Fig. 7.4 An article on tower blocks, *The Guardian*, 17.3.2000.

Birmingham targets 300 tower blocks for bulldozer

First they decided to pull down that ultimate symbol of post-war brutalism, the Bullring shopping centre. Now Birmingham city council has taken demolition to its heart by signalling the end of another great Sixties institution – high-rise living.

Faced with a multi-million pound repairs backlog, it is drawing up plans to demolish up to 300 tower blocks – the largest number in any English city – and replace them with more conventional low-rise homes. The council, which is the biggest municipal land-lord in the country, believes it is throwing good money after bad by spending tens of millions propping up the troublesome, system-built blocks, which cost considerably more to maintain than conventional homes. The tower blocks are seen as a financial liability.

Graham Farrant, Birmingham's housing director,says demolition is a popular choice among some tenants, although others still preferred high-rise living. He insists tower blocks fulfilled a need in the 60s. "The name of the game then was to build as many flats in the shortest possible time – the driving forces were speed and efficiency – but now the agenda has changed, and people are more concerned about the quality of their environment."

He added : "Forty years ago, there was a lot of optimism – streets in the sky and all that – but in reality they turned out to be rather different with people complaining of social isolation. They can be very effective if they are well maintained and in the right location. But in the wrong place they can be very unpopular – they can move very quickly form one extreme to the other."

A contrite city council has not been afraid to admit past errors. One town hall report has spoken of the need for a concerted effort to "remedy the mistakes of the past ... moving forward from the concrete jungle." Sixties planning, it concluded, produced a physical environment that did not stand the test of time.

Enterprise Zones

Between 1981 and 1984, the government created 23 EZs. EZs had a 10-year life. They offered incentives to attract new businesses, such as exemption from some taxes, financial assistance and a simplified planning procedure. In the 1990s, a further 10 EZs were created. Most of these were former coal mining areas rather than inner cities.

Urban Development Corporations (UDCs)

UDCs were set up in the early 1980s. They aimed to reclaim derelict land, provide new roads and other infrastructure, and attract new businesses to some of the most run-down areas of the country. UDCs were independent of local councils. They received some government money but were mainly financed by the private sector.

In total, the 13 UDCs reclaimed nearly 3000 hectares of derelict land, created 187 000 jobs and attracted more than £12bn of investment. However, more than half of the investment went to the London Docklands, which included the Canary Wharf development. By 1996, all the UDCs had been wound up.

Partnership schemes

The partnership schemes of the 1990s were a new approach to urban regeneration. Public bodies, such as councils, the police and health authorities, joined forces with businesses and the local community to tackle the problems of poverty, inadequate housing, dereliction and crime within small areas.

City Challenge: Douglas Valley Partnership, Wigan

In 1992, Wigan won a £37.5m share of the government's City Challenge initiative. The Douglas Valley Partnership was formed to carry out the City Challenge programme. Over a five-year period, the partnership attracted £151m from the private sector and £40m of public funds. This money was spent on environmental improvement, education, training, housing, health services and crime prevention. The partnership either created or preserved nearly 11 000 jobs.

Single Regeneration Budget (SRB)

The SRB was established in 1994. Government funding was made available through competitive bidding. The SRB supports local programmes of regeneration. Many are in urban areas that suffer significant deprivation.

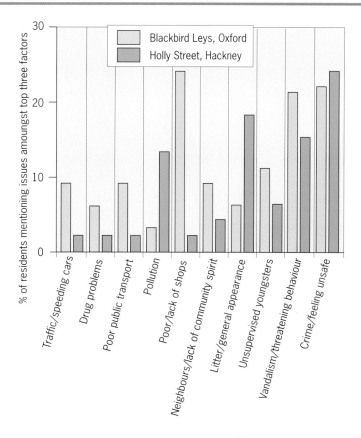

Fig. 7.5 Residents' major dislikes about their estate (1997)

Fig. 7.6 Derelict urban land in England: 1998

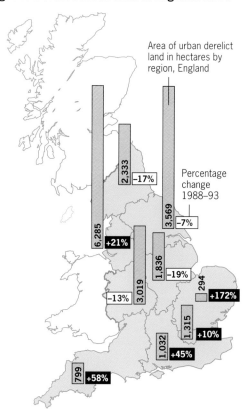

Fig. 7.7 Canary Wharf in London's Docklands.

7.5 Urban sprawl

Every year, 11 000 hectares of rural land in England are swallowed up by building. This loss of countryside to towns and cities is called **urban sprawl**. But the number of people living in towns and cities has hardly changed in the last 20 years. Why is this? There are several explanations.

- There are more households (e.g. young adults leave their parents earlier, couples split up, etc.).
- More people can afford larger houses, which take up more space, and there has been a boom in second homes.
- Businesses have followed people to new sites in the suburbs. Here, on the edge of the city, farmland has been converted to shopping centres, office parks, industrial estates and new roads.

The fight against urban sprawl

In the UK, planners decided that **green belts** were the best way to stop urban sprawl. Green belts are areas of rural land around conurbations and large cities (Fig. 7.9). Within these green areas, strict planning controls operate to prevent urban growth. As well as stopping urban sprawl, green belts provide countryside for recreation and leisure for urban dwellers.

In the last 60 years, green belts have been effective in slowing urban sprawl, but they have a number of disadvantages:

- They protect poor soils and land of little scenic value from development, while higher-quality land beyond the green belt, which is not protected, becomes urbanised.
- Those who gain most from green belts tend to be the higher-income groups who can afford to live on the edge of the city. Poorer people, living in the inner city, and often without cars, may derive few benefits from green belts.
- Green belts cannot stop a city from expanding. They simply interrupt its growth, which continues beyond the green belt.

Because of these disadvantages, many European countries have used a different approach. For example, in Copenhagen in Denmark, planners have opted for **green wedges** (Fig. 7.10). These wedges radiate from the city centre and are separated by corridors of growth. They give everyone equal access to green areas, and at the same time allow for controlled expansion of the city.

7.6 Planning for urban growth: new towns

We have seen that green belts do not stop cities from growing. Therefore, to protect the green belts, there needs to be provision for transferring the growth elsewhere. In the UK, overspill (surplus) population from large urban areas has been moved to purpose-built new towns sited beyond the green belt.

New towns in south-east England

Up until 1939, London's growing population was housed in estates on the edge of the city. This led to urban sprawl. By 1945, there was a serious housing problem in the capital.

Fig. 7.8 Derelict land in the Don Valley, Sheffield.

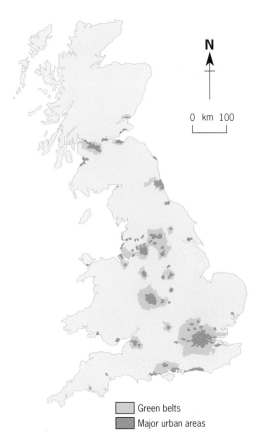

N

0 km 100

Green belts
Major urban areas

Fig. 7.9 Green belts in Britain.

◆ Many houses were slums
◆ There were acute housing shortages caused by bombing and the lack of building during the war. About one million people needed re-housing in 1945.

A radical plan was proposed to solve the problem. A green belt, on average eight kilometres wide, was thrown around the capital. Meanwhile, the overspill population was moved to eight new towns and to several expanded country towns outside the green belt (Fig. 7.12). The new towns were to be self-contained communities with their own employment, rather than commuter settlements for London. They had populations between 30 000 and 60 000, and were built from scratch on **greenfield sites** (farmland). Similar plans were adopted around most of the other conurbations in the UK.

By the mid-1960s, the situation had changed. The population of the south-east of England had grown more rapidly than expected. It was forecast that population growth would continue into the 1980s, adding an extra 3.5 million people. Thus, in 1964, a further three new towns were planned. They were located well outside London's commuter range and were bigger than the original eight new towns. Milton Keynes was built on a greenfield site, but Northampton and Peterborough were built on to existing centres.

Sustainable urban growth

Government forecasts suggest that an extra 4.4 million new homes will be needed in the UK between 1998 and 2016 (Fig. 7.11). This increase is not due to population growth, but to a dramatic rise in the number of households due to:
◆ marriage breakdown;
◆ old people living longer;
◆ single people wanting homes of their own.

Developers would prefer to build new homes on greenfield sites. But this would lead to further urban sprawl. The destruction of the countryside is both unacceptable and unsustainable. Moreover, urban sprawl means longer journeys to work by car, more pollution and more traffic congestion.

A return to urban living

Sustainable urban growth is possible only if more people return to live in cities. In some countries, such as France and Germany, people live in city centres at far higher densities than in the UK.

REMEMBER
Urban sprawl destroys the countryside and is therefore an example of unsustainable growth. Urban growth is sustainable only if it takes place on brownfield sites.

Counter-urbanisation creates many problems, including urban sprawl, long journeys to work, congestion and pollution. As a result, many governments are encouraging re-urbanisation and a return to urban living.

EXERCISES
3a Describe the disadvantages of green belts.
b Explain the advantages of green wedges as an alternative to green belts.

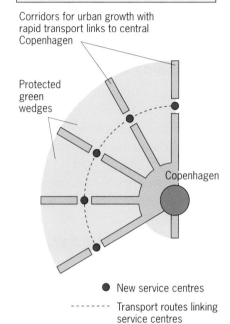

Corridors for urban growth with rapid transport links to central Copenhagen

Protected green wedges

Copenhagen

● New service centres
------- Transport routes linking service centres

Fig. 7.10 (above) Green wedges plan for Copenhagen

Fig. 7.11 (below) Government forecast of new homes

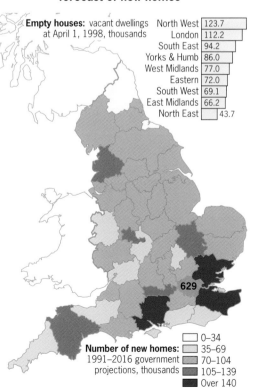

Empty houses: vacant dwellings at April 1, 1998, thousands

North West	123.7
London	112.2
South East	94.2
Yorks & Humb	86.0
West Midlands	77.0
Eastern	72.0
South West	69.1
East Midlands	66.2
North East	43.7

629

Number of new homes: 1991–2016 government projections, thousands
☐ 0–34
☐ 35–69
☐ 70–104
☐ 105–139
■ Over 140

Large resident populations in and around city centres support services such as restaurants, bars and clubs, which make the city centre an attractive place to live.

In the UK, the central areas of some cities, e.g. Newcastle and Leeds, are becoming fashionable places to live, especially for young people and middle-aged professionals without children. Living near the city centre gives them access not only to services, but also to work.

Developing brownfield sites

Large areas of inner-city land in the UK are derelict (Fig. 7.6). In the past, these **brownfield** sites supported manufacturing industries and slum housing. Their reclamation and development could reduce the pressure of urban sprawl on the countryside. The British government has a target to build 60 per cent of new houses needed by 2016 on brownfield sites.

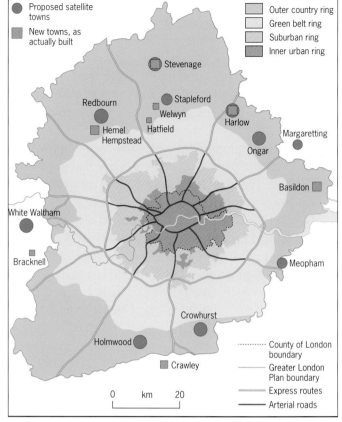

Fig. 7.12 (right) The plan for south-east England, 1945.

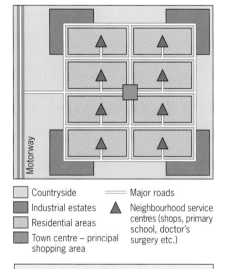

Fig. 7.13 (left) A plan for a typical new town.

Fig. 7.14 (below) The layout of Harlow new town.

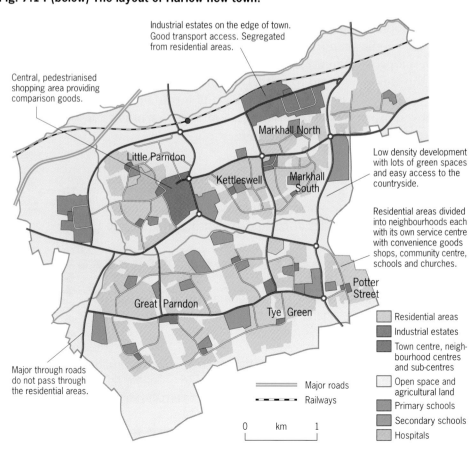

Industrial estates on the edge of town. Good transport access. Segregated from residential areas.

Central, pedestrianised shopping area providing comparison goods.

Low density development with lots of green spaces and easy access to the countryside.

Residential areas divided into neighbourhoods each with its own service centre with convenience goods shops, community centre, schools and churches.

Major through roads do not pass through the residential areas.

Major roads
Railways

0 km 1

EXERCISES

4 Study Fig. 7.6.
a Which parts of England have the largest areas of derelict land?
b* Compare Figs. 7.6 and 7.14. Explain why the development of brownfield sites alone cannot prevent urban sprawl in south-east England.
5 Study Fig. 7.5
a What are the main dislikes of residents on (1) the Blackbird Leys estate in Oxford (2) the Holly Street estate in Hackney?

Fig. 7.15 Harlow from the air.

7.7 Traffic congestion

Traffic congestion is a major problem in most large cities. The average speed of traffic in central London today is only 15 km/h: no more than it was 100 years ago. Why? The central areas of our cities – narrow streets with roads converging on the central business district – were not designed for the motor car. Also, since 1960, car ownership in the UK has increased rapidly. Today, three out of every five families own a car. Traffic congestion imposes both economic and environmental costs. Delays cost the country between £15bn and £20bn a year. Meanwhile, pollution from car exhausts reduces air quality and is a major source of ill health.

Cities have responded to traffic congestion in a number of ways. They have:

◆ built ring roads to divert traffic from the centre, and expressways to give easy access to the centre;

◆ encouraged motorists to leave their cars in the suburbs with park-and-ride schemes;

◆ restricted parking in city centres, and devised elaborate one-way systems;

◆ developed new public transport systems such as Tyne and Wear's rapid transit railway (Metro), and the tramway systems of Sheffield (Supertram) and Manchester (Metrolink);

◆ encouraged car sharing and promoted cycle lanes and bus lanes. In future, cities may reduce the demand for car travel by road pricing.

Tyne and Wear Metro

The Tyne and Wear Metro is an integrated rapid transit system serving the Tyneside conurbation. Developed in the 1980s from the region's underused

EXERCISES

6a Study Figures 7.13 and 7.14. Make a list of the similarities between Harlow new town and a typical new town plan.
b* Using the evidence of Figures 7.14 and 7.15 make a list of the possible advantages of living in Harlow compared to the inner city.

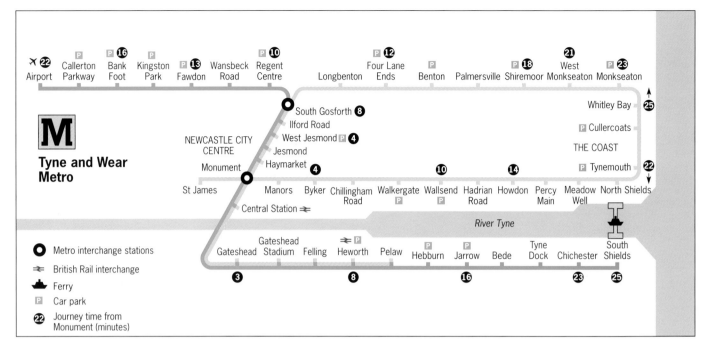

Fig. 7.16 Tyne and Wear Metro.

EXERCISES

7 Study Figure 7.16. This is a **topological** map. It consists of a series of routes (lines between stations) and nodes (stations). Unlike other maps it does not show actual distances or the real position of places.

a Why do you think that the Tyne and Wear Metro uses a topological map rather than a conventional map?

b Which stations are • most accessible • least accessible? Explain your answers.

c What physical feature reduces the overall accessibility of the Metro?

d Suggest one additional route that would increase overall accessibility on the Metro.

e Where would you change trains if you travelled by the most direct route from
• South Shields to Palmersville
• Airport to Wallsend?

rail network, its purpose was to relieve road traffic congestion. The hub of the system is a 6.4-km underground railway in central Newcastle. Forty-five stations on the network link Metro stations to local bus and rail services, and to Newcastle airport (Fig 7.16). Trains run every 10 minutes during the day, and every 5 minutes during the morning and evening rush hours. Parking is available at most stations, encouraging passengers to use the Metro as a park-and-ride scheme. The Metro has been a great success. It carries about 50 million passengers a year. In 2000, a £100m scheme to extend the Metro to Sunderland by 2002 was announced.

7.8 Air pollution in cities

Coal-burning smog

Large concentrations of industry, housing and traffic in cities often leads to air pollution and health hazards. Winter smogs were commonplace in British cities until the mid-1950s. In London, in December 1952, 4000 people died from breathing problems caused by the effects of smog. The smog was a lethal mixture of soot and sulphuric acid produced by coal-burning factories, power stations and domestic fires.

Thanks to laws that prevent coal-burning in British cities, London's 'pea soupers' are a thing of the past. However, Beijing, the capital of China, is not so fortunate. It still depends heavily on coal for power, and suffers from smogs similar to those once found in London. So bad is the problem, that 'oxygen bars' have been opened where people can sit and rent an oxygen mask to recover!

Photochemical smog

Although coal-burning no longer causes smog in Western cities, air pollution has again become a serious problem. Nowadays, a murky brown photochemical smog caused by gases from car exhausts often covers our

Fig. 7.17 Photochemical smog in Los Angeles.

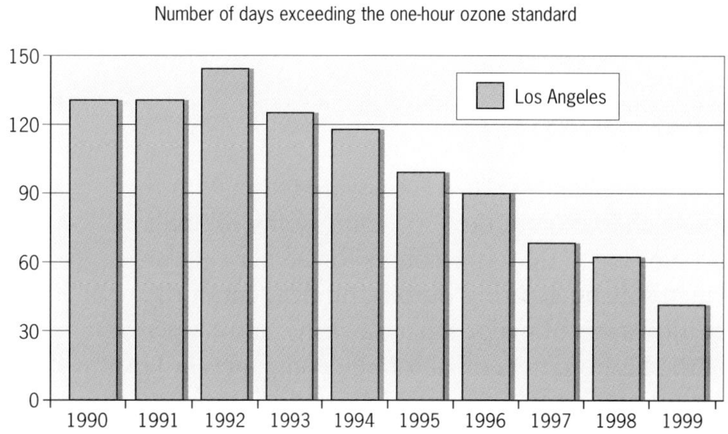

Number of days exceeding the one-hour ozone standard

Los Angeles

Fig. 7.18 Chart showing air pollution levels in Los Angeles.

cities. On still, sunny days, these gases (nitrogen oxide and hydrocarbons) react with sunlight to produce ozone. Ozone is a poisonous gas and high concentrations are dangerous to asthma sufferers and people with breathing difficulties. In October 1997, several days of photochemical smog almost brought the city of Los Angeles, USA, to a halt (Fig. 7.17).

Los Angeles is particularly badly affected by photochemical smog (Fig.7.18). On most days, a dirty haze hangs over the city making it the most polluted city in the USA. The cause is Los Angeles's dependence on the motor car – more than eight million of them. But the problem is made worse because the city is sited in a natural basin. Cold air accumulates in the basin pushing the warm air up above it, forming a **temperature inversion**, which traps ozone and other pollutants.

For two decades, Los Angeles has been fighting the smog. Old cars must pass an annual smog test, catalytic converters are compulsory, drivers who share transport are given access to a clear lane on the freeways, and by 2003, 10 per cent of cars must be electric. However, cleaner cars will not cut pollution unless something is done to reduce the growing number of cars on the road. Measures such as road pricing, car pooling, better public transport and the promotion of bicycling and walking may be the ultimate answer.

EXERCISES

8 Read Figure 7.19.
a Describe the measures used in Paris to reduce levels of pollution in the city centre.
b Why wouldn't the measures used to reduce air pollution in Paris work in London?
c What, according to the article, could be done to reduce air pollution in London?

Fig. 7.19 Article from *The Guardian* 2.10.97.

When air pollution stops Paris

Stopping one out of three cars from entering Paris yesterday might almost seem like a miracle cure. But it was only achieved at a high price – a level of atmospheric pollution which left Parisian eyes smarting and throats burning. The restrictions on car transport are part of a package of measures – passed by the last government – in anticipation of this sort of crisis. But they do nothing to prevent the recurrence of high pollution.

Some of the measures in operation yesterday in Paris could be extended. Drivers were asked to drive 20 kilometres slower than the speed limit. Why not just lower the limits? Public transport was provided – just yesterday – for free. Why not reduce fares permanently? But more serious structural change is needed too.

The Parisian scheme wouldn't work in London, the RAC claims, because public transport is already overcrowded. That is partly true of rush-hour tubes though their frequency could be improved with new signalling. But the buses are under-utilised because they move so slowly. The system needs dedicated bus lanes – not just token stretches – computer-linked traffic lights and extension of the bus indicator scheme. Buses could become immensely more efficient for a small investment. Every day of the week, not just when nitrogen dioxide levels rise.

7.9 | Tokyo

The Tokyo metropolis – the city, together with the three adjacent counties – contains nearly 33 million people (Fig. 7.21). It accounts for 23 per cent of Japan's manufacturing output, 60 per cent of the headquarters of major Japanese firms, and 88 per cent of the headquarters of all foreign companies in Japan. Together with New York and London, it is one of the world's three leading cities and has a wide-reaching influence on the global economy.

Fig. 7.20 (right) The Tokyo region: land-use zones

Fig 7.21 (below) Tokyo metropolis: multi-centred development

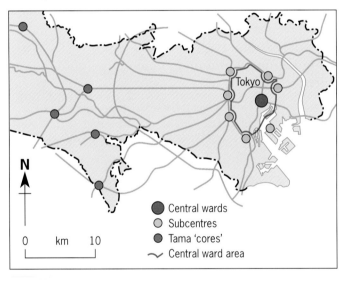

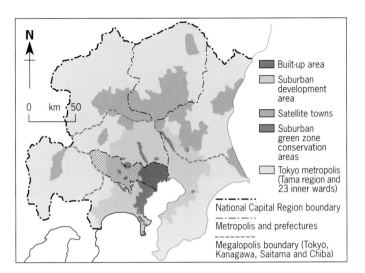

Table 7.2 Tokyo's population

Area	Cumulative population
Tokyo's inner 23 wards	7.89
Tokyo's Metropolis (inner 23 wards and the Tama region)	11.77
Tokyo Megalopolis (Tokyo and Kanagawa, Saitama and Chiba prefectures)	32.58

Table 7.3 Daytime and resident population changes in Tokyo: 1980–95

	1980	1985	1990	1995
Inner 23 wards				
Daytime population (m)	10.61	10.96	11.29	11.19
Resident population (m)	8.35	8.35	8.17	7.89
Ward area and Tama area				
Daytime population (m)	13.49	14.00	14.48	14.57
Resident population (m)	11.62	11.83	11.86	11.77

EXERCISES

9a Using the data in Table 7.3 draw line graphs, either manually or using Excel, to show changes in Tokyo's resident and daytime population between 1980 and 1995 in (1) the inner area of 23 wards (2) the combined ward and Tama areas.
b Approximately how many people commute into the inner ward and Tama areas each day?
c What evidence in Table 7.3 suggests that Tokyo's population is beginning to decentralise?

Planning problems

Tokyo's recovery after the war was rapid. Its population grew quickly as thousands of people migrated to the capital from other parts of Japan. Initially, urban growth was haphazard, and housing and transport systems were inadequate. Gradually, these problems were tackled. Today, all households in the city's inner 23 wards are served by sewerage systems. And Tokyo's subways, suburban rail network, monorails and buses are among the best in the world. Some problems, however, remain.

◆ Within the inner 23 wards, population densities (averaging 13 000 per sq km) are among the highest in the developed world. Millions of people live in cramped conditions.
◆ Chronic traffic congestion and massive long-distance commuting.
◆ Environmental concerns including air pollution, waste disposal, water supplies and shortages of parks and green spaces.

Planning responses

Decentralisation

Planners have addressed the problems of overcrowding, traffic congestion and long-distance commuting by encouraging decentralisation. They aim to develop a multi-centred city with population and economic activities dispersed throughout the Tokyo region.

Tokyo region

Since 1965, 19 satellite towns have been built in the national capital region (Fig. 7.20). Massive new business centres have also appeared. The largest is Makuhari in Chiba prefecture (Fig. 7.22). Developed since 1989, Makuhari houses the Japanese headquarters of several foreign trans-national companies and research and development activities. Makuhari also has Japan's largest convention centre and many futuristic apartment buildings. It has excellent expressway links to central Tokyo and Narita international airport.

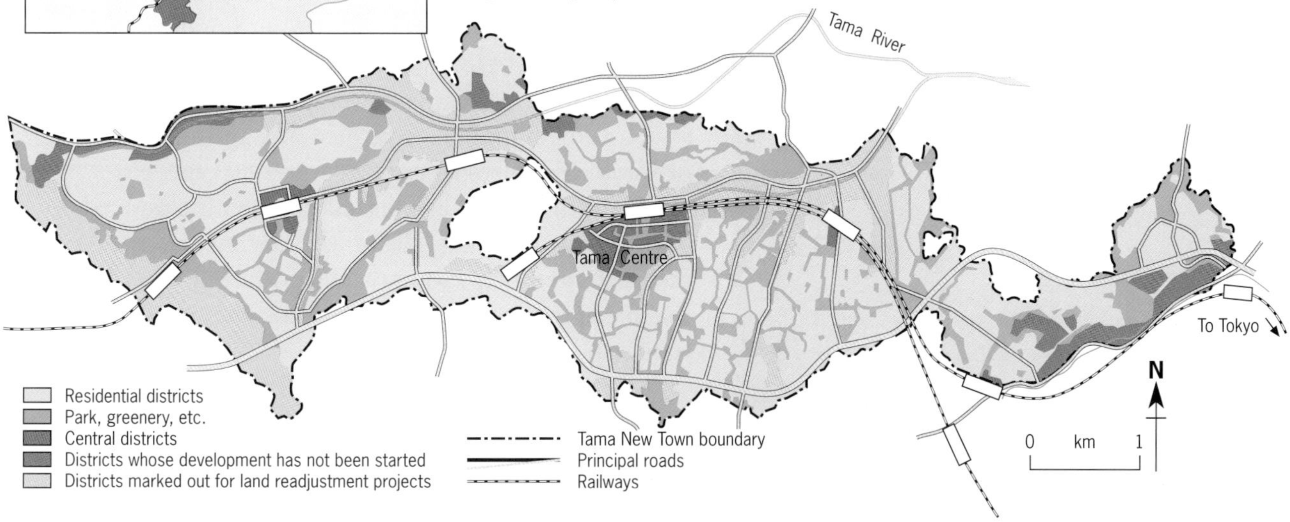

EXERCISES

10a Describe the pattern of land use in Tama New Town (Fig. 7.23).
b Suggest possible differences in land use and density between Tama New Town and the central wards of Tokyo.
c What evidence in Figs. 7.23 and 7.24 suggest that Tama might function as a commuter settlement?

Fig. 7.22 The Makuhari business centre, Chiba.

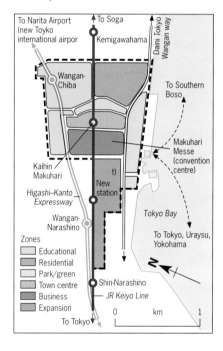

Table 7.4 Planned land use in Tama

Land Use	% area
Residential areas	35.2
Commerical/Business	6.0
Educational facilities	10.4
Other community facilities	10.3
Roads	19.4
Parks, green spaces	18.5
Other public facilities	0.2
Total	100

Tama region

The Tama region has five 'core' centres, which are focal points for growth, employment and services, including one new town (Fig. 7.23). Started in 1965, Tama new town (Fig. 7.24) has a population of 180 000 and a target population of 300 000. The town has large areas of open space and has been built at a relatively low density. Residential and working areas are close together and there are fast road and rail connections to central Tokyo. However, the aim is to create a largely self-sufficient community and reduce the need to commute to Tokyo.

Fig. 7.23 (below) Tama New Town development plan.

Fig. 7.24 (left) Location of Tama New Town.

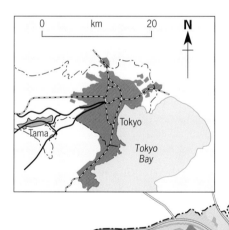

Legend:
- Residential districts
- Park, greenery, etc.
- Central districts
- Districts whose development has not been started
- Districts marked out for land readjustment projects
- —·—·— Tama New Town boundary
- ——— Principal roads
- ········· Railways

Tokyo's central wards

Around the three central wards, seven large sub-centres have been created. Shinjuku is the largest (Figs. 7.25, 7.26). It already has a greater concentration of high-rise buildings than Tokyo's CBD, is the location of the metropolitan city government, and has Japan's busiest railway station. Shinjuku is a major centre of office employment. Retail and leisure activities are important too, with several large department stores and innumerable restaurants and bars. The newest sub-centre is Rainbow Town (Fig. 7.21) built on reclaimed land on Tokyo Bay's waterfront. Due for completion by 2025, it will provide employment for 70 000 people and housing for 42 000. Rainbow Town is linked by a new rapid-transit system to central Tokyo.

EXERCISES

11 Study the photograph of Shinjuku (Fig. 7.26). What evidence suggests that **a** demand for land in Shinjuku is extremely high.

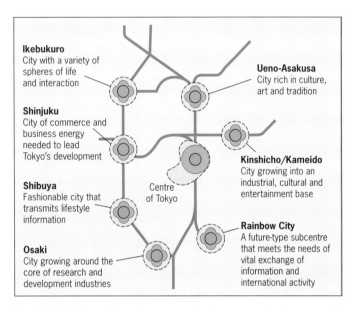

Ikebukuro
City with a variety of spheres of life and interaction

Shinjuku
City of commerce and business energy needed to lead Tokyo's development

Shibuya
Fashionable city that transmits lifestyle information

Osaki
City growing around the core of research and development industries

Ueno-Asakusa
City rich in culture, art and tradition

Centre of Tokyo

Kinshicho/Kameido
City growing into an industrial, cultural and entertainment base

Rainbow City
A future-type subcentre that meets the needs of vital exchange of information and international activity

Fig. 7.25 (Above) Development of sub-centres in the central ward area of Tokyo.

Road improvements

Despite multiple-level expressways and flyovers, traffic congestion in central Tokyo is severe. Decentralisation will help to reduce congestion. However, improvements to the road network are also needed. New loop roads that link radial roads leading out of Tokyo will be built. Meanwhile, the existing arterial roads will be improved.

Creating a sustainable city

Cities need resources such as water, clean air and green spaces. In Tokyo, as in other cities, urban growth has often degraded these resources. Rivers are polluted by domestic and industrial waste, overpumping of groundwater leads to a fall in the water table, motor vehicles and industries pollute the air (Fig. 7.27), urban sprawl swallows up the surrounding countryside, and wastes are dumped on landfill sites around the city. The planners aim to make Tokyo a sustainable city that will conserve rather than degrade water, land, atmosphere and energy resources.

Water

The quality of river water – the major source of drinking water – has declined through pollution. Tokyo has improved water quality through the construction of effective sewerage systems. Water saving campaigns aim to reduce wastage and the reuse of water. Measures to prevent water leakage and recycling of waste-water have also been introduced. Saving rainwater that falls on the city increases water resources and helps to prevent flooding. Even so, the quality of treated sewer water needs to be improved to reduce pollution in Tokyo Bay.

Fig. 7.26 Commercial district of Shinjuku, Tokyo, at night.

Refuse

Tokyo generates more than 4 million tonnes of refuse a year. As the amount of refuse has grown, pressure on landfill sites has increased. Reductions in rubbish volume and recycling are being urged in order to keep landfill sites open for as long as possible.

District heating and cooling

A system of boilers, refrigerators and other equipment in single heating and cooling plants are being developed to supply whole neighbourhoods with central heating, air conditioning and hot and cold water. Such plants save energy and reduce emissions of CO_2 and other pollutants.

Open space, greenery and lakes

There is an urgent need to provide more open space for leisure activities in Tokyo. The per capita park space in Tokyo is only 5.18 sq m – far lower than other international cities. Many brownfield sites are targeted for conversion to urban parks in future.

Fig. 7.27 Urban expressways in Tokyo.

7.10 Urban problems in LEDCs

We saw in Chapter 6 that cities in LEDCs are growing at an alarming rate. So rapid is this growth that the cities are unable to provide adequate housing, services and jobs for their inhabitants. Moreover, poverty has meant that environmental quality in urban areas has taken second place to economic development.

Housing: shanty towns

Most cities in Africa, Asia and Latin America do not have the resources to meet even the most basic housing needs. Their attempts to build low-cost housing have been largely unsuccessful. Poor people either cannot afford to pay rent or find it cheaper to build their own low-cost homes. The result is huge areas of informal settlements (shanty towns). They go under various names: *favelas* in Brazil; *barrios* in Colombia; *bustees* in India; *bidonvilles* in North Africa; *gecekondu* in Turkey, and so on. All are evidence that the poor have solved the housing problem for themselves.

Fig. 7.28 Poor *barrios* in Bogota showing recently installed electricity.

Location

Shanty towns are likely to spring up on any vacant plots in the city. Often these plots have been left unoccupied for good reasons. Some have steep slopes and are affected by landslides and mudslides. Others may be in valleys where flooding is a serious risk. So why do the homeless settle there? Mainly because they have no choice. Because they are poor, they have to accept the risks and occupy whatever land is available.

Upgrading shanty towns

To start with, shanties are little more than clusters of flimsy shacks without any basic services, but over time they are improved (Fig.7.28). Houses are transformed from shacks to solid and permanent structures.

> **REMEMBER**
> Cities in MEDCs and LEDCs have many economic, social and environmental problems in common. The difference is in the scale of the problems and the resources available to solve them.

Boom builds hope in shanties

When the Brazilian government introduced its economic stabilisation plan almost three years ago, no one believed it would work. But the plan, which involved the introduction of a new currency – the real – miraculously, so it seemed, brought inflation down to single figures.

The effect on the lives of ordinary Brazilians has been dramatic.

On the hot and dusty outskirts of Sao Paulo, at the entrance to the Jardin das Palmas shanty town, a skinny ginger kitten scrambles up the half-built breeze-block walls of a two-room house. Inside, Jose Martins Podesta, a butcher by trade, gestures around one of his two rooms, which boasts a fridge, new microwave and food-mixer. 'From here to here is going to be the kitchen, over there I want to build a room upstairs and this will become the living room,' he says.

Over the last year or so, Mr Podesta – who earns around £500 a month – has been replacing the scraps of wood used to build his home in Sao Paulo with concrete blocks bought on credit. 'My life has changed, it's easier now, food is no longer a problem and I am planning to buy a telephone line by the end of the year.'

He is one of millions of Brazilians who have been able to afford to improve their housing conditions in the past few years. The cement industry has been experiencing growth rates of between 54 and 56 per cent, generated largely by the self-build programmes of lower-income families.

At the end of the alley a small stream runs, stinking, through thick undergrowth. Adailton Santos de Araujo, aged 25, lives opposite with his wife and four small children in a two-room shack which once had water seeping up through the floor. 'We can dream about a future now,' he says. 'Before, inflation killed off our dreams.'

He recently built another storey on to his house, adding two rooms. He has also managed to buy a car and a phone.

Shopping malls are being built in working class areas largely ignored for decades. Apartment blocks targeted at lower income families are springing up.

Fig. 7.29 Article by Candace Piette in _The Guardian_, 3.4.97.

The city authorities may provide clean drinking water, electricity and proper drainage. Eventually, after 25 or 30 years, the shanties may become mature suburbs and respectable parts of the city.

In some cities, planners have tried to tackle the housing problem by introducing site-and-service schemes. Land is divided into plots (sites), which are provided with basic services. People rent the plots and build their own houses on them. The Dandora project in Nairobi is an example of such a scheme.

EXERCISES

12 Read Figure 7.29.
a Why have many poor people in Brazil become better off in recent years?
b Describe how Jose Martins Podesta and Adailton Santos de Araujo have improved their houses in Sao Paulo's Jardin das Palmas shanty town.
c* From the evidence of Fig. 7.29, in what way can shanty towns be described as 'slums of hope'?

Employment

Just as cities in LEDCs cannot provide housing for their inhabitants, so paid employment in factories, workshops and offices is not available to everyone. This doesn't mean that unemployment is high. Because there are no welfare payments for the unemployed, people must work to survive. Again, the poor have no option but to rely on self-help and create their own jobs. About one-third of people in cities in LEDCs are self-employed. Most work in petty service activities such as street vending, shoe shining, waste recycling and so on. But within the shanty towns there are all kinds of businesses from motor-vehicle repairing and welding to shoe making and weaving. Earnings are usually very low. Indeed, most households survive only because children as well as adults work and contribute to the family income.

Environment

Air pollution is a major problem in many cities in LEDCs. This comes as no surprise. Poverty and pollution often go together, as they did in the industrial revolution in British cities. Mexico City, for example is one of the most polluted cities in the world. Its air pollution comes from its 4 million vehicles, 30 000 factories and the waste from millions of dogs, rats and people. Ozone levels are well above the safe limits defined by the World Health Organization (WHO).

In Delhi, India, more than 70 per cent of air pollution comes from motor vehicles. More than half of the city's children suffer from asthma, and lung cancer is 12 times the national average.

CASE STUDY

7.11 Nairobi

FACTFILE

- *Nairobi is Kenya's capital and largest city.*
- *Nairobi's population is growing rapidly (Fig. 7.30)*
- *Current estimates (2000) suggest a population of between 2.5 and 2.9 million.*
- *Nairobi's population doubled in the 1990s. This growth was due to both rural-urban migration and natural increase.*
- *Fifty-five per cent of Nairobi's population lives in shanty towns (Fig.7.31) on just 6 per cent of the city's residential land area.*
- *Overcrowding is a major problem. Dwellings usually consist of a single room.*
- *The average density of population in Nairobi's shanty towns is about 73 000 per sq km (Fig. 7.33).*

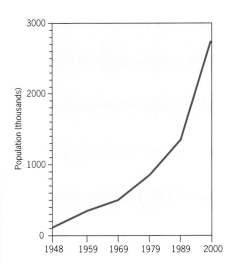

Fig. 7.30 Population growth in Nairobi 1948–2000.

Fig. 7.31 Distribution of shanty towns in Nairobi.

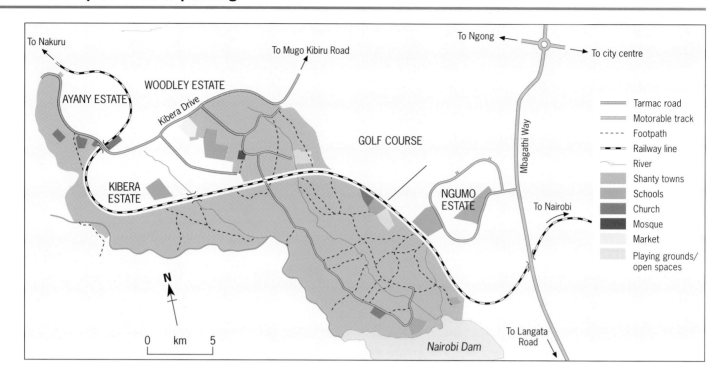

Fig. 7.32 Kibera shanty town, Nairobi.

Fig. 7.33 Mathare Valley – the largest slum in East Africa.

Kibera – Nairobi's largest shanty town

Situated seven kilometres from the city centre, Kibera has an estimated population of 500 000.

Infrastructure problems

Imagine a city the size of Leicester, where the houses are made from mud, wattle and corrugated iron. There is no planning and the city authority provides neither roads, sewerage, drainage, water nor electricity. Most people have to buy water from tanks (or kiosks) at inflated prices because there are not even any standpipes. Some use the nearby Nairobi Dam, which is polluted. The only sanitation consists of pit latrines that are shared between anything from 50 to 500 people. Human excreta litters the settlement and is a major health hazard, particularly in the rainy season when the area floods. Few houses have electricity and there is no street lighting. Roads are unpaved. There is no official refuse collection. Refuse is thrown anywhere and contributes to the health hazards.

Health problems

Mortality rates are high owing to overcrowding (the average population density exceeds 110 000 per sq km), poor sanitation, lack of clean water, poor drainage and accumulating refuse. Diarrhoea, associated with poor sanitation and poor water supplies, is a major cause of death in children.

Education

There are just five primary schools. Average class sizes are 50 to 60 pupils. One-third of children receive no education beyond primary school.

Economic activity

About two in five people have jobs as casual labourers, watchmen, servants, cleaners etc., mainly in the nearby industrial areas and estates and in the city centre. Of the self-employed about one-third (mainly women) cultivate small plots of land, and the rest have small business interests. Trading of goods such as food, cigarettes, fuel and water is the most popular business, but there is a wide range of more productive activities in Kibera, including metal working, machinery repair, carpentry, construction and shoe making.

7.12 Summary: Urban problems and planning

KEY SKILLS OPPORTUNITIES
C1.2: Ex. 1, 2, 3, 4, 5, 6, 7, 8, 11, 12, 13; **C1/2.3**: Ex. 1, 3, 5, 6, 8, 9c, 12, 13; **N1/2.2**: Ex. 9b; **IT1.2**: Ex. 9a

Key ideas	Generalisations and detail
Cities in both the developed and developing worlds face a number of urgent problems.	The main urban problems are: • housing (shortages and sub-standard housing) • poverty • congestion and environmental pollution • urban sprawl The scale and seriousness of these problems is greater in LEDCs.
Planners have tackled the inner city problems of poverty, crime, unemployment, social exclusion and urban decay in MEDCs with a variety of measures.	Planning responses include: • urban renewal involving demolition of slums and the building of high-rise flats e.g. Hulme in Manchester and Sarcelles in Paris • urban improvement • enterprise zones, urban development corporations, partnership schemes.
Urbanisation and the increasing number of households in MEDCs has led to urban sprawl.	• In the UK, green belts have been used to curb urban sprawl. • Green wedges and corridors of growth have been preferred in some other European countries, such as Denmark, France and the Netherlands.
New towns have been developed to accommodate rising urban populations and increasing numbers of households in MEDCs.	• In the UK, new towns have been developed around major conurbations and beyond the green belt. In south-east England, a total of eleven towns have been built since 1945. • Paris has five new towns located in the city's twin axes of development.
Congestion in the central areas of cities in the MEDCs has led to the decentralisation of economic activities.	• New towns, e.g. Tama in Tokyo, have assisted decentralisation. Business centres, industrial estates and office parks (e.g. Makuhari in Chiba, Tokyo) have been developed outside the CBD or at edge-of-town locations in the last 30 years.
Air pollution from traffic is a serious hazard in the urban environment in all large cities.	• 50 years ago, air pollution was caused by burning coal, which caused winter smog. This is still a problem in poorer countries such as China. • In the MEDCs, air pollution is caused mainly by car exhausts. The result is photochemical smog and high concentrations of ozone. Restrictions on the use of private cars in cities, and new public transport schemes (e.g. rapid-transit, trams, etc.) aim to reduce both pollution and congestion.
Urban problems in the LEDCs concern the very survival of city dwellers.	• Rural-urban migration caused massive expansion of cities in LEDCs after 1950. City authorities do not have the resources to solve housing, employment and environmental problems. Most people rely on self-help. This is evident in the growth of (a) huge shanty towns and (b) informal employment based on small-scale services and businesses. Environmental concern has little priority at the moment in most cities.
There is an increasing awareness that cities and urban living should be sustainable.	• Many city authorities in MEDCs are planning to ensure the sustainable use of resources such as water supplies, clean air and green spaces. In the UK, the recycling of urban land – brownfield sites – will be given priority in an effort to protect the countryside from further urban sprawl.

8 Agricultural systems

8.1 Introduction

Agriculture is 'the control and use of plants and animals for the production of food, and fibre and raw materials for industry'. It differs from other economic activities in two main ways.

◆ Unlike manufacturing and services, agriculture relies heavily on the physical environment, and the life-cycles of plants and animals. Both are largely outside the control of farmers.

◆ Agriculture uses a larger proportion of the Earth's surface (about 37 per cent of the land area) and provides more employment worldwide than any other economic activity.

Fig. 8.1 Distribution of the world's agricultural land, and regional value of agricultural output.

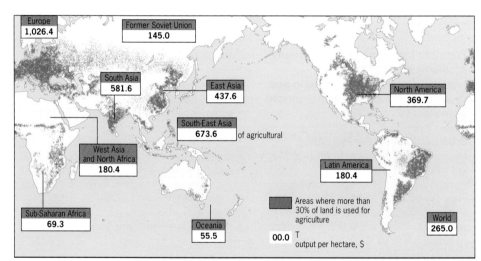

Fig. 8.2 The farm system.

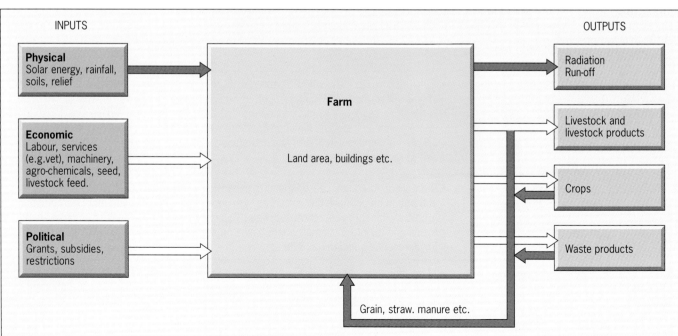

8.2 Agricultural systems

Farms are both ecological and economic systems (Fig. 8.2). First let's consider a farm as a simplified ecosystem (see Section 4.2). It contains only those species of plants and animals that are useful to the farmer. Useless species that compete with crops and farm animals (weeds and pests) are destroyed. Like any ecosystem, a farm relies on climatic inputs of solar energy and rainfall, and on plant nutrients from the soil. Unlike natural ecosystems, most farms are not self-sustaining. Crops and livestock products remove nutrients from the system and must be replaced by artificial fertiliser.

Agriculture is also an economic system. For example, in addition to climatic and soil inputs, an arable farmer in the UK would also require inputs of labour, seeds, agro-chemicals (fertilisers, pesticides) and machinery. These are all part of the costs; and, as commercial farmers aim to make a profit, the value of farm outputs must exceed costs.

Table 8.1 How farmers can modify the physical environment

Physical environment	Modifications
Rainfall	Irrigation. By diverting rivers or using underground supplies, farmers can supplement direct rainfall.
Temperature	Crops can be grown in glasshouses (heated or unheated) or under cloches. South-facing slopes can be cultivated.
Soil	Soils can be drained. If they are acidic they can be limed. Shortages of nitrogen, phosphorus, potassium etc. can be made up by using fertiliser. Field operations, e.g. ploughing, can alter the structure.
Relief	Steep slopes can be terraced.
Wind	Shelter belts, hedgerows and other wind breaks protect crops.
Pests and diseases	Crops can be sprayed with pesticides. Weeding.

EXERCISES

2 Study Fig. 8.3
a Describe the changes in the percentage employment in agriculture between 1950 and 2000.
b What percentage of employment was in agriculture in MEDCs and LEDCs in 2000?
c* State and explain two possible reasons for the difference in employment in agriculture between MEDCs and LEDCs in 2000.

8.3 Types of agriculture

Usually we refer to types of agriculture in one of three ways:
◆ by the dominant **enterprise**;
◆ by the intensity of production;
◆ by the extent to which farming is for cash.

Enterprise

The simplest definition of farming is by enterprise – what a farm produces (Table 8.2). Thus we refer to dairy farms, which specialise in milk production; arable farms, where crops dominate; and mixed farms where there is a combination of both crops and livestock.

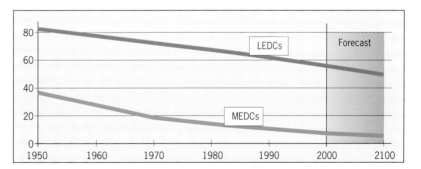

Fig. 8.3 Agricultural employment as a percentage of total employment.

Intensity of production

The intensity of production is more concerned with farming methods.
◆ Intensive farming involves high inputs of labour, agro-chemicals, machinery, etc. per hectare, with resulting high outputs, or yields, per hectare. Often this type of farming develops where land is either in short supply or has very high fertility. Typical intensive farming systems are wet rice cultivation in South-east Asia (Fig. 8.6) and horticulture in Holland.
◆ Extensive farming has low inputs per hectare, which give low outputs per hectare. Very large farms or those with poor-quality land often use extensive methods, such as hill sheep farming in the Pennines and cattle ranching on the High Plains in the USA (Fig. 8.7).

EXERCISES

3 Most farmers make some attempt to modify the physical environment for agriculture, even though their impact overall is small. Study Table 8.1 and decide which physical factors farmers are ● most able ● least able to change?
Explain your choices.

Table 8.2 Major world agricultural systems

Type	Features	Examples
SHIFTING CULTIVATION	Temporary cultivation of small plots cleared in the rainforest. Simple technology e.g. axes, hoes. Low population density. Plots abandoned after harvest.	Tribal groups in rainforests of Amazonia, central and west Africa and South-east Asia.
NOMADIC PASTORALISM	Constant movement of pastoralists and livestock in search of pasture and water. A response to meagre environment resources. Cattle kept in wetter areas. Sheep, goats and camels in drier parts. Extensive use of land.	Semi-arid areas such as fringes of the Sahara and Arabian deserts. Also movements between upland and lowlands known as transhumance e.g. Zagros mountains in Iran.
PEASANT AGRICULTURE	Sedentary cultivation around permanent settlements. High population density. Farmers may be tenants, sharecroppers or owner occupiers. They may own their tools and other working capital. Often highly labour intensive e.g. wet rice cultivation.	Easily the most important type of farming in LEDCs. Found throughout Asia, Africa and Latin America. May be dry farming (based on direct rainfall) or irrigation farming. Wet rice cultivation in South-east and south Asia supports hundreds of millions of people.
PLANTATION AGRICULTURE	Cultivation of cash crops e.g. palm oil, bananas, tea, rubber, etc. for export. Crops grown on estates. Owned by foreign trans-national companies e.g. Unilever, but using local labour.	Most plantation agriculture is based on tropical and sub-tropical crops and is found in LEDCs.
HORTICULTURE	Intensive (both capital and labour) cultivation of soft fruit, vegetables and salad crops. Cultivation of small plots, much of it in glasshouses.	Mainly found in MEDCs, serving large urban markets. Horticulture in MEDCs is small-scale and related to the growth of air transport and international tourism.
MECHANISED ARABLE FARMING	Large-scale cultivation of cereals, sugar beet, potatoes, etc. Capital intensive. High inputs per person of agro-chemicals.	Middle to high latitudes in North America (prairies), Europe and Australia.
DAIRY FARMING	Intensive livestock farming for milk. Needs good transport links between farms and markets.	Middle to high latitudes in MEDCs. Often found in regions of higher rainfall and heavier soils.
INTENSIVE LIVESTOCK	Pigs, poultry, calves, etc. produced indoors in intensive off-land enterprises.	Mainly found in MEDCs where there is a market for expensive eggs and meat products.
EXTENSIVE STOCK RAISING AND RANCHING	Sheep farming and cattle raising in uplands. Cattle ranching and sheep in semi-arid regions. Extensive farming on poor land with low outputs per hectare.	Hill sheep in upland areas in Europe, such as the Highlands of Scotland. Ranching in semi-arid regions like the High Plains, USA and Pampas in Argentina.
MEDITERRANEAN AGRICULTURE	Based on traditional drought-resistant crops such as olives and vines. Also wheat and sheep. With irrigation, citrus fruits and salad crops are important.	Found in regions that have a summer drought e.g. Mediterranean basin, California, South Africa, south and west Australia, central Chile.

☐ Commercial agriculture   ☐ Non-commercial agriculture

Farming for cash or subsistence

There is an important distinction between commercial and non-commercial farming (Table 8.2). In MEDCs, virtually all farming is commercial. This means that farmers produce crops and livestock products for sale, in order to make a cash profit. In LEDCs, non-commercial agriculture remains important. In this system, farmers and their families grow crops mainly for their own consumption. What's left may be sold or traded for other products in local markets (Fig. 8.4). We often call this type of self-sufficient farming **subsistence** agriculture.

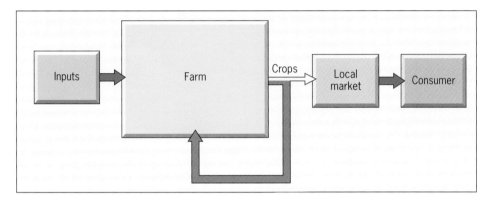

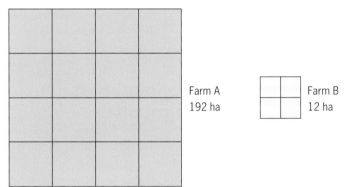

Farm A 192 ha   Farm B 12 ha

EXERCISES

4a Study Figure 8.6. What features shown in the photograph are typical of intensive farming?
b Draw a diagram similar to Figure 8.4 to illustrate a commercial farming system.
c* Figure 8.5 shows two farms: A (192 hectares) and B (12 hectares). Assume that each farm needs to make a profit of £24 000 a year to survive.
• How much profit per hectare must each farm make to be profitable?• Which farm will be more intensively cultivated and why? • Suggest a possible enterprise for each farm.

Fig. 8.4 (above left) A non-commercial farming system.

Fig. 8.5 (left) Farm size and farming intensity.

Fig. 8.6 (below left) Intensive rice cultivation in Bali, Indonesia.

Fig. 8.7 (below right) Cattle ranching on the High Plains, USA.

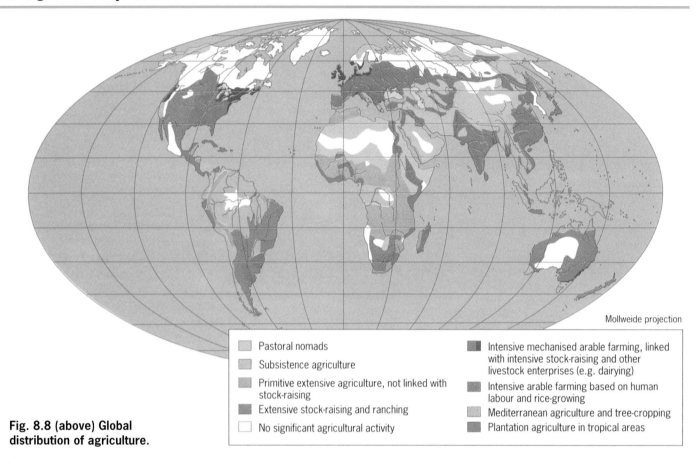

Fig. 8.8 (above) Global distribution of agriculture.

Legend:
- Pastoral nomads
- Subsistence agriculture
- Primitive extensive agriculture, not linked with stock-raising
- Extensive stock-raising and ranching
- No significant agricultural activity
- Intensive mechanised arable farming, linked with intensive stock-raising and other livestock enterprises (e.g. dairying)
- Intensive arable farming based on human labour and rice-growing
- Mediterranean agriculture and tree-cropping
- Plantation agriculture in tropical areas

Mollweide projection

Fig. 8.9 Arctic tundra, the Mackenzie Delta, Canada.

Fig. 8.10 Hot desert, Wadi Rum, Jordan.

8.4 The global distribution of agriculture

On a global scale, the distribution of agriculture is most influenced by climate (Fig. 8.8). Large parts of the planet are unsuitable for farming.

Temperature

All crops have minimum heat requirements. Growth usually begins when the mean daily air temperature rises above 6°C, and most crops need this temperature for at least 120 days. As you go towards the poles, temperatures fall and the growing season shortens. This is the main reason why cultivation rarely extends beyond latitude 60° in the northern hemisphere.

Precipitation

Crops also have moisture requirements. The world's hot deserts are simply too dry for cultivation unless water is available for irrigation. Extensive farming systems based on nomadic herding of camels, sheep, goats and cattle are found only around the edges of deserts. High mountains, such as the Himalayas and Andes, support few farming activities – as well as severe climates they have steep slopes and thin soils.

8.5 Distribution of agriculture in the UK

On the national scale, climate is the most important factor affecting the distribution of agriculture. In the UK, there is a simple pattern: the east is mainly arable, the west mainly pastoral (Fig. 8.11).

Arable farming in the east

In the drier eastern side of the country, precipitation is between 600 and 800 mm, which favours crops such as wheat, barley, oilseed, sugar beet and potatoes. The slightly warmer summers give crop production an advantage.

Livestock farming in the west

In the west, precipitation is too high for most arable crops to be grown profitably, but it is ideal for grass. Thus dairying and beef cattle are the leading enterprises in western areas. Pastoral farming is also found in the uplands. However, the harsh climate, steep slopes and poor soils limit upland farming to hill sheep and cattle rearing.

EXERCISES

5a Figures 8.9 and 8.10 show two harsh environments for agriculture. List the evidence in each photo that suggest that farming would be difficult in each environment.

b Suggest any actions that people could take to make farming possible in these environments (e.g. modifying physical factors Table 8.1; introducing special types of farming, etc.).

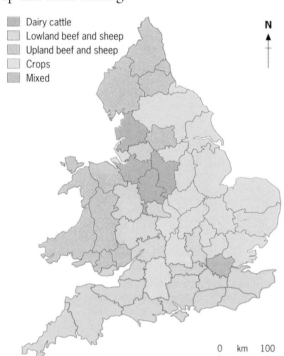

Dairy cattle
Lowland beef and sheep
Upland beef and sheep
Crops
Mixed

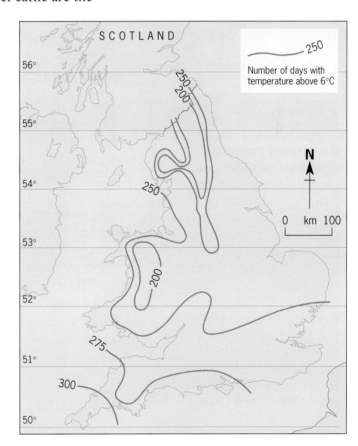

Fig. 8.11 (above left) Distribution of types of farming in England and Wales.

Fig. 8.12 (above right) The length of growing season in England and Wales.

Table 8.3 Climatic factors and crop growth

	July temp °C	Jan temp °C	Growing season (days)	Precipitation mm
Cheshire	16–17	4–5	250–275	?
Suffolk	?	3–4	225–250	?
South Devon	17–18	?	?	750–1500
Central Wales	16–17	3–4	?	?

EXERCISES

6a Using the information in Figures 8.11, 8.12, 3.18, 3.19, and 3.21 complete Table 8.3.

b Locate each region with the help of an atlas, and identify the main farming type (Fig. 8.11).

c Explain how the physical factors in Table 8.3 might have influenced the choice of farming in each region.

127

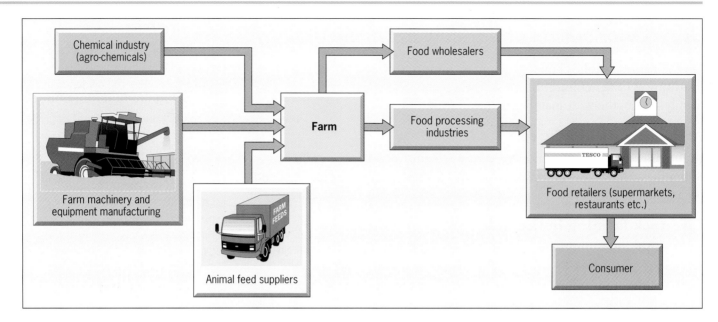

Fig. 8.13 The food system.

8.6 Agriculture and the food system

Farming is the production side of a chain of activities that eventually lead to food consumption (Fig. 8.13). This **food system** includes industries that supply essential farm inputs, such as agro-chemicals and machinery, and food wholesalers, food retailers and food manufacturers, who handle the outputs from the farm.

Geographically, food systems vary in length. Some are worldwide; others extend no further than the farm gate.

◆ In LEDCs, most farm produce is still consumed on the farm. This means that food systems are short. Those crops that are not consumed on the farm are probably sold in the local village market.

◆ In MEDCs, food systems are much longer. For example, in the UK, lamb is imported from New Zealand, citrus fruits from South Africa, and coffee from Colombia.

However, even in the UK, some food systems are short. Increasingly, farmers (especially those living close to large towns and cities) sell directly to customers through their own farm shops and pick-your-own schemes.

Food retailers and the food system

Leading food retailers like Marks & Spencer (M & S), Sainsbury's and Tesco have an important influence on farmers, controlling what is grown, how it is grown and its quality. Although M & S gets most of its food from the UK, it increasingly buys some fresh fruit and vegetables from overseas. A new trend is that more and more of the UK's fresh food comes from LEDCs. This means that geographically, food systems are getting longer, and that farming, like manufacturing, is increasingly a global industry. Why is this?

One reason is that more and more customers want fresh foods all year round, and not just for the few weeks when they are in season in the UK. Air freighting of highly perishable products like strawberries makes this possible. When M & S searches for new suppliers, climate is crucial. Obvious sources are the tropics, where farming is possible all year, providing water is available; or further south, where summer corresponds to the British winter.

8.7 Shifting cultivation

Shifting cultivation is the traditional method of farming in the tropical rainforest (Fig. 8.15). It is a form of subsistence agriculture, often combined with hunting, and practised by small tribal groups like the Iban in Sarawak in South-east Asia.

Methods of cultivation

We saw in Section 4.3 that the rainforest has very poor soils – so poor that permanent cultivation is impossible. Shifting cultivators get round this problem by making temporary clearings in the forest (about 2 hectares for a family of six). The Iban make these clearings in June and July, and burn the leaves and branches in August, which is a relatively dry month. The ash from the burnt vegetation fertilises the soil and allows cultivation for up to two years. Hill rice, which does not require irrigation, is the main crop. Seeds are sown directly into the ash using a simple digging stick.

Initially, rice yields are good. However, cropping and heavy rainfall quickly removes plant nutrients from the soil, and weeds become an increasing problem. After two years, cultivation is no longer worthwhile, and the Iban abandon their plots and make fresh clearings in the forest.

Sustainable cultivation

Shifting cultivation is a **sustainable** type of farming. This means that it does no long-term damage to the environment, providing the intervals between cultivation are long enough to allow the forest trees to regenerate and the soil to recover its fertility. In the case of Sarawak, a

Fig. 8.14 Hand picking beans in Zimbabwe, for export to MEDCs.

Fig. 8.15 (above) Shifting cultivation in the Orinoco river basin, Venezuela.

Fig. 8.16 (left) Cycle of cultivation of the Iban.

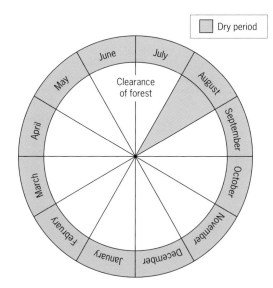

Dry period

Clearance of forest

June | July | August | September | October | November | December | January | February | March | April | May

Timetable
Date

1.6	Begin clearance of forest plots.
1.8	Clearing complete.
14.8	Trees are burned.
18.9	Sowing of rice begins.
27.10	Sowing completed.
12.2	Quick-ripening rice harvested.
26.3	Threshing of quick-ripening rice.
22.4	Late-ripening rice harvested.
2.5	Storing of rice.

NB weeding takes place from the completion of burning to the final harvesting of rice.

EXERCISES

9 Copy Figure 8.16. Add notes to your diagram about the sequence of tasks during the farming year using the timetable given beside it.

15-year cycle of cultivation is needed. There are two threats to the sustainability of shifting cultivation.
- Population growth, which may force farmers to re-cultivate plots before they have recovered their fertility.
- Logging. In Chapter 4, we saw how commercial logging is devastating Sarawak's rainforests. If this continues for much longer, then the shifting cultivators of this region will be forced to abandon their unique way of life.

CASE STUDY

8.8 Nomadic herding

Like shifting cultivation, nomadic herding is a response to harsh environmental conditions where resources for farming are too sparse to allow permanent, settled agriculture. Although nomadic herding is found in some sub-Arctic areas and high mountain ranges, it is most closely associated with the fringes of tropical deserts like the Sahara (Fig. 8.8).

Nomadic herding in Mauritania

On the southern edge of the Sahara Desert in Mauritania, rainfall averages only 100 to 250 mm. Because of this low and unreliable rainfall, settled agriculture is impossible. Thus farmers have no option but to follow a nomadic existence. They keep cattle, camels, sheep and goats which, apart from longer stays at summer and winter encampments, are constantly on the move in search of water and pasture. They follow the seasonal rains, moving northwards between July and October, and spending winter in the south. Each year, and at the same time, they visit the same wells and pastures. A typical annual cycle might involve a journey of 800 kilometres (Fig. 8.17).

Fig. 8.17 (below left) Seasonal movements of nomads in Mauritania.

Fig. 8.18 (below right) Mean annual rainfall in Mauritania.

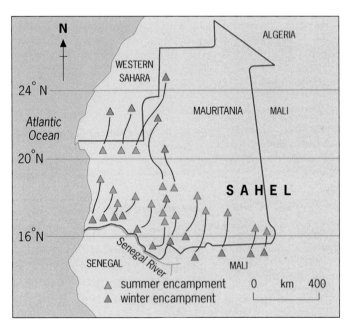

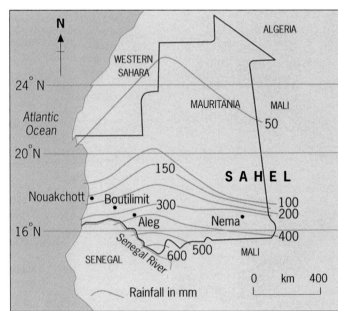

Features of nomadic herding

Nomadic herding is an extensive farming system. Meagre supplies of water and pasture mean that a large area is needed to support each animal. Thus output per hectare of meat, wool, milk, hides and other items is small. Food chains are short. Items that the nomads cannot produce themselves, such as cereals, will be exchanged for livestock products with village cultivators.

Threats to nomadic herding

Nomadic herding is a sustainable farming system, well adapted to a harsh environment. But like shifting cultivation, it is currently under threat as a way of life because:

◆ governments wish to stop traditional migrations across international borders, and force the nomads to live in villages where they can be taxed;
◆ population growth leads to more livestock and overgrazed pastures;
◆ a succession of drought years since the early 1970s greatly reduced the land's **carrying capacity** – its ability to support nomads and their animals.

Southern Mauritania lies within the semi-arid .... belt. The rest of the country is .... and apart from scattered oases is uninhabited. Nearly ....of Mauritania is too dry to support any kind of agriculture. The rains follow a predictable seasonal pattern. The winter is a period of .... Most rain falls between July and October, advancing from the south and gradually petering out northwards. The extreme south of Mauritania is the only part of the country which can support .... agriculture.

REMEMBER
Human mismanagement and population growth are often to blame for farming systems becoming unsustainable. In future, climate change associated with global warming may increase the frequency of drought. As a result, livestock farming may be abandoned in many of the world's drylands.

EXERCISES

10 Study Figures 8.17 and 8.18, then copy the paragraph opposite, inserting the missing words from the list below.

Missing words:
desert, drought, settled, Sahel, three-fifths.

CASE STUDY

8.9 Arable farming in eastern England

FACTFILE

• *Grange Farm is located close to sea level near Scunthorpe in North Lincolnshire*
• *The farm has ideal conditions for arable farming: gentle slopes, mean July temperatures of 16°C, mean annual precipitation between 600 and 650 mm, a long growing season (March to November), and rich alluvial soils.*
• *Some crops, e.g. potatoes, require irrigation during dry spells.*
• *Crop yields are well above the UK average for most arable crops.*
• *Grange Farm is part of a large-scale 'agribusiness' enterprise.*

EXERCISES

11* Study the Factfile and Table 8.4 and explain how physical conditions favour arable farming at Grange Farm.

Physical environment

Grange Farm in North Lincolnshire is situated in the arable core of eastern England (Fig. 8.22). The local climate, relief and soils are ideal for most arable crops.

The physical environment in this part of Lincolnshire places few limits on farming. However, Grange Farm lies very close to sea level. As a result, the land has to be drained artificially. Pumps lift the water from the fields and into the nearby River Trent.

Potatoes, sugar beet, wheat and peas are grown on an eight-

Table 8.4 Crops yields: UK and Grange Farm

| | Average yields per hectare | |
	UK	Grange Farm
Wheat	6.5	10.0
Sugar beet	40.3	60.0
Potatoes	38.0	40.0

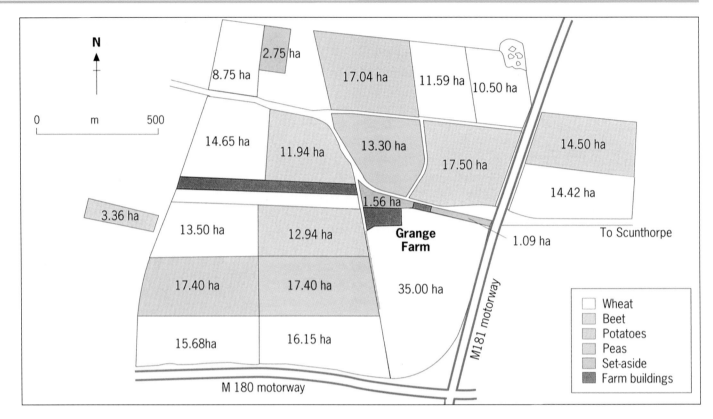

Fig. 8.19 Lay-out and land use: Grange Farm.

Fig. 8.20 Land use: Grange Farm.

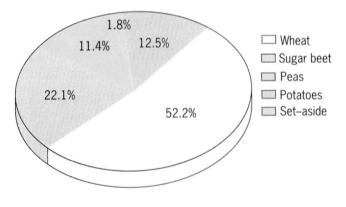

Fig. 8.21 Combine harvesting at Grange Farm

year cycle (**rotation**) (Fig. 8.19). No one crop is grown in the same field in successive years. This helps to maintain the soil's fertility and control any weeds and pests associated with particular crops.

Agribusiness

Grange Farm is typical of arable farming in much of eastern England today: it is a large-scale, highly efficient farm, organised on scientific and business principles. This type of farming, which includes a chain of suppliers of inputs (e.g. seed, fertiliser), food producers (i.e. farmers), and food processors and retailers, is known as **agribusiness**. Grange Farm belongs to a group of seven farms, which cover nearly 2500 hectares in North Lincolnshire. The farms belong to a single family business. Grange Farm has 272 hectares of arable land, six full-time labourers and various casual workers employed at different times of the year.

Being part of a large business enterprise gives Grange Farm several advantages. The main one is that it can reduce the costs of its inputs. For instance, buying fertiliser and pesticides (agro-chemicals) in bulk is cheaper; machinery can be shared between the seven farms; the cost of administration can be dealt with at a central office, and so on. We refer to these advantages of size as **economies of scale**.

Cultivation at Grange Farm is intensive. Crop yields are high, partly because of the favourable climate and soils, and partly because inputs of agro-chemicals and capital equipment, such as tractors, combines, grain driers, refrigerated stores, etc., are high.

Government farm policies

Government policies can also influence farming.

◆ In the European Union (EU), the choice of crops and methods of farming often depends on subsidies from the Common Agricultural Policy (CAP) and individual governments. For example, shortages of vegetable oil in the EU in the 1970s led to CAP subsidies for growing oilseed rape.

◆ The CAP also guarantees to buy cereals, potatoes, sugar beet and peas at a given minimum price. This led to over-production and huge food surpluses in the EU in the 1980s. We can see one effect of this at Grange Farm. Some land is 'set-aside' and is not used for cropping. By paying farmers to take arable land out of cultivation, the EU hopes to reduce food surpluses. Overall, 18 per cent of the arable land at Grange Farm and its 'sister' farms is in 'set-aside'.

Markets

The choice of crops and methods of cultivation at Grange Farm are also affected by the location of markets. Several crops are grown under contract to large food companies such as Birds Eye. These companies often insist on strict conditions for cultivation (e.g. inputs of fertiliser, types of seed, previous crops, etc.) as well as crop quality.

EXERCISES

12 Study Figures 8.19 and 8.21. Suggest how the size and shape of fields assist the use of machinery on the farm. What other feature of Figure 8.21 helps the use of machinery?

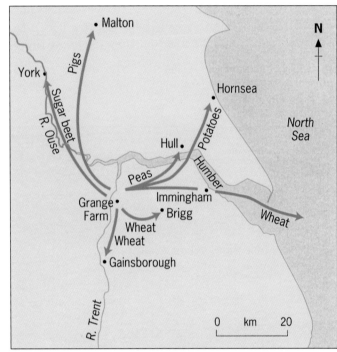

Fig. 8.22 Main markets for Grange Farm products.

FACTFILE

The Common Agricultural Policy (CAP)

The CAP covers the countries of the European Union. It provides a wide range of grants and subsidies to farmers that aim to:

• *ensure a fair standard of living for the agricultural community and stablise farm incomes;*
• *ensure food safety and food quality for consumers;*
• *develop alternative job and income opportunities for farmers and their families;*
• *conserve and protect rural environments;*
• *make farming more sustainable.*

The CAP has been reformed on several occasions, most recently in 2000.

• *Price subsidies: arable farmers growing cereals, oilseeds, proteins and linseed receive a minimum price for their crops if prices fall below an agreed threshold. They also receive area payments i.e. a subsidy for each hectare of arable land. Beef and sheep farmers get a subsidy for each animal. In 2000, the special premium scheme for*

beef cattle was worth between £76.45 and £100.27 per head. Area payments were also made to upland farmers on a maximum of 700 hectares of rough grazing land (£13 for the first 350 hectares; £6.50 for the next 350 hectares). However, this money was paid only to farmers who had stocking levels of less than 1.2 animals per hectare. This incentive was designed to de-intensify farming and protect upland environments from overgrazing.

• *Grants: grants are available for farm modernisation, conservation, converting farmland to woodland and off-land enterprises such as tourism, golf courses etc.*

• *Set-aside: farmers are paid to withdraw arable land from cultivation. The purpose of set-aside is to prevent over-production. Currently, farmers who take part in the set-aside scheme must withdraw 10 per cent of their arable land from cultivation for 5 years. In the UK in 1999, out of 4.3 million hectares of arable land, 586 000 were set-aside. Set-aside has also brought significant environmental benefits to the countryside.*

Vining peas are grown under contract to Birds Eye on Grange Farm because Birds Eye have a freezing plant nearby at Hull (Fig. 8.22). This means that peas can be delivered to the plant within 40 minutes of picking. Sugar beet, also grown under contract, is sent to the sugar refinery at York. Wheat is sent to Brigg for milling as animal feed, and to Gainsborough for milling for biscuits and bread. Some wheat is also exported through the Humber port of Immingham. Potatoes are grown on contract to a large food processing firm at Hornsea in East Yorkshire. However, the bulk of the potato crop is kept in a huge refrigerated store on the farm, and sold direct to wholesalers and supermarkets when prices are favourable. Finally, pigs are sent to a bacon factory at Malton in North Yorkshire, which supplies Tesco and Safeway supermarkets.

CASE STUDY

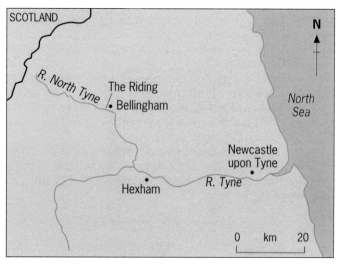

Fig. 8.23 Location of The Riding.

Fig. 8.24 The Riding.

8.10 Hill farming in the UK

The Riding is a hill farm in the North Pennines in Northumberland (Fig. 8.23) Covering 385 hectares, the farm extends from the flood plain of the River North Tyne on to the surrounding moorland (Fig. 8.25). High precipitation, cool summers and poor soils place severe limits on upland farms such as The Riding.

FACTFILE

- *Altitude: 110–300 m*
- *Mean July temperature: 13.7°C*
- *Mean annual precipitation: 900 mm*
- *Growing season: May to September*
- *Soils: Poor – acidic, clayey and peaty. Better quality, sandy soils in the valley bottom.*

Livestock enterprises

Like most farms in highland Britain, The Riding specialises in livestock, in this case lambs and calves. About 950 lambs a year are produced and 'finished' (i.e. fattened for market) on the farm. About 100 calves are also reared each year for beef. All of the lambs and calves are sold to a farm co-operative near Newcastle-upon-Tyne. Wool from the ewes provides additional income.

Farming systems in the uplands are extensive (Fig. 8.27). At The Riding, the poor-quality grazing supports sheep densities of only 3 to 4 per hectare. Inputs of chemical fertiliser are low. Indeed the farm is largely self-sufficient. All winter feed (hay, silage, turnips, barley) is grown on the farm (Fig. 8.28).

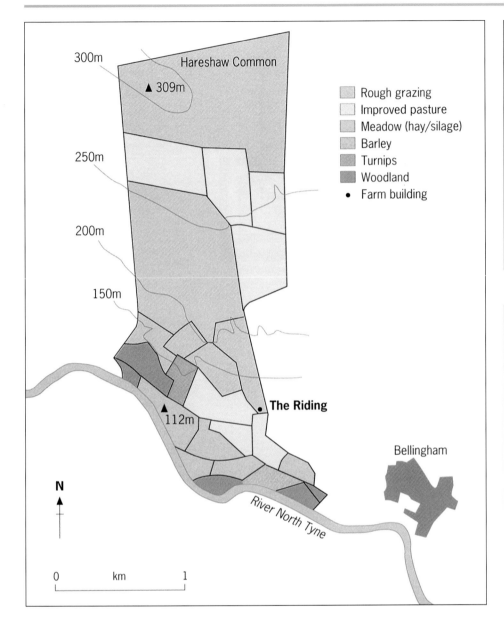

EXERCISES

14a Study Figure 8.25 and suggest reasons for the location of hay/silage, barley and turnips on the farm.
b* Describe the location of The Riding's farm buildings in relation to the farm's area. What advantages does this location have?
c* Suggest the possible advantages of using contract labour rather than full-time labour.

EXERCISES

15a Trace an outline sketch of the main features in Figure 8.24. On your outline, show the main types of land use (i.e. rough grazing, meadow, improved pasture, and woodland)
b* Using the evidence of your outline sketch and Figure 8.25, describe and explain how land use is influenced by slope and altitude.
c Read the section on the CAP (page 133), then comment on stocking densities at The Riding. What are their possible effects on the upland environment.

Fig. 8.25 (above) Lay-out and land use: The Riding.

Labour

The Riding is a tenant farm run by a manager, Mr Lurati. He is the only full-time worker. Until 1979, there were three full-time workers. Today Mr Lurati gets around the farm on a four-wheeler motor bike. This has enabled him to run the farm by himself. At busy times like during sheep clipping, dipping and harvesting, contract labour is also used.

Fig. 8.26 (right) Sheep shearing, The Riding.

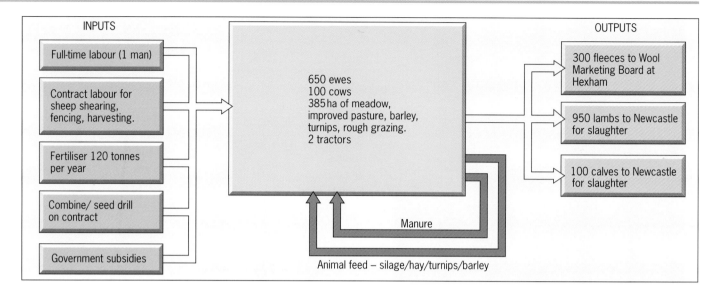

Fig. 8.27 The Riding: farm system.

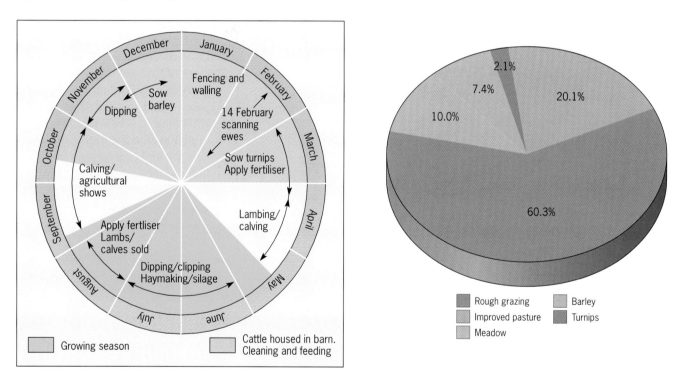

Fig. 8.28 (above left) The farming year at The Riding.

Fig. 8.29 (above right) Land use: The Riding.

Subsidies

We often describe hill farming as marginal. This means that it is barely profitable. The CAP helps farmers in 'less-favoured areas' like the North Pennines by giving subsidies for each head of livestock, and area payments. Without this assistance, many farms and rural communities in the uplands could not survive. Grants for woodland planting, land drainage, stonewalling, etc. are also taken up by The Riding.

8.11 Horticulture in the Netherlands

FACTFILE

- *Horticulture occupies approximately 58 000 hectares or just 3 per cent of the Netherlands' agricultural area.*
- *There are nearly 15 500 horticultural holdings in the Netherlands.*
- *Horticulture accounts for 35 per cent of the value of Dutch agricultural products.*
- *Horticulture accounts for 25 per cent of the value of Dutch agricultural exports, and about 5 per cent of the value of all Dutch exports.*

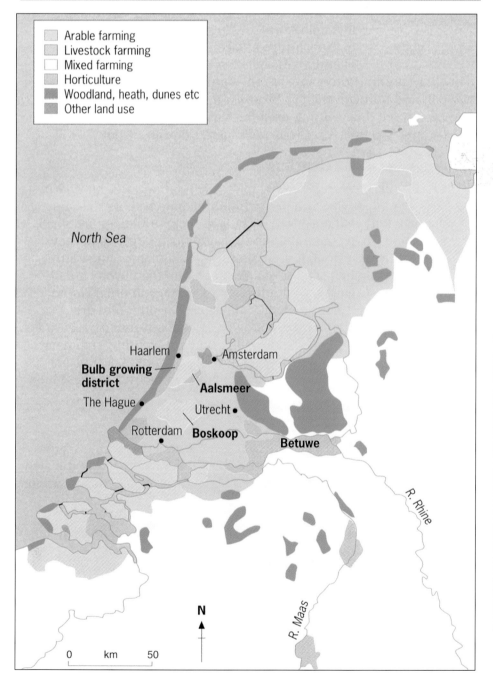

Arable farming
Livestock farming
Mixed farming
Horticulture
Woodland, heath, dunes etc
Other land use

North Sea

Haarlem
Bulb growing district
The Hague
Rotterdam
Boskoop
Amsterdam
Aalsmeer
Utrecht
Betuwe
R. Rhine
R. Maas

N

0   km   50

Fig. 8.30 Distribution of types of agriculture in the Netherlands.

REMEMBER
Intensive farming has high inputs (labour, fertiliser etc.) per hectare, and high outputs (yields) per hectare. Dutch horticulture is highly intensive. Extensive farming has low inputs and low yields per hectare. Farming in upland Britain, e.g. The Riding, is extensive.

EXERCISES

17 Study the Factfile on Dutch horticulture. Calculate the average size of horticultural holdings in the Netherlands.
18a Study Figure 8.30. Describe the distribution of horticulture in the Netherlands.
b What physical advantage do bulb growers have in the area shown in Fig. 8.31?
c What evidence in Fig. 8.31 suggests that farming in this bulb-growing area is intensive?
d* List and explain the possible physical disadvantages for horticulture in this area.

Fig. 8.31 Bulb fields in the Netherlands.

EXERCISES

19* Growers in Westland still face some physical and economic risks, in spite of the artificial conditions provided for plants by glasshouses. Suggest what these risks might be?

Horticulture, or market gardening, is the intensive cultivation of high-value crops such as fruit, vegetables, flowers, bulbs and garden shrubs. It is a major branch of agriculture in the Netherlands. There are a number of specialist horticultural regions in the Netherlands (Fig. 8.30). They include the world-famous bulb fields of the Haarlem area, the glasshouses growing salad crops in the Westland, ornamental trees and shrubs at Boskoop, and orchards in the Betuwe.

Horticulture is both labour intensive and capital intensive. Because of the small size of horticultural holdings (in the crowded western Netherlands smallholdings of less than one hectare are common) intensive methods and reliance on the high value of crops are essential.

The success of Dutch horticulture is due partly to technology and organisation. It is a sophisticated, high-tech type of farming. Growers are supported by scientific research and advisory services. There are many horticultural co-operatives. They provide the credit to growers for materials and horticultural products. Co-operative auctions, where growers can sell their output, exist for many horticultural products. One of these – at Aalsmeer – is the world's largest flower auction.

Bulb growing near Haarlem

The famous bulb-growing area occupies just 3000 hectares on the coast near Haarlem (Fig. 8.31). Situated behind the dune belt, its soils are well-drained, lime rich and ideal for bulb growing. Holdings are small (just 5 hectares on average) though they are much larger than they were 30 years ago. Although the bulb fields are a major tourist attraction in the spring when the flowers are in bloom, the flowers are of secondary interest. They are cut off at an early stage in order not to exhaust the bulbs. Crocus, daffodil, tulip and hyacinth bulbs are exported all over the world. Bulb growing is a labour-intensive business. Demand for labour is particularly high at times of planting, removing flower heads, harvesting, peeling, grading and packing. Local casual labour (including children during school holidays) is used at these busy times.

The Westland: 'glass city'

The Westland is a small, highly urbanised region between the Hague and the Hook of Holland. Horticulture was initially attracted to the area by its sandy soils. Today, there are no longer any physical advantages for horticulture in the Westland: virtually all production takes place in heated glasshouses (Fig. 8.32). The main specialisms are salad crops (tomatoes, lettuce, cucumbers), cut flowers and pot plants. Capital investment is very high. Heating, ventilation, humidity, watering and fertilising are computer controlled. Even the soils are often artificial! The average size of each holding is barely one hectare. None the less, because of the intensity of production, such small holdings are profitable.

Fig. 8.32 The 'glass city'.

8.12 Summary: Agricultural systems

KEY SKILLS OPPORTUNITIES
C1.2: Ex. 1b, 1c, 2b, 3, 4a, 5a, 8a, 10, 11, 12, 14a, 15b, 18a, 18c, 18d, 19;
C1/2.3: Ex. 1b, 1c, 2a, 2c, 14b, 15c, 16, 18a, 18b;
C2.2: Ex. 7c; **N1/2.2**: Ex. 4c, 6a, 8b, 17; **N1/2.3**: Ex. 6b, 6c, 8c

Key ideas	Generalisations and detail
Agriculture is an important economic activity.	• About 40 per cent of the world's economically active population works in agriculture. • 95 per cent of the agricultural workforce is in LEDCs. • Agriculture is the biggest user of land: 37 per cent of the world's land area is used for agriculture.
Agriculture is different from other economic activities.	• Agriculture relies heavily on the physical environment (especially climate). Farmers have limited control over climate. Agriculture also depends on the biological cycles of crops and animals.
Farms are both ecological and economic systems.	• Farms are systems, with inputs, outputs (yields) and food chains. • Outputs comprise crops and livestock products. • The main inputs are sunlight, precipitation, soil nutrients, agro-chemicals, labour, capital (machinery etc.). • The amount of inputs and outputs per hectare determine the intensity of farming.
Agriculture is just one link in a much larger integrated food system/chain.	• Food systems are chains of activities, from agricultural suppliers to supermarkets. • Farms are the production side of the food system, which includes industries supplying the farm, such as fertiliser and agricultural machinery makers, and purchasers of farm products, such as food processors and retailers.
Types of agricultural enterprise are defined according to several different criteria.	• The dominant enterprise – crops or livestock – defines agriculture. • Intensity of farming is determined by the level of inputs and outputs per hectare. • Commercial farming is a profit-making form of agriculture and non-commercial is a subsistence form.
On a global and national scale, climate is the major influence on agriculture.	• Climate determines the broad limits of what a farmer can grow. On a global scale, insufficient warmth and moisture explains the absence of farming in many high-latitude, hot desert and mountainous areas. • In the UK, the contrast between the arable east and pastoral west is largely related to climate.
Many traditional agricultural systems are sustainable but under threat.	• Shifting agriculture and nomadic herding are well adapted to harsh environments and are sustainable systems, i.e. they can be practised without long-term damage to the environment. However, both systems are under threat from population growth, habitat destruction, government policies and natural hazards, such as drought.
Modern farming in much of the economically developed world is agribusiness.	• Large-scale farming, based on scientific and business principles, is known as agribusiness. Agribusiness is capital intensive, employs expert farm managers and is geared to contract farming. In addition to local climatic and soil conditions, crops grown and animals reared are influenced by local market opportunities and government policies.
Farming in upland areas is strongly limited by the physical environment.	• Climate, soils and relief place strict limits on farmers' choice of enterprise in the uplands. • Farming in highland Britain is extensive and livestock based. Without assistance from the Common Agricultural Policy, most upland farms would not be profitable.

9 Agriculture: problems and change

9.1 Introduction

Over the last thirty years, agricultural change in LEDCs has been closely related to population growth. There has been an urgent need to increase food production to feed the increasing population. Some countries have responded with high-tech solutions; others have preferred a low-tech approach. Whatever the approach, the pressure to produce more food has often caused serious damage to the environment.

In the MEDCs, recent agricultural change has most often been due to government policies. In the 1970s and 1980s the European Union's (EU) policies favoured expanding food production. Not only did this cause huge economic problems through over-production, but it was also ruinous for the environment. As a result, policies in the 1990s shifted. Now, the emphasis is on reducing food production and protecting the environment.

CASE STUDY

9.2 Low-tech change in Ethiopia

FACTFILE

- *Ethiopia is the ninth-largest country in Africa, and has an area four times greater than the UK's.*
- *In 2000, its estimated population was 64.12 million.*
- *Ethiopia's population is rising rapidly: its current doubling time is 29 years.*
- *Ethiopia is one of the world's poorest countries: half the employed population works in agriculture.*
- *The physical environment creates problems for agriculture: much of the country is mountainous, and the lowlands that surround the mountains are dry and desert-like.*
- *The mountains have higher rainfall than the lowlands, and greater potential for agriculture.*
- *Population density averages 50 persons per sq km in the highlands, compared to just 10 per sq km in the lowlands.*

Fig. 9.1 Location of Adami Tulu.

Fig. 9.2 Using a simple ox-drawn scratch plough.

Traditional farming in Adami Tulu

Physical environment

Adami Tulu is a district in Ethiopia's central highlands about 180 kilometres south of the capital Addis Ababa (Fig. 9.1). About the same size as a small English county, it has a population of 100 000 and is one of Ethiopia's more favoured agricultural regions. Rainfall at about 800 mm a year is well above the country's average (Fig. 9.4). There are also large water resources awaiting development in lakes Ziway, Abriyala and Langaro. But despite the region's above-average rainfall, the growing season (the period when crops can be produced) is short – crops can be grown only during the summer rains. Another problem is the shallow, infertile sandy soil.

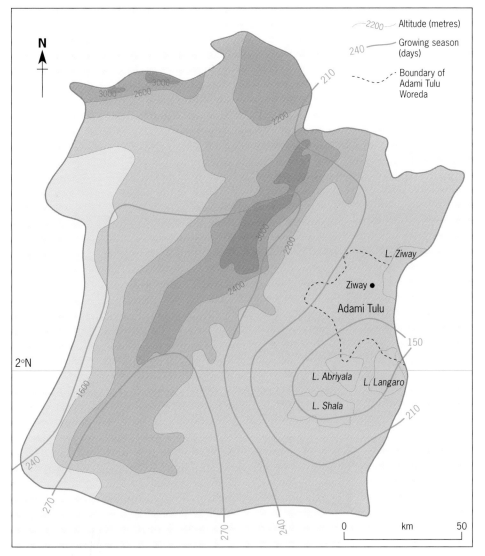

Fig. 9.3 Adami Tulu: altitude and length of growing season.

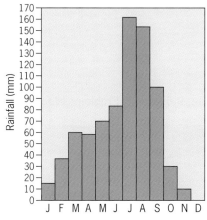

Fig. 9.4 (above) Average monthly rainfall: Adami Tulu.

Cropping and livestock herding

Traditional farming in Adami Tulu is a combination of cropping and livestock herding. The farmers live in permanent villages, though many were nomadic herders until recently, when they were forcibly settled by the Ethiopian government. Unlike the shifting cultivators of the rainforest (Chapter 8), the farmers of Adami Tulu cultivate the same land every year. There is no irrigation. The farmers rely on the summer rains to water their crops – a system known as **rain-fed agriculture**. Because the rains last only for a few months, the land produces only one crop a year.

Farming technology in Adami Tulu is very simple. Farmers till the land with primitive ox-drawn ploughs, which only scratch (rather than turn) the soil (Fig. 9.2). Sowing, weeding and harvesting are done by hand. Threshing is done by walking oxen on the harvested grain. The main crops are maize, teff (a type

Fig. 9.5 (below) Annual rainfall at Adami Tulu.

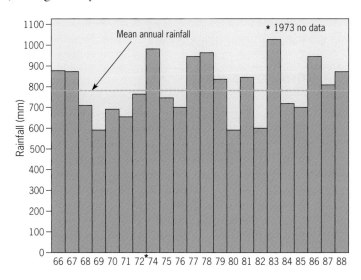

141

Mountains too high and steep for cultivation.

Rainfall is low and erratic. Drought between 1984 and 1987 caused crop failure.

Problem of fetching water from distant wells and ponds. Lack of facilities for grinding cereals.

Traditional crops are low yielding and mature slowly.

Too few ponds for water storage. Ponds help to overcome droughts and make water available in the dry season.

Maize cultivated as a monoculture, exhausting the soil. Diets lack balance. Too much dependence on cereals.

Soil erosion. Wind blows topsoil from overgrazed pastures and deforested areas.

Deforestation caused by overgrazing and felling trees for firewood.

Soil erosion. Gullies formed by rainwater running off the fields.

Overstocking of livestock on unfenced pasture. Overgrazing destroys vegetation and leads to soil erosion.

Lack of firewood. Farmers forced to burn dung – a valuable fertiliser.

Fig. 9.6 (above) Problems of farming in the Ethiopian Highlands.

Fig. 9.7 Fetching water from the river,

Fig. 9.8 Gully erosion.

Fig. 9.9 Overgrazed pasture.

of cereal) and haricot beans. Livestock, mainly cattle and goats, is kept for milk, meat, hides, dung and draught purposes. There are no inputs of fertiliser from outside. Overall, farming is of low intensity.

Farmers produce crops and livestock both for food and for sale. They belong to co-operatives, which provide seeds, tools and credit. Until the overthrow of Ethiopia's communist government in 1989, all cash crops were sold through the co-operatives to the government. Today, farmers are once again free to sell their produce at local markets.

Fig. 9.10 Making irrigation channels in Adami Tulu.

FACTFILE

The aims of the Self-Help project in Adami Tulu
- *To make the region self-sufficient in food production (after drought in the 1980s had forced the people to depend on food aid).*
- *To make farming* **sustainable**, *so that it no longer harmed the environment.*
- *To develop irrigation (Fig. 9.10). This would give higher crop yields, two or more crops a year, and widen the choice of crops to include fruit and vegetables. The last would improve people's diets and provide money through cash sales.*
- *To use the local farmers' knowledge and skills. Thus, when the project ended, it was hoped that farmers would be able to maintain the improvements themselves.*
- *To make a start on the long-term improvement of the environment. Measures were taken to reduce soil erosion, stop overgrazing, and encourage reafforestation (Figs. 9.8, 9.9, 9.11).*

The development project

In 1984, a ten-year aid project designed to improve farming in Adami Tulu began. The project was funded by an Irish charity called Self-Help, working in partnership with the Ethiopian government and the local farmers. Poverty and environmental degradation were the two most urgent problems that had to be tackled (Fig. 9.6). The project adopted a low-cost, low-technology approach (see Factfile).

Results

By 1994, most of the project's aims had been achieved.
- New varieties of seed were introduced and proved popular among farmers. As a result, crop yields increased greatly.
- Farmers fenced off their pasturelands to provide forage for livestock in the dry season and prevent overgrazing.
- Farmers planted hundreds of thousands of trees for firewood and as shelter belts to protect soils from erosion.
- Tree nurseries and a research centre for fruit and vegetables were set up, and 38 hectares of farmland irrigated. This will rise to 200 hectares.
- The introduction of irrigation allowed fruit and vegetables to be grown. There is a ready market for these crops in the capital Addis Ababa, which is linked to Adami Tulu by a 150-kilometre tarmac road.
- Several flour mills for grinding cereals were built and the number of ponds and boreholes was increased. The ponds provide water in the dry season, extend the growing period, and help farmers to overcome drought. Boreholes provide clean drinking water.
- Because water is more available, it makes the lives of women easier. Traditionally, women have been responsible not only for cooking, but also for the laborious task of carrying water. (Fig. 9.7).

Fig. 9.11 Tree planting in Adami Tulu.

EXERCISES

3 Study Figure 9.12.
a Explain how • reafforestation • fencing-off pasture • irrigation and using improved varieties of seed can break the vicious circle in Figure 9.12.
b* Even with the improvements such as reafforestation, irrigation and fencing of pastures, the farming system in Figure 9.12 is likely to be unsustainable in the long term. Can you explain why?

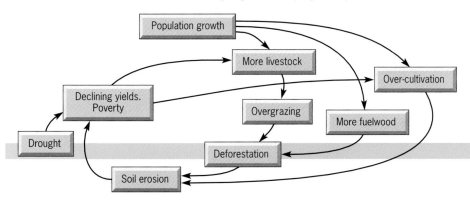

Fig. 9.12 Population growth, poverty and environmental degradation.

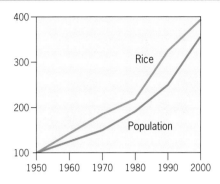

Fig. 9.13 Population growth and rice production in India: 1950–2000.

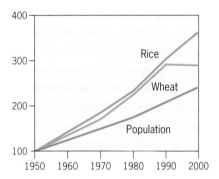

Fig. 9.14 World population growth compared with wheat and rice production: 1950–2000.

EXERCISES

4 Study Figure 9.14.
a How do you think the increase in rice production in the world and the growth of population are related?
b Millions of people still suffer food shortages and famine in spite of the increase in production shown in Figure 9.14. Can you suggest reasons for this?

9.3 High-tech change: the green revolution

In the last forty years, high-yielding varieties (HYVs) of rice and wheat have been introduced into many LEDCs. The resulting increase in food production has been dramatic (Fig. 9.13). This innovation has become known as the green revolution. Plant breeders in the Philippines and Mexico developed HYVs, which then spread to many parts of the economically developing world (especially Asia) in the 1960s and 1970s (Fig. 9.15). For example, India, which until the 1960s had suffered frequent food shortages, became self-sufficient in cereals. As well as increased output, crop yields became more reliable, and the faster-maturing HYVs allowed for more than one crop a year. And because the HYVs gave more food per hectare, farmers could use more of their land for other crops, such as vegetables.

Despite its successes, the green revolution has not benefited everyone.

◆ HYVs of rice need irrigation. This is a problem because many of the poorest parts of the world (e.g. Ethiopia) depend on rain-fed agriculture.
◆ HYVs rely on chemical fertilisers and pesticides, which are often unavailable (or unaffordable) to peasant farmers.
◆ Seeds from HYVs are infertile so farmers must buy seed every year.
◆ Cultivation of HYVs based on chemical fertilisers is unsustainable in the long term.

Traditional wet rice cultivation in East Asia

The green revolution has enabled continuous cropping of rice and has replaced traditional wet rice farming in large parts of East Asia. But is this an improvement on the traditional sustainable farming systems?

For hundreds of years, wet rice cultivation in China and Japan has been highly successful (Figs. 9.16, 9.17). It is in balance with the environment and provides an adequate diet for millions of people. Traditional wet rice cultivation is based on small farms and plentiful supplies of labour, and is highly intensive. As a result, yields per hectare are high and support rural population densities, which are among the highest in the world.

Methods of cultivation

The basis of wet rice farming is management of water. Rice is cultivated in tiny fields (padis) surrounded by earth embankments, which keep the water in when the fields are flooded. Rice seedlings are planted by hand in nursery beds, in damp, carefully prepared soil. When they are about 30 centimetres tall they are transplanted into the flooded fields (Fig. 9.15). A few weeks before harvesting, the fields are drained. The land is then used for other crops. All of this takes a great deal of labour, but gives overall food yields similar to HYVs.

Sustainable cultivation

This farming system is known as a **polyculture** (Fig. 9.17). It means that several different crops are grown, including vegetables and mulberries for silkworms.

Fig. 9.15 Transplanting high-yielding rice, Java.

Even the field embankments are cultivated. Manure from the silkworms, and even human sewage, is returned to the fields. Tanks that supply water for irrigation are stocked with fish to provide protein. The whole farming system is self-sustaining and does not rely on inputs from outside.

Technological fix – unsustainable rice monoculture

In many parts of East Asia the green revolution has replaced traditional rice polyculture with a rice **monoculture** – a type of commercial agriculture that may not be appropriate for the economically developing world. It relies on large inputs of chemical fertiliser and pesticides from outside. Smaller farmers struggle to pay for these chemical inputs. Thus the benefits of higher yields go to more prosperous farmers who can buy agro-chemicals in bulk and produce rice more cheaply. The small farmers are forced off the land to become paid labourers on larger farms, or migrants to nearby cities.

Fig. 9.16 Water buffalo ploughing a rice paddy, Java.

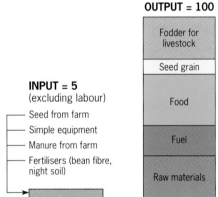

Fig. 9.17 Inputs and outputs: traditional wet rice polyculture in East Asia.

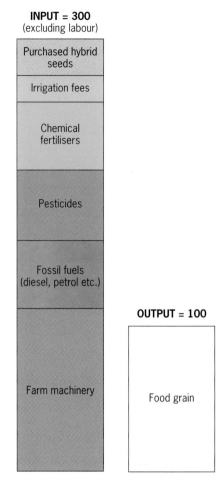

Fig. 9.18 Inputs and outputs: green revolution rice monoculture in East Asia.

Although the green revolution has brought prosperity to large irrigated farms, millions of farmers have gained little. This is especially the case for farmers who depend on rain-fed agriculture and grow coarse grains, such as sorghum, millet and lentils. Attention is now being switched to these farmers. This is good news for Africa, which so far has shared few of the benefits of the green revolution.

9.4 Agriculture and the environment

In this section, we see how modern agriculture has contributed to environmental degradation in the UK. We shall also look at the attempts of governments to make agriculture more environmentally friendly.

The EU spends nearly half of its annual budget on agriculture through the Common Agricultural Policy (CAP). If the CAP has been costly for the taxpayer, it has imposed even higher costs on the environment. Hedgerows have been destroyed, soils eroded, and groundwater supplies contaminated. Meanwhile, many wild plants and animals are in decline. We refer to all these changes as **environmental degradation**. The worst effects have been felt in the intensively farmed arable regions such as eastern England (Fig. 9.19).

EXERCISES

5 Make a table to compare the main features of traditional wet rice polyculture and green revolution rice monoculture in East Asia (Figs. 9.17, 9.18). Use the following headings: farm sizes, fertiliser inputs, farm machinery, labour, yields, variety of crops.

6* Write a report summarising the advantages of traditional wet rice polyculture over green revolution monoculture.

145

Fig. 9.19 Agricultural prairie, South Downs, Sussex.

EU farm policies

The CAP has been one of the main reasons for environmental degradation in the UK in the last 30 years. Arable farmers were encouraged to produce as much as possible, because the CAP guaranteed to buy everything that farmers produced (at prices well above the world's average). In a free market, if there was a surplus of wheat or barley, prices would fall and farmers would automatically grow less. Under the CAP, the EU set a minimum price for cereal crops, sugar beet, oilseed and potatoes. If farmers could not find buyers at this price then the EU stepped in and bought the crops. As output rose, so too did the mountains of unsold grain, beef, butter and other products.

How did farmers achieve these increases in production? Essentially they did two things: they cultivated more land, and they farmed existing land more intensively.

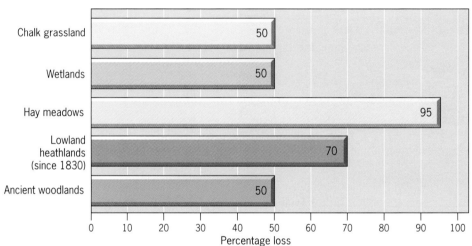

Fig.9.20 Loss of wildlife habitats in the UK: 1945–98.

Farming more land

The CAP made it profitable for farmers to plough up almost any kind of uncultivated land – chalk grassland, woodland, heathland and marshes – in order to increase output. For example, since 1945, the UK has lost 50 per cent of all its chalk grassland and 95 per cent of its limestone grassland (Fig. 9.20). Not only are these areas attractive countryside, they are also valuable wildlife habitats, supporting many rare plants and animals.

Farming the land more intensively

Because the CAP paid farmers for everything they produced, farmers naturally tried to produce more from their land. They achieved this mainly by farming more intensively. By using more chemical fertilisers and pesticides, their yields rose dramatically (Table 9.1).

9.5 The impact of farming on the countryside

Modern intensive farming, encouraged by the CAP, caused serious environmental damage in the 1970s and 1980s, especially in the arable areas of eastern England.

EXERCISES

7a Using Excel, draw a bar graph to illustrate the information in Table 9.1.
b Compare the percentage increase between 1939 and 1968, with that between 1968 and 2000. Present this exercise as a word-processed document, complete with an imported bar graph.

Table 9.1 Wheat yields (tonnes/ha): UK 1939-1994

1939	2.0
1944	2.2
1958	2.7
1968	3.5
1978	5.3
1988	6.1
1994	7.4
2000	7.9

Loss of hedgerows

The most obvious change to lowland landscapes has been the removal of hedgerows to create huge prairie-like fields (Fig. 9.19). Between 1947 and 1990, 377 000 kilometres of hedges were ripped up in the UK. For many years, the government gave subsidies to farmers to remove hedges because small fields are inefficient compared to large ones: tractors and combine harvesters have to turn more often and, in order to turn, they have to leave broad strips alongside hedges uncultivated. Also, in small fields, a relatively large area is occupied by hedges and cannot be cultivated.

The destruction of hedges not only affects the appearance of the countryside. Hedges are an important habitat for wildlife, particularly birds, insects and small mammals. Loss of habitat leads to the disappearance of wildlife and reduces the number of species (**biodiversity**) in the countryside.

> *EXERCISES*
>
> **8** Study Figures 9.21 and 9.22
> **a** Explain how the landscape in Figure 9.21 is: (1) efficient for modern agriculture; (2) of little value to wildlife.
> **b*** Compare the landscape in Figure 9.21 with that in Figure 9.22. Which do you find more attractive? Justify your choice in class discussion.

Fig. 9.21 Intensive arable farming, Fens, East England.

Fig.9.22 Traditional farming landscape, Cheshire.

Pesticides and pollution

The increased use of pesticides also has reduced biodiversity. After treatment with pesticides, traditional hay meadows, with their colourful flowers, become monocultures of grass. Insects and birds that depend on the wild flowers lose a valuable food source and decline too. This is one reason why 24 bird species that breed on farmland declined between 1970 and 2000.

Chemical fertilisers pollute streams and rivers. Nitrates are easily washed from the soil by rainfall and run into water courses where they have a fertilising effect. Algae grow rapidly, use up the oxygen in the water and fish and aquatic insects die. This process is called **eutrophication** (Fig. 9.23).

Fig. 9.23 Eutrophication of a water course.

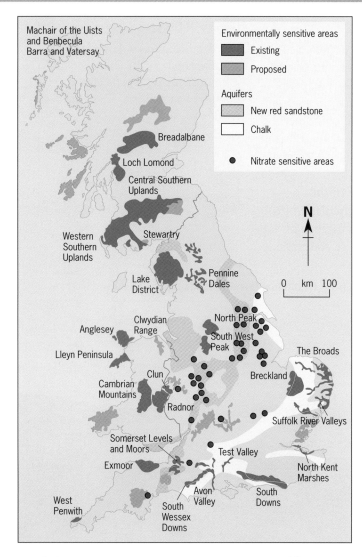

Fig. 9.24 (above) Environmentally and nitrate-sensitive areas and major aquifers in Britain.

Fig. 9.25 Set-aside land, Hampshire.

Water containing nitrates sinks underground into porous rocks (**aquifers**). These are the main sources of drinking water in eastern England (Fig. 9.24). There is concern about the long-term effects on human health of nitrates in drinking water. They have been linked with stomach cancer, blood pressure problems and 'blue-baby' syndrome. In 1990, 1.7 million people in the UK relied on drinking water that had nitrate levels above recommended safe limits.

Soil erosion

Soil erosion occurs wherever farming takes place (see Section 9.8). It is an increasing problem in the arable districts of eastern England, where the increased use of chemical fertilisers and heavy machines has altered the soil's structure. The removal of hedges makes the situation worse. Hedges protect soils (especially the lighter ones) from being blown away.

9.6 Modern farming and environmental protection

Modern intensive farming is not sustainable. It survives only through massive inputs of chemicals, which damage the environment. Since the late 1980s, the EU has recognised the problems and introduced measures to make farming more environmentally friendly. But agro-environmental schemes represent only 3 per cent of the CAP's spending on subsidies.

Extensification

In the 1990s, the EU made strenuous efforts to reduce the output of farming. Indirectly this also benefited the environment.

Set-aside

Since 1988, arable farmers have been paid to grow nothing. Currently, they have to set aside 10 per cent of their land as a condition for receiving subsidies of £264 per hectare. By 2000, 14 per cent of arable land in the UK lay unused. Not only did this cut production, it also had benefits for wildlife.

Area payments

Since 1992, the level of price support (per tonne) for crops has been reduced. Gradually, price support is being replaced by fixed payments for each hectare cultivated. This should make it less attractive for farmers to get more from each hectare cultivated. The result – lower inputs of fertilisers and pesticides – should also benefit the environment.

Agro-environmental policies in the UK

A number of schemes provide grants to farmers to protect the environment and improve the countryside. Among these schemes are:

Figs 9.26 – 9.30 Landscapes and wildlife habitats under threat.

Countryside Stewardship

This is the government's main scheme. It aims to improve the natural beauty and diversity of the countryside, and improve public access. Agreements last for 10 years, and, in return for annual payments, farmers have to manage the land in an environmentally friendly way.

Environmentally Sensitive Areas (ESAs)

ESAs safeguard areas of countryside where the landscape, wildlife and historic interest is of national importance (Fig. 9.24). Farmers receive payments to compensate for using low-intensity, traditional farming methods. There are 22 ESAs, covering 10 per cent of farm land in Britain.

Farm Woodland Premium (FWP)

The FWP provides annual payments to farmers who convert agricultural land to woodland. In 1998, 3000 hectares entered the scheme.

Organic Farming Scheme (OFS)

The OFS gives grants to farmers to help them convert from conventional to **organic farming**. Organic farming is based on the sustainable use of the soil, avoiding the use of chemical fertilisers and pesticides. Similarly, antibiotics, hormones and other treatments are not used in livestock production.

Nitrate Sensitive Areas (NSAs)

There are 32 NSAs in England and Wales (Fig. 9.24) covering 35 000 hectares. In these areas, farmers receive compensation for using lower levels of nitrate fertiliser. Nitrates are a major polluter of water supplies and are harmful to people's health.

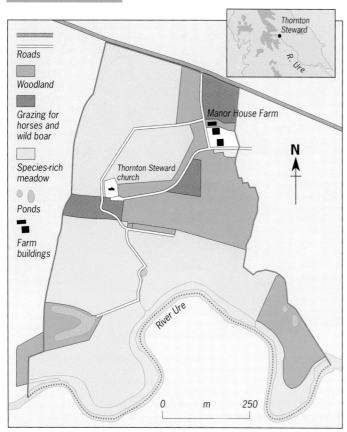

Fig. 9.31 (above) Manor House Farm.

Fig. 9.32 (above right) The farm meadows and woodland planting.

9.7 Conservation as a crop

Manor House Farm

Manor House Farm in Wensleydale, North Yorkshire (Fig. 9.31) was bought by its present owner Mr Jo Crossley in 1981. At the time, it was a run-down dairy farm of 100 hectares. It occupies a gentle south-facing valley slope and includes part of the flood plain of the River Ure (Fig. 9.32). The land is of good quality and, until 1973, most of it was used for cropping.

Mr Crossley is an experienced farmer. Previously he had farmed an intensive arable farm in North

Yorkshire. However, his main purpose at Manor House Farm is not food production, but environmental conservation. This does not give Mr Crossley the highest return, and he still has to make the farm profitable.

Grants for environmental protection and improvement
Manor House Farm receives a number of environmental grants from the British government.

◆ The meadows on the flood plain form an ESA. They are rich in wild flowers, insects and ground-nesting birds, so Mr Crossley gets compensation for using traditional, low-intensity methods to farm them. No chemical fertilisers or pesticides are permitted. Hay can be cut only once a year, and not before 15 July. This gives birds time to complete their nesting, and flowers time to seed.

◆ A FWP is paid for 25 hectares of mixed woodland (both deciduous and coniferous trees) which Mr Crossley has planted. Eventually these woodlands will produce timber, though they will take thirty years to mature.

◆ A hedgerow incentive scheme pays Mr Crossley to plant and maintain hedgerows on the farm.

◆ The Countryside Stewardship scheme has allowed Mr Crossley to make ponds for fishing and for wildlife habitats.

However, environmental grants alone do not provide sufficient income. Thus Mr Crossley rents out his meadows to local farmers for hay and for

EXERCISES

12a Draw a systems diagram (see Fig. 8.27) to show the inputs and outputs of Manor House Farm.

b Compare Manor House Farm with Grange Farm (see Section 8.9). What are the main differences in their approaches to farming? Try to explain them.

c* Should we pay farmers to look after the countryside rather than produce food? Write about your views on this matter and be prepared to defend them in discussion in class.

fattening lambs. He also lets 2.5 hectares to a small business specialising in breeding wild boar, and three hectares to a local livery stable for grazing. All of these enterprises are carried on at low intensity to encourage the greatest diversity of plant and animal life.

9.8 Soil erosion in the UK

Soil erosion is the removal of topsoil by water and wind faster than it can be replaced by natural processes. It is a worldwide problem, found wherever farming occurs. In the UK, soil erosion is most severe in eastern England. In this mainly arable farming region, an average of 20 tonnes of soil per hectare is lost each year. These losses are very serious. In just a few years, erosion can destroy soils that have taken thousands of years to develop.

Causes of soil erosion

In nature, the soil is usually covered with vegetation. Plants provide a protective cover, shielding the soil from erosion by wind and rain. Their roots also bind the soil together.

Cultivation

Cultivation removes the protective cover of vegetation, exposing the soil to erosion. For example, ploughing up the natural grasslands of the Great Plains of the USA led to massive wind erosion in the 1930s. So bad was the erosion that this region became known as the 'dust bowl' and huge areas of farmland were abandoned.

Overgrazing and deforestation

Lack of plant cover may occur not just through cultivation but because of overgrazing and deforestation. Both are common causes of soil erosion in LEDCs (Figs. 9.8, 9.9).

Mismanagement

Other causes of soil erosion include:
- cultivating steep hillslopes and ploughing up and down them rather than across, so that the furrows act as drainage channels, greatly increasing the rate of erosion;
- wheelings (tracks made in fields by farm machinery), which create artificial channels and erosion problems;
- cultivating land with heavy machinery, which compresses (compacts) the soil, damaging its natural drainage and increasing run-off and erosion;
- over-cultivation, which exhausts the soil and removes most of the humus that binds the soil particles together;
- the use of chemical rather than organic fertilisers, which degrades the topsoil into tiny, loose particles that are easily removed by wind and rain.

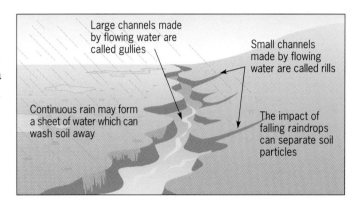

Fig. 9.33 Different types of water erosion.

Fig. 9.34 A landscape vulnerable to soil erosion.

Fig. 9.35 Soil erosion and gullying, Nottinghamshire.

EXERCISES

13 Study Figure 9.34.
a Suggest possible reasons why the landscape in Figure 9.34 is at risk from soil erosion.
b Describe and explain the types of soil erosion that might take place.

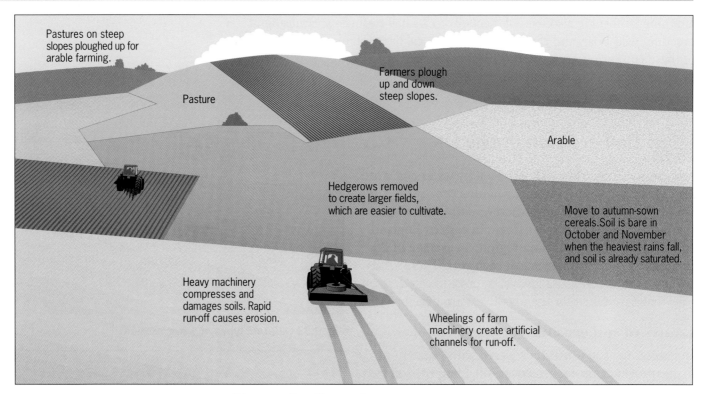

Pastures on steep slopes ploughed up for arable farming.

Pasture

Farmers plough up and down steep slopes.

Arable

Hedgerows removed to create larger fields, which are easier to cultivate.

Move to autumn-sown cereals.Soil is bare in October and November when the heaviest rains fall, and soil is already saturated.

Heavy machinery compresses and damages soils. Rapid run-off causes erosion.

Wheelings of farm machinery create artificial channels for run-off.

Fig. 9.36 A landscape vulnerable to soil erosion.

EXERCISES

14* Trace the outline of Figure 9.36 and modify the farming landscape to reduce the risk of soil erosion. Add notes to your sketch explaining the effects of the changes you have made.

Types of soil erosion

There are two main agents of soil erosion: water and wind.

Water erosion

Water erosion is the main problem in the UK, especially in autumn and winter. Rain runs off the surface carrying with it particles of soil, as well as seeds and fertilisers. As the water runs off the land it is concentrated in channels (Fig. 9.33). The smaller channels (rills) are not usually a problem because they can be ploughed out. However, larger gullies that cannot be crossed by farm machinery may develop (Fig. 9.35). The problem is particularly severe on steeply sloping fields.

Wind erosion

Wind erosion in the UK is a more localised problem. Areas with light, sandy and peaty soils are most at risk, e.g. the Vale of York, the Fens in Cambridgeshire and Lincolnshire, and the Breckland in Norfolk.

Early spring, when soils begin to dry out and winds are strong, is the most hazardous time. Tiny soil particles are lifted into the air and may be carried long distances. Coarser particles either bounce along (saltation) or roll along the surface (creep).

The effects of soil erosion

As well as the loss of soil, erosion decreases soil fertility and crop yields, thus increasing the farmer's costs of production. For example, seeds may be washed or blown away, roads and drains blocked by eroded soil, and crops sand-blasted by the wind, or smothered by wind-blown material. Off the farm, soil erosion increases the silt load of streams and rivers. As waters become muddy, aquatic plants, insects and fish may disappear. However, farmers can take measures to protect soils from erosion. (Table 9.2)

Table 9.2 Methods of protecting the soil from erosion in the UK

Contour ploughing	Ploughing across slopes.
Use of machinery	Avoid cultivating wet soils with heavy machinery.
Cover crops	Keep fields partly covered with some crops or crop residues left after harvest.
Wind breaks	Plant trees and hedges to protect the soil from strong winds. Lines of trees provide shelter for up to ten times their height.
Strip cropping	Grow several different crops in one field in strips. The crops ripen at different times so there is always some crop cover to give protection.
Crop rotations	Build up the soil's fertility and its organic content.
Convert arable to pasture	Pasture gives a 100 per cent plant cover. Soil erosion is minimal.
Plant fewer autumn cereals	If cereals are planted in spring, stubble and plant residues can be left in fields throughout the winter, thus reducing rates of water and wind erosion.

Fig. 9.37 Wind erosion.

9.9 Summary: Agriculture: problems and change

KEY SKILLS
OPPORTUNITIES
C1.1: Ex. 8b, 12c; **C1.2**:
Ex. 1a, 3a, 4a, 5, 10a, 11,
12b, 13a; **C2.1**: Ex. 8b,
12c; **IT1.2**: Ex. 7a, 7b;
IT2.3: Ex. 7a, 7b

Generalisations	Detail
There are both high- and low-tech approaches to increasing agricultural production in LEDCs.	• In Adami Tulu, a low-tech aid project designed to increase food production and improve the environment has been successful. • The green revolution is a high-tech approach to increasing food production. It has increased food output significantly in some LEDCs. However, many small farmers, and many areas in the economically developing world, have not benefited.
Low-tech improvements in agriculture in the economically developing world are likely to be more sustainable than high-tech ones.	• Low-tech improvements are affordable to poor peasant farmers. The use of simple technology allows the skills of local people to be used. • High-tech improvements are expensive and tend to benefit the rich more than the poor. • Low-tech improvements are more likely to be environmentally and economically sustainable.
There are chronic shortages of food in many of the poorest LEDCs.	• Food shortages stem from drought, rapid population growth, civil wars, etc. In times of famine many poor countries have to rely on food aid from MEDCs.
Population growth and agriculture have contributed to environmental degradation in the economically developing world.	• Rapid population growth has meant extending and intensifying agriculture to increase food production. This has put the environment under pressure in many parts of the economically developing world. The result is over-cultivation, overgrazing, deforestation, soil erosion, etc.
The Common Agriculture Policy has caused economic and environmental problems in the EU.	• The CAP encouraged the intensification and extension of farming. The result was huge food surpluses and environmental degradation (destruction of habitats, pollution, soil erosion, etc.). • In the 1980s and 1990s the CAP introduced measures to reduce surpluses (e.g. set-aside) and improve the environment (ESAs, woodland and hedgerow planting, nitrate reduction, landscape/habitat protection and improvement).
Soil erosion invariably accompanies cultivation.	• Soil erosion is widespread in the UK and especially in the arable areas of eastern England. Wind and rain are responsible for most soil erosion. • Soil erosion not only results in the loss of topsoil, it increases the costs of cultivation and reduces crop yields.
There is a range of conservation measures that can significantly reduce rates of soil erosion.	• Wind erosion can be lessened by planting shelter belts. • Strip cropping, the growing of cover crops and leaving crop residues in the fields reduces both wind and water erosion. Contour ploughing helps to conserve soils on hill slopes. • Keeping soils fertile with the use of manure makes soil erosion less likely.

EXERCISES

1 Study Figures 10.1–10.6.
a Identify each of the economic activities.
b State to which of the three main economic sectors each activity belongs.
c Explain why you selected that sector for each activity.

10.1 Introduction

We divide economic activities into four main sectors: **primary**, **secondary**, **tertiary** and **quaternary**. Service industries are so large and diverse that they occupy two separate sectors.

◆ The primary sector produces food and raw materials. It includes agriculture, fishing, forestry, mining and quarrying.
◆ The secondary sector is manufacturing industry.
◆ The tertiary sector comprises transport, communications and utilities such as water, gas and electricity.
◆ The quaternary sector includes producer services for commerce and industry (e.g. banking, research and development, advertising etc.) and services for individual consumers, such as education, health care and tourism.

Figs 10.1 – 10.6 Economic activities.

10.2 The distribution of industrial activities

From Figure 10.7, you can see that the importance of manufacturing industry varies from one country to another. Manufacturing is least important in the world's poorest countries. For example, LEDCs in Africa, such as Burundi, Uganda and Malawi, have fewer than 5 per cent of their working population in manufacturing industry. In contrast, manufacturing employs at least 20 per cent of the working population in most MEDCs.

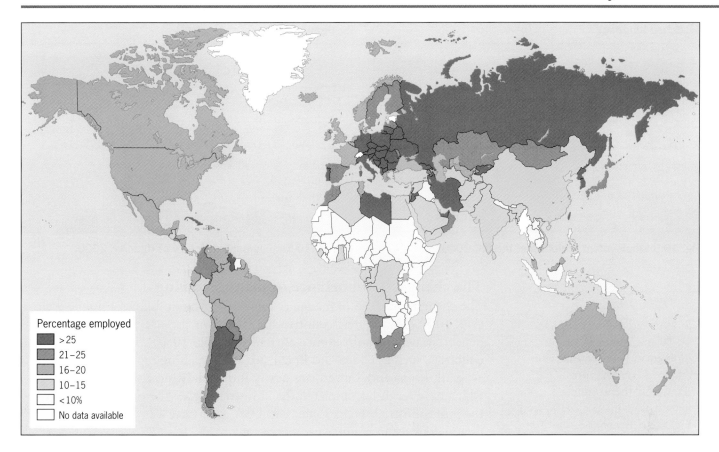

Explaining the global distribution of industrial activities

Figure 10.8 explains why the importance of manufacturing varies so much between countries. If we turn the clock back in Europe to the early-18th century, we find that most people worked in agriculture. This was the pre-industrial phase.

Industrialisation

Around 1750, a remarkable change began to take place. Industries started to use coal as a source of power, new machines were invented, and manufacturing moved from cottages and workshops to factories. As a result, industrial production increased massively. We refer to these changes as the **industrial revolution**. The industrial revolution both transformed industry and changed the lives of millions of people who left farming for the newly built factories in the towns (see Chapter 6). This so-called industrial phase (Fig. 10.8) lasted until the mid-20th century.

Post-industrial phase

Today, much of the economically developed world is in the **post-industrial** period. As manufacturing increases in efficiency and machines replace workers, more and more people move to work in the service sectors. Meanwhile, people become better off, and spend more on services such as health care, leisure, tourism, travel and so on. As a result, more jobs develop in the service sectors. Thus, in the UK, as in other MEDCs, we now live in a world where employment is dominated by services (Fig. 10.9), and services drive the nation's economy.

Fig. 10.7 Global distribution of employment in manufacturing industry.

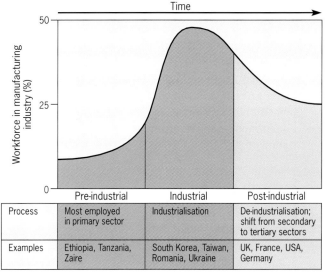

Fig. 10.8 The changing importance of manufacturing industry.

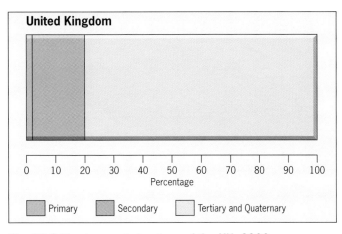

Fig. 10.9 Employment structure of the UK, 2000.

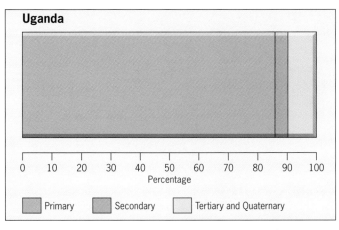

Fig. 10.10 Employment structure of Uganda, 2000.

The changing importance of manufacturing

The changing pattern of manufacturing employment follows a simple cycle (Fig. 10.8). The poorest countries are still in the pre-industrial stage and depend heavily on **subsistence agriculture** (Fig. 10.10). In contrast, some countries, such as China and Brazil, are industrialising rapidly. Others, such as South Korea and Taiwan, are **newly industrialising countries** (NICs), which have recently completed the industrial stage. The rich countries are in the post-industrial stage. Some (e.g. USA, UK) have a smaller proportion of their workforce in manufacturing than many LEDCs.

10.3 Types of manufacturing industry

Manufacturing industries do three things: they process raw materials; fabricate products; and assemble parts to make finished goods. Because of the work and materials involved in all three types of manufacturing, the final products have **added value**.

Manufacturing industries that refine raw materials (e.g. iron-and-steel) are known as processing industries. Their main purpose is to supply other manufacturing industries with essential materials. Another group of industries, e.g. textiles and pottery, fabricate products, such as cloth and crockery, directly from raw materials. Assembly industries buy manufactured parts from other firms, and put them together to make a finished product. Motor vehicle manufacture is probably the best-known example of an assembly industry.

Table 10.1 Matching exercise: manufacturing industries, raw materials and products

Industry	Raw material	Semi-finished product	Finished product
Printing	timber →	wood pulp →	paper/cardboard
Motor vehicles	cotton	molasses	ethylene
Aerospace	bauxite	alumina	syrup
Fashion	sugar cane	refined oil	aluminium
Construction	iron ore	pig iron	sheet steel
Paint	crude oil	yarn	concrete
Food processing	limestone	cement	cloth

CASE STUDY

10.4 The pottery industry in Stoke-on-Trent

> **FACTFILE**
>
> - *Stoke-on-Trent comprises a small conurbation of 270 000: apart from Stoke, the conurbation includes the neighbouring towns of Hanley, Longton, Burslem, Fenton, Tunstall (the so-called 'six towns') and Newcastle-under-Lyme.*
> - *The pottery industry supports about 20 000 jobs in Stoke-on-Trent, or nearly half of all employment in pottery manufacturing in the UK.*
> - *The factory-based pottery industry was first established in Stoke-on-Trent in the mid-18th century.*
> - *Stoke-on-Trent's initial advantages for the development of the pottery industry were local supplies of clay and coal.*
> - *The pottery industry's survival in Stoke-on-Trent is due to* **industrial inertia** *and its skilled workforce.*

Fig. 10.11 (above) Location of Stoke-on-Trent.

Early history

Pottery manufacturing has a long history in Stoke-on-Trent. It was first recorded in the 14th century, when it was a **cottage industry** (see Section 10.10). Large-scale factory production only occurred after 1750.

Factory-based production

The initial attractions for the factory-based industry were local materials, especially clay, and coal for firing the kilns. During the 18th century, a number of developments made local materials less important.

◆ Ball clay (from Dorset) was used to make earthenware products.

◆ Flint and china clay (from Cornwall) were introduced to make porcelain.

These imported bulky materials were expensive to transport, especially when overland transport relied on horse-drawn carts and packhorses. This problem was solved in 1777 with the opening of the Trent-Mersey Canal. It then became possible to transport raw materials from Dorset and Cornwall by sea to the Mersey estuary and then by canal to Stoke-on-Trent.

Many of these changes came about with the help of one man, Josiah Wedgwood. He built a new factory, called Etruria, alongside the Trent-Mersey Canal in 1769 (Fig. 10.12). The Wedgwood works survives today, although it now occupies an edge-of-town site at Barlaston (Fig. 10.11).

Fig. 10.12 (above right) Etruria in the 1850s.

Fig. 10.13 (bottom right) John Tams factory, Stoke-on-Trent.

157

Fig. 10.14 Location of John Tams production sites and its local suppliers.

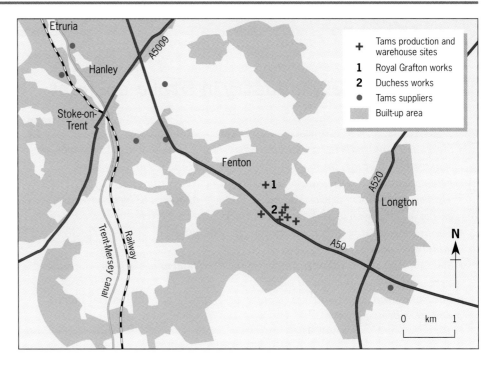

The survival of pottery making in Stoke-on-Trent

By the mid-20th century, most of the **initial advantages** that first attracted the pottery industry to Stoke-on-Trent had disappeared. Local clays were no longer used, and gas and electricity had replaced coal for firing the kilns. And yet Stoke-on-Trent continued to dominate the UK pottery industry. One reason for this is the difficulty and expense of moving factories and heavy machinery to new locations. Even if this were possible, it would not be worthwhile so long as the factory remained profitable. We call this **industrial inertia**. It is an important influence on industrial location and means that industries tend to stay where they first started.

John Tams plc: a Stoke-on-Trent pottery firm

The John Tams pottery firm illustrates some of the reasons for the survival of pottery manufacturing in Stoke-on-Trent. Founded in 1875, it is a family-run business that makes earthenware and bone china. It does not rely on local materials (Fig. 10.15), but its location in Stoke-on-Trent has advantages.

◆ Materials and machinery are sourced from local firms that are specialist suppliers to the pottery trade. These suppliers play a vital part in the production chain. Their linkages with pottery manufacturers are known as **external economies** and are not available in other regions.

Fig. 10.15 John Tams plc; a pottery manufacturing system.

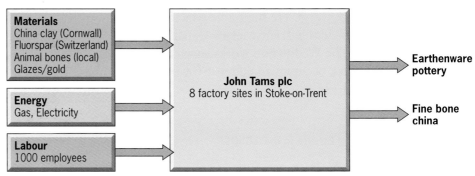

◆ Until February 2000, Tams employed 730 people, most of whom were either skilled or semi-skilled workers. Some skills, such as gilding and decorating china are highly specialised and were concentrated in the Stoke-on-Trent region.

However, in the late 1990s, John Tams plc struggled to remain profitable. With more than half its production exported, the firm was badly hit by the unfavourable exchange rate. Its problems were made worse by cheap imported pottery from Asia. In February 2000, the company went into receivership. Two months later, a management buy-out ensured the survival of the firm and secured nearly half the jobs in the company.

10.5 The UK iron-and-steel industry

Iron-and-steel making is an important industry for a modern industrial economy. Many industries, such as car making, construction and engineering use steel as their basic material.

Iron-and-steel making operations

There are three main operations in iron-and-steel making.
◆ Coking coal and limestone are used to smelt iron ore in a blast furnace to make iron.
◆ The iron is refined in a furnace to produce steel.
◆ The steel is shaped to make a range of products, such as beams, rails, plate, coil and so on.

Integrated steel-making

In a modern integrated iron and steel works, all three operations take place

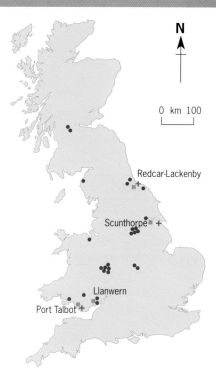

- ▪ Integrated iron and steel works
- + Deep water teminal for ore and coal
- ● Works making steel products (e.g. tubes, strip etc.)

Fig. 10.16 Distribution of the UK iron-and-steel industry.

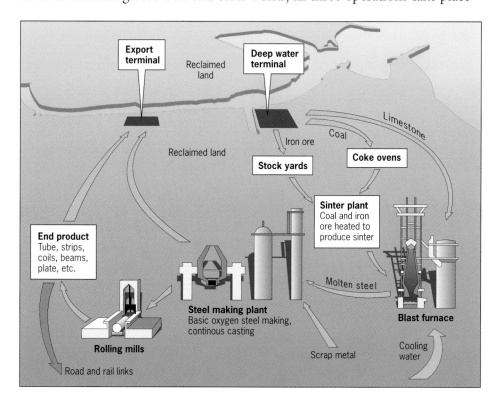

Fig. 10.17 A modern, integrated iron and steel works.

REMEMBER
Advances in technology will alter the locational factors that affect an industry. The result of technological advance is often a change of location e.g. in the iron-and-steel industry.

on the same site (Fig. 10.17). This helps to cut both transport and fuel costs. For example, molten iron is taken directly from the blast furnace to the steel-making plant. Such integrated iron-and-steel plants are very large and may occupy sites covering six or seven square kilometres. Large plants are essential if the costs of making steel are to be kept as low as possible. We call the savings associated with large plants, **economies of scale**.

FACTFILE

- *Iron-and-steel is a heavy industry, using heavy, bulky raw materials in large quantities.*
- *The costs of transporting the raw materials for iron-and-steel making are a large proportion of total costs.*
- *In order to keep transport costs low, the iron-and-steel industry locates as close as possible to its sources of raw materials.*
- *In Europe and the USA in the 19th and early-20th centuries, iron-and-steel making used domestic raw materials, and the industry located on the coalfields and iron orefields where these materials were sourced.*
- *The modern iron-and steel-industry relies on imported raw materials. Its location has shifted to the coast where these materials are imported in large bulk-carrying ships.*

Since 1945, the industry has relied increasingly on imported materials. This has led to a movement to coastal locations. Here, imported iron ore and coking coal, brought in by 200 000-tonne bulk carriers, can be processed more cheaply.

EXERCISES

6 Figure 10.18 shows four possible locations (A–D) for a new iron-and-steel works. The works will use imported iron ore and coal, and local limestone. It will employ about 3000 people. and will need a flat site covering 6 sq km.

a In 1850, the region had a thriving iron industry. Explain why the industry developed here.

b Suggest which location (A-D) it probably occupied, giving reasons.

c Choose a location for the new iron-and-steel works. Explain your choice.

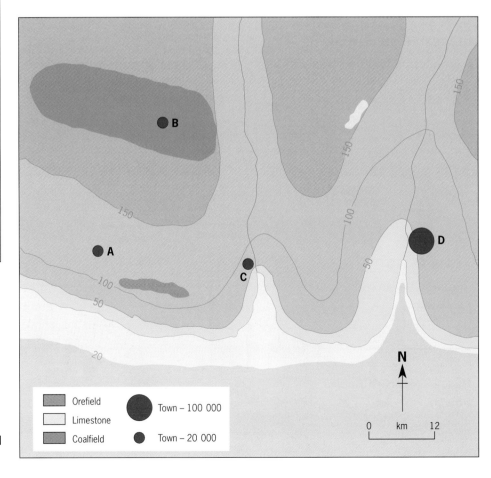

Fig. **10.18 Locating an iron-and-steel works.**

CASE STUDY

10.6 The Redcar-Lackenby iron-and-steel works

Redcar-Lackenby on Teesside is one of four integrated iron-and-steel works in the UK operated by Corus, the giant UK-Dutch steel maker. Iron-and-steel making started on Teesside in the mid-19th century. The initial advantages were iron deposits in the nearby Cleveland Hills, and coking coal from the Durham coalfield (Fig. 10.19). By 2000, the Teesside iron-and-steel industry no longer used local materials, with the exception of limestone.

Modern iron-and-steel making on Teesside

Geography has been important for the survival of iron-and-steel making on Teesside. As Teesside is located on

Fig. 10.19 (right) Iron-and-steel making on Teesside.

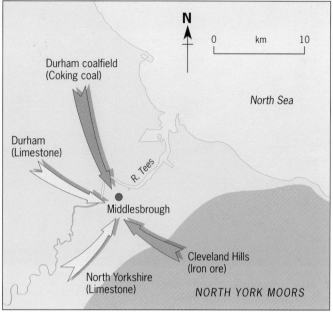

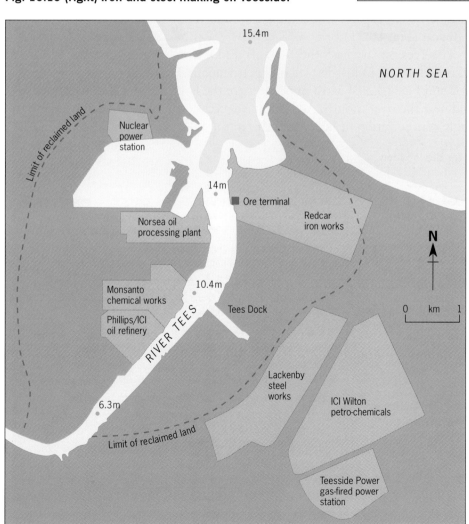

Fig. 10.20 The heavy industrial complex at the mouth of the River Tees.

EXERCISES

7a Draw a field sketch of Figure 10.21.
b Use Figure 10.20 to help you label as many features as possible.

REMEMBER

Iron-and-steel making on Teesside has survived since 1850 because the location has continued to offer advantages to the industry. The initial advantages of local supplies of coking, coal and iron ore, were later replaced by the advantage of the deep water of the Tees estuary for transporting materials by ship.

Fig. 10.21 Redcar-Lackenby steel works at the mouth of the River Tees, looking south.

EXERCISES

8* Heavily industrialised estuaries may have disadvantages for local people and for wildlife. Write an essay about some of these possible disadvantages.

a deep-water estuary, iron-and-steel works could easily switch to using imported materials. Thus, in 1976, a new iron works with its own deep-water terminal (capable of handling 200 000-tonne bulk carriers) was built at Redcar (Fig. 10.21).

The Tees estuary has other advantages for iron-and-steel making and for heavy processing industries, such as petrochemicals and oil refining (Table 10.2 and Fig. 10.20). Most important are the large areas of flat, reclaimed land near the river mouth. As a result, the Tees estuary now has the largest single concentration of heavy industry in the UK.

Table 10.2 Advantages of the Tees estuary for the location of heavy industries

Industrial sites	Large expanses of flat, reclaimed land. Ideal for heavy, space-using industries such as Redcar-Lackenby iron-and-steel works, BASF/du Pont Wilton (petrochemicals), Monsanto (chemicals), Phillips North Tees oil refinery, Hartlepool nuclear power station, Wilton Teesside gas power station.
Access to tidewater	Deep-water channel in the Tees estuary allows bulk carriers (up to 200 000 tonnes) to bring oil, iron ore and coal to heavy processing industries. Refined oil products and steel are exported by sea.
Remoteness	The Teesside industrial complex is near the mouth of the river and downwind of the main urban areas. This location helps reduce the risk of accident and minimises air pollution.
Access to water	Water is extracted from the river for industrial processes, while polluted water can be discharged into the estuary.

FACTFILE

- *Redcar-Lackenby is the largest and most modern iron-and-steel works in the UK.*
- *Redcar is the site of iron making: the Redcar blast furnace produces 3.5 million tonnes of iron a year.*
- *Iron ore is imported from Australia, Canada, West Africa, Brazil and Sweden.*
- *Coking coal is imported from Australia and the USA, and limestone comes from nearby Durham and Wensleydale.*
- *Molten iron is transferred by rail to the steel-making plant at Lackenby (a distance of two or three kilometres).*
- *Using basic oxygen furnaces and continuous casting methods Lackenby converts the molten iron to steel slabs and finished products such as steel beams and steel coil.*
- *Steel products are transported to the UK market by rail, and are exported by sea from Tees Dock.*

10.7 Car-making industry

Car making is an assembly industry. Parts such as engines, radiators, spark plugs, windscreens, seats etc., made by hundreds of different firms, are put together at an assembly plant. We refer to this system as horizontal organisation (Fig. 10.22).

Car making is a leading industry in the developed world (Fig. 10.23). Although production is growing rapidly in some LEDCs, such as Brazil and Mexico, nine out of every ten cars are still made in the developed world.

Huge **trans-national corporations** (TNCs) dominate world car production. The six largest car-making companies produce three-quarters of the 45 million cars sold every year. Many of these companies, such as Ford and VW, are household names. TNCs operate assembly plants and parts factories in many different countries. In the next section we shall look at the most international of all motor vehicle TNCs: Ford.

Ford Motors

Ford is an American TNC with its headquarters in Detroit, USA. After General Motors, it is the world's second-largest car maker. In the 1900s, Ford first developed the mass-production of vehicles using moving assembly lines.

Fig. 10.22 Horizontal and vertical types of organisation.

Fig. 10.23 World car production, 1999.

EXERCISES
9a Study Figure 10.22. Describe how the organisation of the car industry differs from the iron-and-steel industry.
b* Suggest possible reasons why it is an advantage for component suppliers in the car industry to locate close to assembly plants.

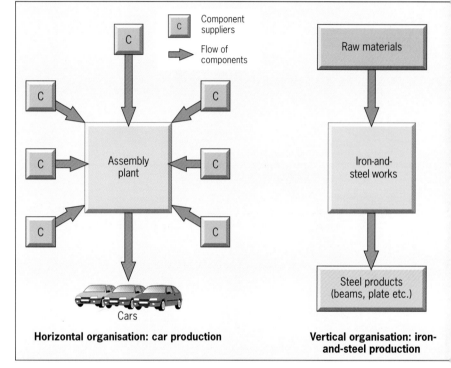

Horizontal organisation: car production

Vertical organisation: iron-and-steel production

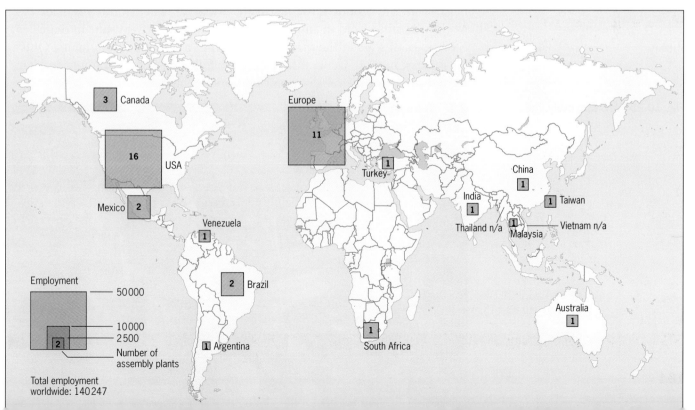

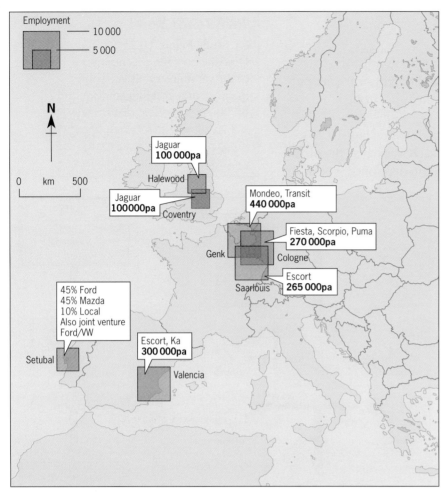

Fig. 10.24 Ford's EU assembly plants.

The company then opened its first overseas plant in Manchester, UK, in 1911. In 2001, it had assembly plants throughout the USA and the EU (Fig.10.24), as well as in Mexico, South America, East Asia, South-east Asia and Australia. In total, Ford employs 350 000 people worldwide.

Integrated production in Europe

In Europe, Ford's operations are fully integrated. It has a common car range for the whole of Europe. For example, the plants at Saarlouis and Valencia (Figs. 10.24) produce all of the Escorts sold in Europe. What advantage does this policy have? Essentially, it lowers costs and makes Ford more competitive. By concentrating on just a few models for the entire European market, Ford can make a large number of cars. This is important because the costs of developing new models are enormous. (Ford spends $6bn a year on global research and development.) Costs are also lowered if a factory specialises in making a single model or part (e.g. Ford's Bridgend engine plant in South Wales). These savings, or economies of scale, are vital to the success of large-volume car producers like Ford.

Globalisation

In 1995, Ford embarked on a global production strategy. Globalisation began with the Mondeo, the first truly global car. The Mondeo is made worldwide and is sold in all major markets. This strategy results in huge economies of scale in the manufacture of the car and its components. Other car makers, notably General Motors, have followed Ford's example and have moved towards the globalisation of production and sales.

Fig. 10.25 Ford assembly line.

10.8 The UK car industry

The UK car industry, together with the manufacture of car components, is a leading sector of the UK economy. The car parts manufacturing industry alone has an estimated turnover of $40bn. Two-thirds of all cars manufactured in the UK are exported, making a huge contribution to the UK's trade.

EXERCISES

10a Describe the changing output of cars in the UK between 1965 and 2000.
b* Describe and explain the main difference in production between the 1960s and 2000.

The early car industry

The car industry first developed in the early-20th century in the West Midlands and the south-east. It grew out of related industries such as coach building and bicycles. Labour skills from these industries were easily transferred to car making. In the West Midlands, there were also long-established engineering and metal-working industries which supplied components for the new car industry.

Although skilled labour is no longer important, the West Midlands and the South-east remain leading centres of car production (Fig. 10.26) and parts suppliers.

Locational change in the 1960s

In the early 1960s, several new car factories were located in Merseyside and Central Scotland. These regions had no tradition of car making. However, the government believed that the car industry would generate new jobs and economic growth in these less prosperous regions. As a result, the government directed investment to the new assembly plants and away from the West Midlands and the South-east. Not all of the new plants were successful, but Ford's plant at Halewood, and Vauxhall's at Ellesmere Port (both on Merseyside) have survived.

Japanese investments in the UK

From 1970 to 1985, the UK car industry was in decline (Fig. 10.27). Output fell from 1.6 million cars in 1970, to less than one million in 1982. Workers' strikes were common and foreign firms took over several British manufacturers.

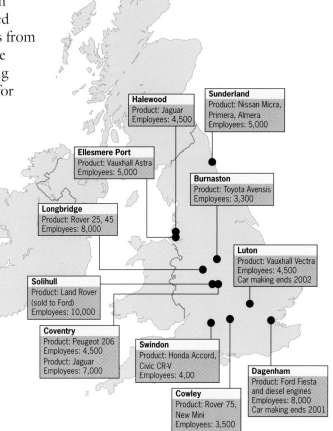

Fig. 10.26 (top right) UK car assembly plants and production.

Fig. 10.27 (right) Production of cars in the UK: 1950–2000.

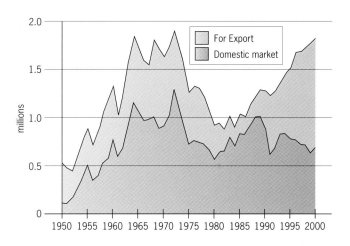

Fig. 10.28 Aerial view of Nissan assembly plant, Sunderland.

Japanese transplants

In 1984, Nissan chose the UK for its first European assembly plant (**transplant**). Within two years, Nissan had begun production on a greenfield site near Sunderland. This was so successful that Nissan was soon joined by Toyota (in Derby) and Honda (in Swindon). The UK provided these Japanese manufacturers with a base from which they could enter the EU market. The advantages of the UK compared to other EU countries were:

◆ the skills and flexibility of British workers;
◆ the lack of competition from British car manufacturers;
◆ government grants.

By 2001, the three Japanese transplants were producing 700 000 cars a year, two-thirds of them for export.

Lean production

Japanese firms did not just boost car production in the UK in the 1990s. They also introduced new production methods. Lean production involved closer co-operation between car assemblers and parts suppliers. Fewer parts were made by the car assemblers and more were outsourced to independent suppliers. Parts were delivered to assemblers a few hours before they were used on assembly lines. This **just-in-time** system meant that assemblers no longer needed to stockpile large quantities of parts. The effect of lean production was to lower costs and make the car industry more productive.

10.9 High-technology industries in the UK

High-technology (high-tech) industries cover a wide range of activities, including micro-electronics, computers, telecoms, biotechnology, pharmaceuticals and many others. Like iron-and-steel and car making, high-tech industries need a lot of investment. However, one special feature of high-tech industries is the importance they give to researching and developing new products.

High tech: large and small

Like car making, large TNCs dominate high-tech industries. GlaxoWelcome is, for example, a British TNC and a world leader in pharmaceuticals. Most foreign high-tech TNCs with factories in the UK are American and Japanese companies. They include electronic giants such as IBM, Motorola, Mashushita and Sony.

However, a feature of many high-tech firms is their small scale and rapid growth. Science-and-technology-based firms in high-growth activities, such as software and genetics, may be worth billions of pounds, yet they employ just a few hundred people.

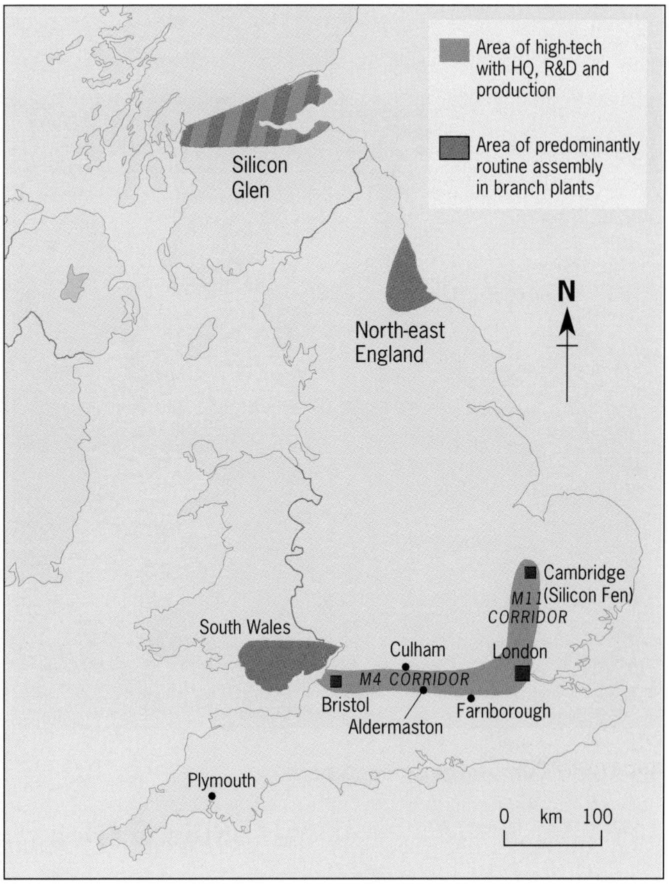

Footloose but not free: the location of high-tech industries

Most high-tech products, such as semi-conductors and pharmaceuticals, have high volume and low weight and bulk. Thus transport costs for high-tech industries are fairly low and play little part in their location. Similarly, other traditional locational factors, such as supplies of materials and energy, have little importance. Industries like high-tech, which are not limited in their choice of location by transport, materials or energy, are called **footloose**. But, despite having a much freer choice of location than heavy industries, high-tech industries cannot locate anywhere they like.

Science parks

Many high-tech firms are sited in purpose-built science and business parks. Often located at the edge-of-town and on greenfield sites, these parks are easy to access and have attractive landscaped grounds and futuristic buildings. There are **45 science parks** in the UK, many of them joint ventures between universities and local authorities. A wide range of activities are found on science parks, from manufacturing to research, development and design.

Silicon Fen

Silicon Fen is the name given to the concentration of high-tech industries in Cambridge and its surrounding region. With more than 1000 high-tech firms generating about $3bn a year, Silicon Fen is the UK's leading high-tech cluster. Cambridge specialises in research in areas such as

Fig. 10.29 Major concentrations of high-tech industry, UK.

EXERCISES

12a Search newspapers, magazines and the internet for advertisements by electronics manufacturers.
b From the advertisements, cut out or print the names of the firms and stick them down in a table with four other columns.
c* In the columns next to the names of the manufacturers, list the products advertised, their cost, their approximate weight and bulk. Comment on the difference between products shown by your table.
d* Try to find out the nationality of the firms and add this to the last column of your table. Apart from the USA and Japan, which other countries have important electronics industries?

Fig. 10.30 Cambridge science park.

biotechnology, telecoms and electronics. Hundreds of small technology-based companies have developed in Cambridge since the establishment of its first science park in 1972. At the opposite end of the scale, Cambridge has also attracted leading companies such as Glaxo and Microsoft. Microsoft is currently investing £60m in a new electronics research centre in the town.

The attractions of Cambridge for high-tech businesses include:

◆ Cambridge University's expertise in science (the recruitment of highly qualified graduates, the link between business and academic researchers in the university, and 'start-up' firms founded by the university's graduates);

◆ Cambridge's proximity to London (access to bankers in the City of London who finance new business ventures, and to Heathrow international airport);

◆ Cambridge's charm as a historic town and cultural centre, which attracts highly paid and highly qualified scientists, managers and technicians.

Silicon Glen

The cluster of high-tech industries in central Scotland, in the triangle between Glasgow, Edinburgh and Dundee, is Silicon Glen. Silicon Glen is one of the largest clusters of high-tech industries in Europe. Traditionally, high-tech industries in Silicon Glen have focused on the production of electronic goods, rather than research and development. American, EU and East Asian TNCs manufacture 28 per cent of Europe's PCs and 15 per cent of its semi-conductors in Silicon Glen.

Fig. 10.31 Alba Centre in Livingston, Scotland.

The initial advantages of Silicon Glen for high-tech industries were:

◆ government grants to create employment in a region that suffered massive de-industrialisation in the 1970s and early 1980s;

◆ a skilled, flexible and relatively cheap workforce;

◆ the proximity of universities in Glasgow, Edinburgh and Dundee.

Many foreign TNCs were also attracted by the quality of life in central Scotland, and the region's excellent transport infrastructure. Scotland's regional development agency – Locate in Scotland – has been very successful in persuading high-tech TNCs to invest in Silicon Glen.

From high-tech manufacturing to knowledge-based industries

In the last five years, Silicon Glen has promoted research, development and design, and knowledge-based industries in the high-tech sector. Foreign-owned plants making high-tech goods are vulnerable to closure if demand falls or firms decide to shift production overseas. Recent developments aim to make Silicon Glen a world centre for micro-electronics design. There is a trend away from large-scale manufacturing towards specialised activities, which add more value. Meanwhile the Glen's growing software sector already employs 20 000 people – nearly half the total number of people employed in the electronics industry in Scotland.

10.10 Industries in LEDCs

Cottage industries

Most manufacturing industries in MEDCs are capital intensive, use advanced technology and highly educated labour forces, and take place in purpose-built factories. We have seen that their products are increasingly sold globally.

Similar industries exist in most large cities in LEDCs. However, most manufacturing in the economically developing world is different.

It is usually:

◆ small-scale;

◆ based on simple technology;

◆ reliant on local materials and traditional skills;

◆ geared to producing goods for the local community.

Such industries are often located in people's homes in rural areas, or in small workshops in towns. These so-called cottage industries were once common in Europe before the industrial revolution.

Appropriate technology

Some LEDCs, such as China, India and Brazil, are building capital-intensive, advanced-technology industries. But most governments and aid organisations do not see these big projects as the best way forward for the developing world. Industries using advanced technology may bring prestige to the country but they rarely benefit the majority of the people. The most successful schemes are based on low technology, use local materials and traditional skills, and cost relatively little to introduce. They involve the local people who are consulted about their specific needs. We shall now look at two schemes in LEDCs that are based on the principle of using technology that is appropriate for local people's needs.

EXERCISES

13a Read through the sections in this chapter on the pottery, iron-and-steel, car and high-tech industries.

b Make a table summarising the factors that influence the location of these industries. Head each column with a type of industry. At the side of your table list the following factors:

• raw materials • labour skills
• transport costs • labour costs,
• energy supplies • external economies • inertia • economies of scale • government policies
• other factors. For each industry in your table tick the factors which are important.

c* In what way do the locational factors for high-tech firms differ from those for more traditional industries?

CASE STUDY

10.11 Making cooking stoves in western Kenya

In 1987, the UK charity Intermediate Technology taught a group of women potters (the Keyo group) in western Kenya (Fig.10.32) how to make the *upesi*, an efficient wood-burning stove. The stove uses less than half the fuelwood of an open fire and it can also burn maize stalks and dry sugar cane. It is also safer and cleaner. The stove is simple and effective and brings benefits to everyone.

- It burns less wood, and therefore saves time collecting fuelwood.
- It saves money for those who normally buy their fuelwood at the market.
- It saves forests and woodlands from destruction.
- It helps to reduce respiratory diseases among the women and their families because the *upesi* produces less smoke than an open fire.

Fig. 10.32 (right) Location of appropriate technology manufacturing projects in India and Kenya.

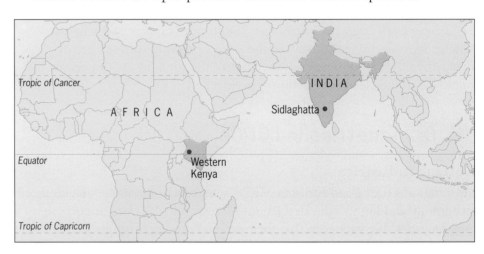

Fig. 10.33 (below) Stove makers with the Keyo women's group, Kenya.

Not surprisingly, the *upesi* is very popular. The Keyo women's group produce 15 000 stoves a year, using local clay and their traditional skills as potters (Fig.10.33). The stoves are sold in rural markets. As a result, the group members receive a useful source of income and the local community benefits from the employment provided by making stoves. Demand for the stoves is expected to grow, provided certain problems are solved. One problem is the difficulty of transporting the heavy stoves to market. Another is the cost of the raw material, clay. Originally, people dug clay locally for free. Now, landowners are charging for the clay.

CASE STUDY

10.12 Silk reeling in India

More than 500 000 people in India work in different stages of the silk industry, from the production of raw silk (sericulture), to reeling (turning the raw silk to yarn) and weaving.

Reeling is mostly a cottage industry. It is labour intensive and a vital source of income and employment for India's rural poor. Reeling involves unwinding threads from silkworm cocoons using a simple reeling machine known as a *charaka*. (Fig. 10.34). Firstly, though, farmers breed silkworms, which feed on mulberry leaves. When the silkworms pupate, they spin silk cocoons, which the farmers then take for auction in local markets. Reelers, who are mainly women, buy these silk cocoons and separate the strands on their *charakas*. The women then sell the yarn to weavers. Some women operate small businesses, buying the raw silk and employing three or four reelers.

Fig. 10.34 Reeling silk, India.

Aid organisations, which are keen to promote appropriate technology, support the silk-reeling industry because it is based on simple technology. For example, in Sidlaghatta in southern India (Fig. 10.32), aid workers have helped to improve the business and marketing skills of local reelers. In addition, they helped to design a new *charaka*. Reelers have tested three new machines, which they found were easier to use, produced better-quality yarn and increased output. All these improvements came through the involvement of local reelers, using their ideas and skills. This development should greatly improve the lives of local people, and at little cost.

REMEMBER
Small-scale, labour-intensive industries based on simple technologies, and serving local markets, offer the greatest scope for economic advancement in LEDCs. Moreover, these activities are, in the long term, sustainable.

> *EXERCISES*
>
> **14a** Draw systems diagrams (see Fig. 8.27) to show stove production in Kenya and silk reeling in India.
> **b*** Appropriate technology is often labour intensive. Why are labour-intensive industries often well suited to many LEDCs?
> **c*** Explain how the making of cooking stoves in Kenya, and silk reeling in India, promote the idea of sustainable development.

10.13 Summary: Industrial activity and location

KEY SKILLS OPPORTUNITIES
C1.2: Ex. 1a, 5a, 6a, 9a, 10;
C1/2.3: Ex. 1a, 1c, 2, 6a, 8, 9, 10, 12c, 14; **C2.2**: Ex. 12d, 13b; **IT1/2.1**: Ex. 3b, 12a; **IT1.2**: Ex. 12b

Key ideas	Generalisations and detail
Economic activity can be divided into four sectors: primary, secondary, tertiary and quaternary.	• Primary activities such as agriculture and mining produce food and raw materials. Secondary activities manufacture goods e.g. iron-and-steel, motor vehicles. Tertiary and quaternary activities are service activities. The tertiary sector includes utilities and transport. The quaternary sector comprises services for other economic activities and individual consumers.
The importance of manufacturing industry varies in time.	• Manufacturing industry in the economically developed world has passed through a cycle in the last 200 years. The percentage of people working in manufacturing was low in the pre-industrial period. It reached its height in the industrial revolution. Today, in the post-industrial period, manufacturing employs between one-fifth and one-quarter of the working population.
The importance of manufacturing varies in different countries.	• Manufacturing is least important in the poorest countries of the economically developing world. In some newly industrialising countries (e.g. Taiwan, South Korea) manufacturing employs between one-quarter and one-third of the working population but in some of the world's richest countries (e.g. USA), it employs less than one-fifth of the working population .
Energy and raw materials influence industrial location.	• Heavy industries, using large amounts of energy and raw materials, (e.g. iron-and-steel), often locate close to sources of energy or raw materials to reduce transport costs .
The location of some manufacturing industries is explained by industrial inertia.	• Although the initial advantages of a location may have disappeared (e.g. local raw materials may no longer be used) some industries remain where they first started e.g. pottery. Inertia often keeps an industry in its original location because of the cost and difficulty of moving.
New reasons for retaining the location of an industry often replace the original ones.	• Acquired advantages such as skilled labour and linkages with nearby firms may also explain the survival of an industry in a region (e.g. pottery at Stoke-on-Trent), even though the initial advantages of the location have long since disappeared.
Changes in technology and the source of materials may change an industry's location.	• In the UK, over the last 200 years, the iron-and-steel industry has shifted from locations on coalfields and iron ore fields to coastal sites. These moves reflect increasing reliance on overseas materials.
Some industries are successful only if they operate on a large scale.	• In the iron-and-steel and motor vehicle industries, large firms can lower their costs because of economies of scale. To achieve these economies, an industry may need a very large site and/or a huge, global market for its products.
Estuaries are often attractive industrial locations.	• Estuaries provide large areas of flat, reclaimed land for heavy, space-using industries like steel and oil refining. They also give access to imported raw materials and energy.
Some industries are dominated by trans-national corporations.	• Trans-national corporations (TNCs) are large international firms with factories and markets in many different countries. Car making and high-tech industries are dominated by TNCs.
Some manufacturing industries are footloose.	• Footloose industries, such as high-tech industries, are those that are not strongly influenced by traditional locational factors i.e. transport, materials, energy. However, footloose industries cannot locate anywhere. In the UK, they are highly concentrated in regions such as the South-east and central Scotland.
Governments influence the location of manufacturing.	• Governments give grants to foreign firms to encourage them to invest. In less-prosperous regions, grants are available to attract industry, which will provide jobs.
In LEDCs, cottage industries are important.	• Cottage industries are based in the countryside. They are usually small-scale, labour- intensive industries, and rely on simple technology.
Appropriate technology is the basis for industrial development in many LEDCs.	• Appropriate technology aims to benefit the people of LEDCs by using their skills and encouraging them to find their own solutions e.g. stove making in western Kenya. Large-scale, capital-intensive industrial development often failed to benefit the people.

11 | Industrial change

11.1 Introduction

In the previous chapter we saw how materials, energy, labour and other factors influence the location of industry. However, in the last 25 years the importance of these factors has changed. One outcome has been new patterns of industrial location. These new patterns, which exist at global, national, regional and local scales are the subject of this chapter.

11.2 The globalisation of industry

Today, manufacturing and service industries are increasingly organised on a worldwide scale (the globalisation of industry). One effect of **globalisation** has been the rapid growth of industry in the developing world. In 1955, the developing world accounted for only 5 per cent of manufacturing industry. By 2005, the proportion should be nearly 30 per cent. This **global shift** of manufacturing will continue for the foreseeable future. Thus, by 2020, we expect China to have the world's biggest economy; and seven of the ten largest economies will be from today's LEDCs.

The global shift of manufacturing is most evident in the Asian countries around the Pacific Ocean (Fig. 11.1). Industrialisation in the Asian Pacific Rim began in the 1950s in Japan. This was followed in the 1970s, 1980s and 1990s by South Korea, Taiwan, Singapore and Hong Kong. Within the next 10 to 20 years, countries like China, Malaysia and Thailand will become the next wave of newly industrialising countries (NICs). (Fig. 11.2).

Explaining globalisation

Several factors explain the globalisation of manufacturing industry in the past 20 years.

EXERCISES

1a From which continent will most of the ten largest economies come in 2020?
b Which continents are not represented in Table 11.1? Suggest reasons for this.
c* What does Table 11.1 tell you about the probable global shift of economic activity between 1992 and 2020?

Table 11.1 The largest economies in the world: 1992 and 2020

1992	2020
USA	China
Japan	USA
China	Japan
Germany	India
France	Indonesia
India	Germany
Italy	South Korea
UK	Thailand
Russia	France
Brazil	Taiwan

Fig. 11.1 (below) Countries of the Asian Pacific Rim.

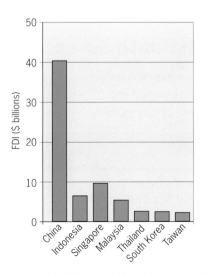

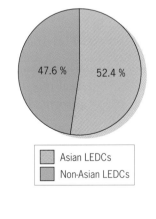

47.6 %   52.4 %

- Asian LEDCs
- Non-Asian LEDCs

Fig. 11.2 (above) Foreign direct investment in Asian LEDCs and NICs: 1997.

Fig. 11.3 (above) Total foreign direct investment in LEDCs: 1997.

◆ Globalisation allows very large trans-national corporations (TNCs) like General Motors, Ford, Nestlé and IBM to make products and buy services in places where they can be purchased cheaply.

◆ Low labour costs in LEDCs encourage labour-intensive industries to locate overseas. In the last 20 years, large numbers of US factories have located just across the border from the USA, in Mexico. Nearly one million Mexicans work in these factories in cities such as Tijuana and Ciudad Juararez for wages that are only a fraction of those in the USA (Fig. 11.4).

◆ TNCs benefit from global organisation because it gives them access to the largest of all markets – the world. By supplying the world market, TNCs can increase output, and this helps to lower their costs, making them even more competitive.

◆ The globalisation of a company's operations helps it to avoid trade restrictions. This is one reason why so much foreign investment has come to the UK since the mid-1980s. Firms like Nissan, Toyota, Sony and Samsung have set up factories in the UK to serve the EU market. As a result, they are exempt from tariffs and quotas, which they would otherwise face if they exported goods from Japan and South Korea. Globalisation has been made possible by great improvements in telecoms. The use of satellites and computer networks allows TNCs to control their operations worldwide. Without modern telecoms, Swiss Air could not have moved all its accounting to Bombay in India, nor could the southern Indian city of Bangalore have become a major software producer for Europe and North America.

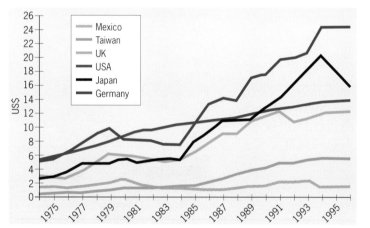

Fig. 11.4 Hourly direct pay for production workers in manufacturing: 1975–1996.

CASE STUDY

11.3 Modern industrialisation: South Korea

Like Japan and the other Asian NICs, South Korea has developed its industries despite having few natural resources of its own. Since the early 1970s South Korea has been transformed from one of the poorest, to one of the richest countries in Asia.

REMEMBER
Industrialisation in NICs is not based on domestic sources of energy and raw materials. The single most important influence has been NICs' highly educated workforce.

FACTFILE

- *Population: 47.47 million (2000) with a workforce of 21.5 million.*
- *Area: 98,480 sq km – similar to the combined area of Scotland and Wales.*
- *Few natural resources apart from some coal, HEP, tungsten and graphite.*
- *24 per cent of the workforce in mining and manufacturing.*
- *Major industries: electronics, cars, shipbuilding, steel, textiles, chemicals and clothing.*
- *GDP per capita: $13 300 (1999) – similar to Portugal and Greece.*
- *Literacy rate: 98 per cent.*

South Korea's industrial miracle

From the start, the South Korean government planned the country's industrial development. It protected its own industries from foreign imports, and it encouraged Korean export industries by giving them subsidies and cheap loans. Firms were told what to make and where to make it.

Heavy industries

Between 1973 and 1979, the South Korean government promoted heavy industries such as metals, chemicals and shipbuilding. The state-sponsored Posco iron-and-steel company is now the largest steel producer in the world. Meanwhile, in 1993, South Korea overtook Japan as the world's leading shipbuilder.

Technology-based industries

Since the mid-1980s the emphasis has shifted away from heavy industries to cars, high-tech (e.g. semi-conductors) and electronic goods (e.g. TVs, videos etc.). By the end of the 1990s, South Korea had four main car makers – Hyundai, Daewoo, Kia and Samsung – with a capacity to produce more than 4 million cars a year.

Chaebols

South Korean industry is dominated by several giant, family-controlled businesses known as *chaebols*. The four largest *chaebols* – Samsung, Hyundai, Daewoo and LG – account for 60 per cent of South Korea's exports. Unlike US or British companies, each *chaebol* has a wide range of business interests. For example, among Samsung's business interests are the manufacture of memory chips, computers, cars, ships, petrochemicals and heavy machinery.

Overseas investment

In the 1990s, South Korea's *chaebols* began to globalise their operations (Fig. 11.7). The four leading *chaebols* invested heavily in the USA and Europe, as well as East Asia (Fig. 11.5). The UK has been South Korea's most popular location for investment in Europe. There were major investments in the electronics industry in North-east England, South Wales and Central Scotland (Fig. 11.6). By 1997, the total value of investment by Korean firms in the UK stood at £2.6bn. These investments provided Korean firms with a manufacturing base from which to export to the EU.

Crisis in the South Korean economy

In 1997–98 South Korea and other East Asian economies, were rocked by a major financial crisis. The government-sponsored *chaebols* with their diverse business interests were inefficient and had amassed huge debts. For the first time in 20 years, the Korean economy slumped. Many overseas investments were put on hold, and some foreign factories closed. By the turn of the century the Korean economy was beginning to recover. Even so, late in 2000, Daewoo's car subsidiary went into liquidation.

Fig. 11.7 Overseas investment by South Korean companies, 1992–1999.

Fig. 11.5 (above) A South Korean shipyard.

Fig. 11.6 South Korea's principal investments in the UK by 1997.

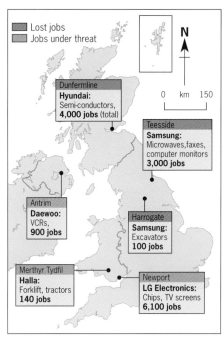

Lost jobs
Jobs under threat

N

0   km   150

Dunfermline
Hyundai:
Semi-conductors,
4,000 jobs (total)

Teesside
Samsung:
Microwaves, faxes,
computer monitors
3,000 jobs

Antrim
Daewoo:
VCRs,
900 jobs

Harrogate
Samsung:
Excavators
100 jobs

Merthyr Tydfil
Halla:
Forklift, tractors
140 jobs

Newport
LG Electronics:
Chips, TV screens
6,100 jobs

EXERCISES

4* Explain the likely reasons for South Korean investment in: (1) the economically developing world, (2) Europe.

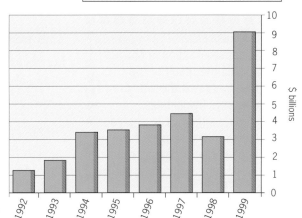

Fig. 11.8 (right) Mothballed Siemens factory, North Tyneside.

Fig. 11.9 (below) Shipbuilding on Tyneside in the 1930s.

11.4 From smokestacks to microchips

De-industrialisation in the North-east

Since the 1930s, the North-east of England has been a problem region. Coal mining, shipbuilding and iron-and-steel brought prosperity to the region in the 19th century (Fig. 11.9). But for most of the 20th century, these industries were in decline. In 1980, County Durham still had 22 working collieries, 25 000 people worked in the iron-and-steel industry at Teesside and Consett, and the shipyards on the Tyne and Wear launched more merchant ships than any other UK region (Fig. 11.10).

Then suddenly, in the 1980s, the old industries collapsed. By 1990, shipbuilding had ended at Sunderland. The last shipyard in the North-east – Swan Hunter on the Tyne – closed in 1994. The same year saw the closure of County Durham's last coal mine. Now, apart from the partly re-opened Ellington colliery in Northumberland, deep mining has ended in the North-east. The steelworks at Consett closed in 1980, and though there is still some steel making on Teesside, it employs less than half the 1980 workforce. This sudden decline of the region's traditional manufacturing industries is an example of **de-industrialisation**. It hit old industrial regions like the North-east hardest. Altogether, 160 000 manufacturing jobs were lost in the region between 1970 and 1990. Also, with the closure of factories, large industrial areas became derelict.

The new North-east: re-industrialisation

Between 1985 and 1995, the economy of North-east England underwent a remarkable transformation. By the mid-1990s, the region had lost its old image of smokestacks, pit heaps and shipyards. In its place was a new North-east: a region of modern business parks and factories producing electronic goods, memory chips and motor vehicles (Fig. 11.11).

These changes came about through foreign investment. By 1995, 380 foreign companies were operating in the North-east. The reasons they chose chose to locate in the North-east included the skilled workforce and government grants. For example, Samsung received a £58m grant for its

REMEMBER
De-industrialisation in MEDCs is partly the result of the globalisation of the world economy. Traditional industries in MEDCs, such as steel and shipbuilding, have been unable to compete with lower-cost producers in NICs and LEDCs.

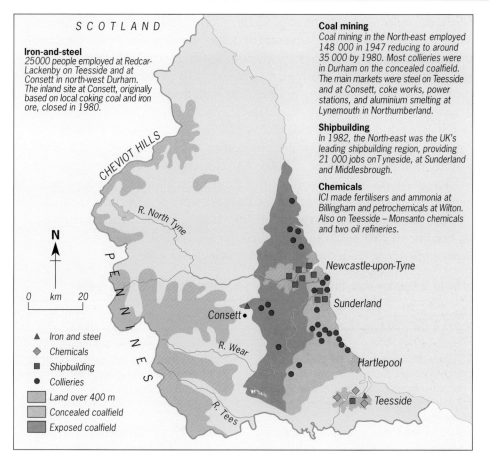

Iron-and-steel
25000 people employed at Redcar-Lackenby on Teesside and at Consett in north-west Durham. The inland site at Consett, originally based on local coking coal and iron ore, closed in 1980.

Coal mining
Coal mining in the North-east employed 148 000 in 1947 reducing to around 35 000 by 1980. Most collieries were in Durham on the concealed coalfield. The main markets were steel on Teesside and at Consett, coke works, power stations, and aluminium smelting at Lynemouth in Northumberland.

Shipbuilding
In 1982, the North-east was the UK's leading shipbuilding region, providing 21 000 jobs on Tyneside, at Sunderland and Middlesbrough.

Chemicals
ICI made fertilisers and ammonia at Billingham and petrochemicals at Wilton. Also on Teesside – Monsanto chemicals and two oil refineries.

▲ Iron and steel
◆ Chemicals
■ Shipbuilding
● Collieries
Land over 400 m
Concealed coalfield
Exposed coalfield

Fig. 11.10 The old North-east: the smokestack industries.

Fig. 11.11 The new North-east: major investments 1984–1995.

EXERCISES

5 Study Figure 11.10. Describe the geographical advantages of the North-east for the development of heavy industries like shipbuilding and iron-and-steel.

electronics on Teesside. Large-scale inward investment in the North-east began in 1984 when Nissan, the Japanese car maker, decided to build a car assembly plant at Sunderland. Not only did this create more than 4000 jobs, it also attracted more than 20 parts suppliers (several of them Japanese) to the region. Nissan's success encouraged others. In the next ten years, Fujitsu, Samsung, LG, Siemens and many smaller firms followed Nissan and located factories in the region.

Globalisation, interdependence and plant closures

The North-east became part of the global economy between 1984 and 1995 when it benefited from massive foreign investment. But in the late

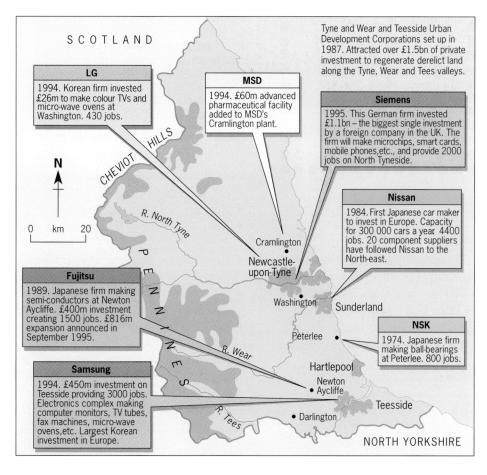

LG
1994. Korean firm invested £26m to make colour TVs and micro-wave ovens at Washington. 430 jobs.

MSD
1994. £60m advanced pharmaceutical facility added to MSD's Cramlington plant.

Tyne and Wear and Teesside Urban Development Corporations set up in 1987. Attracted over £1.5bn of private investment to regenerate derelict land along the Tyne, Wear and Tees valleys.

Siemens
1995. This German firm invested £1.1bn – the biggest single investment by a foreign company in the UK. The firm will make microchips, smart cards, mobile phones, etc., and provide 2000 jobs on North Tyneside.

Nissan
1984. First Japanese car maker to invest in Europe. Capacity for 300 000 cars a year 4400 jobs. 20 component suppliers have followed Nissan to the North-east.

Fujitsu
1989. Japanese firm making semi-conductors at Newton Aycliffe. £400m investment creating 1500 jobs. £816m expansion announced in September 1995.

Samsung
1994. £450m investment on Teesside providing 3000 jobs. Electronics complex making computer monitors, TV tubes, fax machines, micro-wave ovens, etc. Largest Korean investment in Europe.

NSK
1974. Japanese firm making ball-bearings at Peterlee. 800 jobs.

1990s, the closure of a number of foreign-controlled factories in the region focused attention on the disadvantages of globalisation. In 1998, the semi-conductor plants at Aycliffe (Fujitsu) and North Tyneside (Siemens) closed with a loss of 1600 jobs. Both plants fell victim to worldwide overcapacity in the semi-conductor industry, and the steep fall in semi-conductor prices. Meanwhile, Samsung, hit by the financial crisis in South Korea, put its plans for the expansion of its Teesside electronics complex on hold. Further closures included the Wilkinson razor factory at Cramlington (1998) and clothing factories at Peterlee (2000). The clothing industry was hit by the decision of Marks & Spencer to source more of its clothes from East and South-east Asia, where labour costs were only a fraction of those in the UK.

These examples of disinvestment show how vulnerable the North-east has become to changes in the global economy. They also demonstrate the increasing interdependence of industries at a global scale.

Table 11.2 Foreign investment: advantages and disadvantages for a region

Advantages	Disadvantages
• Creates jobs. • If jobs don't come to the UK they will go to competing countries. • Initial investment may attract other firms (e.g. car assembly attracting parts suppliers). • Good for the image of a region to attract a major TNC. This may attract further investment. • May introduce new production methods that improve the output of local firms. • Boosts exports and helps the country's trade balance.	• Factories are controlled from overseas. • Factories may close because of changes in the global economy, which are unrelated to conditions in the UK. • No control over decisions to close factories. • Foreign firms will compete with UK firms, which may be forced out of business. • Factories are often branch plants. They employ only low-skilled workers. There are few highly paid jobs in administration and research and development.

Help for disadvantaged regions

To help the most disadvantaged regions in the UK, the government set up policies with the primary aim of reducing unemployment in these areas.

Table 11.3 Grants available to firms in the UK's assisted areas in 2001.

Regional selective assistance grants (RSAs)	RSAs are designed to attract new investment and create new jobs or safeguard existing ones. RSA grants cover up to 15 per cent of the cost of new investment in plant, machinery, buildings and land preparation.
Regional enterprise grants (REGs)	REGs are available to very small firms. They provide money for capital investment and financial assistance of up to 50 per cent of the costs of projects.

Urban development corporations and enterprise zones

In the North-east, most traditional heavy industries were concentrated in the lower Tyne, Wear and Tees valleys. De-industrialisation therefore created a massive dereliction problem in these areas. The government tackled this problem by setting up two urban development corporations (UDCs) and two enterprise zones (EZs).

The Tyne and Wear UDC, and the Teesside UDC were set up in 1987. Their task was to reclaim derelict land and make new sites for industry. By 1995, the UDCs had secured more than £1.5bn of private investment. Among the major schemes are the East Quayside leisure and office project in Newcastle; the Sunderland enterprise park; and the Hartlepool marina (Fig.11.13).

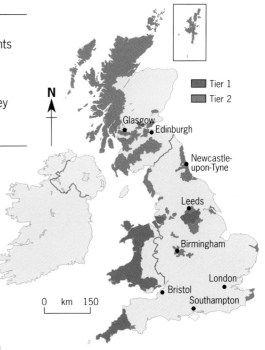

Fig. 11.12 (above) Assisted areas in Britain.

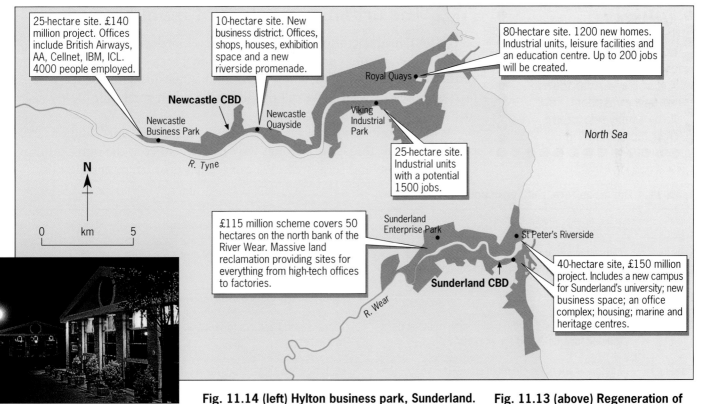

Fig. 11.14 (left) Hylton business park, Sunderland.

Fig. 11.13 (above) Regeneration of the Tyne and Wear riverbanks.

Since 1983, the North-east region has had six Enterprise Zones (EZs). Most have covered derelict riverside areas in Newcastle, Sunderland, Hartlepool and Middlesbrough. EZs have a life-span of 10 years. They aim to regenerate run-down areas by offering special tax allowances and reduced

Fig. 11.15 (below left) Newcastle Central Business and Technology Park

Fig. 11.16 (below right) West Quayside business park, Newcastle.

planning controls to businesses. The success of the EZ idea is shown best by the MetroCentre. Located on former derelict land in the Gateshead EZ, MetroCentre is one of largest and most successful planned shopping centres in the UK. Four of the six EZs in the North-east have now expired. The two remaining EZs are in East Durham (expires in 2005) and Tyne Riverside (expires in 2006).

11.5 The urban-rural shift of manufacturing

Since 1960, manufacturing industry in the developed world has declined steeply in conurbations and large cities (Section 11.4). Meanwhile, in many small towns and rural areas, employment in manufacturing has actually increased (Section 11.6). We call this trend the urban-rural shift of manufacturing.

As old factories closed in the inner areas of cities, new ones did not replace them. Instead, new factories were located either in the outer suburbs or in small towns and rural areas. We can explain this change through the

Table 11.4 The urban-rural shift: push and pull factors

	Push factors (inner city)	Pull factors (small towns/rural areas)
Space	Sites in inner city areas are cramped. Lack of space for single-storey buildings, parking and expansion.	Sites in small towns and rural areas are more spacious.
Cost	Land/rents/taxes are high.	Land/rents/taxes are usually cheaper.
Access	Narrow roads and traffic congestion make access difficult for trucks and for workers' cars.	There is good access to motorways, trunk roads and by-passes.
Buildings	Factories are often old multi-storey buildings, unsuitable for modern production lines.	Factories are single-storey and often purpose-built on industrial estates and business parks.
Environment	The physical environment is often run-down and derelict. There may be problems of vandalism.	There are attractive purpose-built estates on greenfield sites. Levels of crime are lower in small towns and rural areas.
Workforce	Inner cities often have a disproportionate number of low-skilled workers.	Skilled and highly qualified workers live mainly in the outer suburbs or in commuter villages and smaller towns.

Fig. 11.17 Hexham in Northumberland.

operation of 'push' and 'pull' factors (Table 11.4) combined with the **urban-rural shift** in population (Chapter 5).

11.6 Mid-Wales: rural industrial change

FACTFILE

- Mid-Wales comprises the county of Powys and the districts of Ceredigion and Meirionnydd, and is a remote part of the UK (Fig. 11.18).
- Most of the region is rugged upland and is sparsely populated.
- Mid-Wales covers nearly 40 per cent of the area of Wales, but has only 7.5 per cent of the country's total population.
- The population of Mid-Wales peaked in the late-19th century.
- Between 1891 and 1971, the population fell by 40 000.
- Rural **depopulation** between 1891 and 1971 was due to out-migration. People left Mid-Wales in search of greater job opportunities, higher wages, and better services.

Population revival

Since 1971, Mid-Wales's population has experienced a strong revival (Table 11.5). In some places, this was the first recorded population growth for more than a century.

The population increase in Mid-Wales is part of a wider trend known as **counter-urbanisation** (Chapter 6). For the last 25 years,

Fig. 11.18 (below) Area covered by the Development Board for Rural Wales.

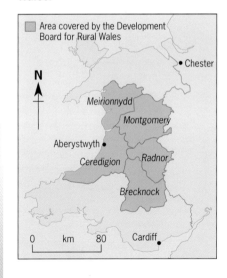

Table 11.5 The population revival in Mid-Wales (% change)

	1961-71	71-81	81-91	91-96
Brecknock	–4.5	+4.6	+1.7	+0.5
Ceredigion	+2.4	+0.8	+10.4	+10.5
Meirionnydd	–8.4	–3.3	+4.9	–1.8
Montgomery	–2.5	+10.6	+8.1	+3.7
Radnor	–1.1	+14.4	+9.8	+2.3

EXERCISES

9 Study Figure 11.19.

a What sort of businesses is the advert trying to attract?

b What is the main selling point in the advert?

c What sort of image of Mid-Wales is the advert suggesting?

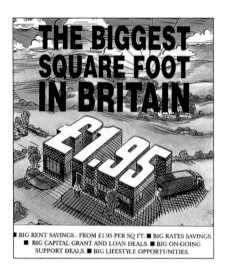

Fig. 11.19 (above) Development Board advert for Rural Wales.

people in MEDCs have been moving out of large cities and conurbations. Most have gone to small towns and villages within commuting range of the cities. However, some have moved much further afield, settling in remote regions like the Scottish Highlands and Mid-Wales. They have been attracted by the higher quality of life, away from the congestion, pollution and crime of large urban areas.

Industrial change

The Development Board for Rural Wales (DBRW)

In the 1950s, the UK government set up a rural development agency in Mid-Wales to deal with the depopulation problem. In 1977, this agency became the DBRW. There was only one other similar body in the UK, responsible for the Highlands and Islands of Scotland.

The DBRW aimed to promote Mid-Wales by bringing new manufacturing and service jobs to the region. Grants and low-interest loans were given to firms wishing to locate in Mid-Wales. The DBRW also built small factory and office units for sale or rent.

The DBRW was helped by the establishment of a new town (Newtown) in the region in 1968, and by assisted area status (for both UK and EU regional policies) for some parts of Mid-Wales (Fig. 11.12). So far, progress has been impressive. Between 1981 and 1991 there was a 14 per cent increase in manufacturing jobs. This compares with a 25 per cent decrease in the UK as a whole. The DBRW has built eleven business parks across the region (Fig. 11.20). By 1995, unemployment in Mid-Wales was 20 per cent below the national average: another indication of the region's success. In 1999, the DBRW was abolished. Its functions were assumed by the Welsh Development Agency.

Small businesses

Most of the firms locating in Mid-Wales since 1977 have been small businesses. They are extremely diverse – their products range from car components and electronic circuit boards, to processed foods and scientific instruments. In the main, firms have gone to the larger centres of population, such as Brecon, Cardigan, Newtown and Welshpool. These towns can offer a wide range of services, a skilled workforce, good communications by road, and modern factory and office space in purpose-built business parks. Companies moving to Mid-Wales have done so for a variety of reasons. Many small firms see the life-style and the high quality of the environment as the major attractions. However, just as important are the availability of greenfield sites, modern factory buildings, low rents and financial assistance.

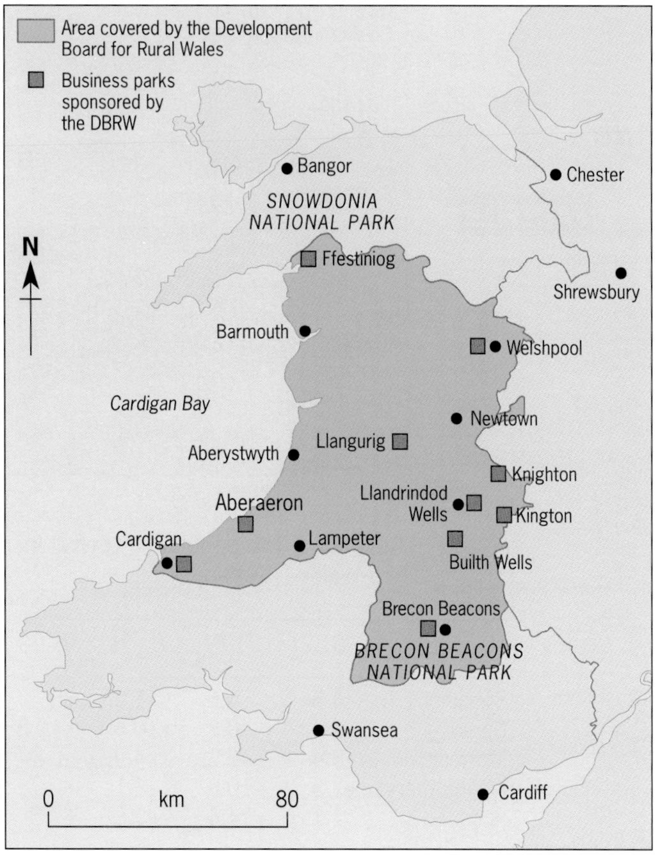

Fig. 11.20 Business parks in Mid-Wales.

CASE STUDY

11.7 Rotterdam port: locational change

FACTFILE

- *Rotterdam is situated at the mouth of two great rivers: the Rhine and the Meuse (Maas).*
- *Rotterdam's situation gives it unrivalled access by river and canal to a vast* **hinterland**, *which includes the Netherlands and much of Germany, Belgium, eastern France and Switzerland.*
- *Rotterdam is the world's leading port.*
- *In 1999, Rotterdam handled 303 million tonnes of cargo.*
- *75 per cent of Rotterdam's trade is bulk cargo, such as crude oil, coal, ore and grain.*
- *General cargoes, such as manufactured goods, account for 25 per cent of Rotterdam's trade. Most general cargo is shipped in containers.*

Growth of the port

Thanks to trade between the Netherlands and its overseas colonies, Rotterdam was already a major port by the 17th century. However, by the mid-19th century, the shallowness of the River Rhine was proving an obstacle to the port's growth. Eventually the problem was solved with the completion of the New Waterway in 1872. This new deep-water (and lock-free) channel linked Rotterdam to the North Sea (Fig. 11.22).

About this time, two other developments worked in Rotterdam's favour:

◆ the Treaty of Mannheim (1868) abolished tolls and allowed free navigation on the Rhine;
◆ the rapid growth of several large industrial regions in its hinterland – the Ruhr and the Saarland in Germany, Lorraine in eastern France, and south Belgium.

Thus Rotterdam's trade expanded as it began to import the raw materials and export the manufactured goods for these new industrial regions.

Because most of its trade is with its international hinterland, we refer to Rotterdam as a **transit** port. Much of the imported cargo is shipped on to Germany, Belgium and other European countries. Most of these cargoes are transported by inland waterways. Also important are pipelines that carry crude oil from Rotterdam to Germany, Antwerp and Amsterdam.

Changing location of port activities

Rotterdam's oldest harbours are close to the city centre. Over the last one hundred years, the port's trade and busiest harbours have slowly shifted

EXERCISES

10 36 per cent of all freight in the Netherlands is transported by inland waterways.
a Refer to an atlas and (1) explain how the physical geography of the Netherlands favours transport by inland waterway, (2) compare the lengths of the Rhine and Meuse with the Thames and Severn in the UK. How do you think that river length might influence navigability?
b* What kinds of cargo are most suited to transport by inland waterway?
c* Suggest two possible advantages and two possible disadvantages of transport by inland waterway.

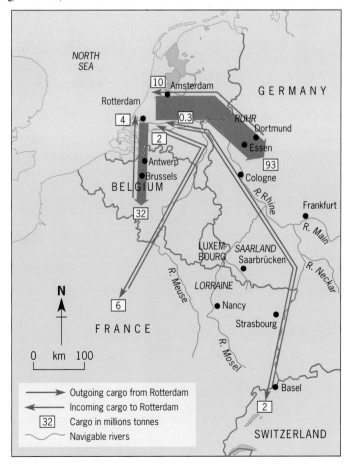

Fig. 11.21 Rotterdam's hinterland.

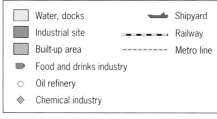

☐ Water, docks		⛴ Shipyard	
☐ Industrial site		▬▬ Railway	
☐ Built-up area		┄┄ Metro line	
🥟 Food and drinks industry			
○ Oil refinery			
◆ Chemical industry			

Fig. 11.22 Rotterdam and Europoort.

Fig. 11.23 (below) Throughput of cargo (thousand tonnes): Rotterdam 1999.

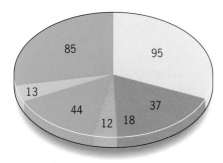

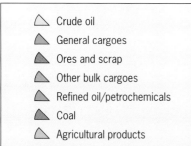

△ Crude oil
△ General cargoes
◣ Ores and scrap
△ Other bulk cargoes
◢ Refined oil/petrochemicals
◣ Coal
△ Agricultural products

Fig. 11.24 (below) Europoort, part of the containerport.

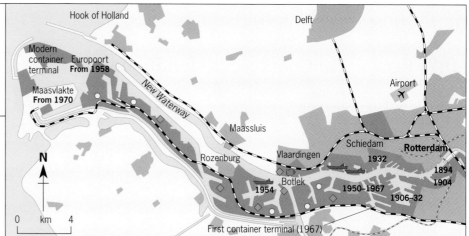

downstream towards the North Sea. They were followed by port industries such as oil refining, petrochemicals, shipbuilding and food processing.

There are two reasons for this movement.

◆ Lack of space. The old, inner harbours were cramped and hemmed-in by existing industries and houses. (Oil refineries occupy sites of between 1 and 3 sq km.)

◆ The increasing size of ships associated with new ways of cargo handling.

Transporting bulk cargoes in large ships reduces costs but requires deep-water terminals. Near the mouth of the New Waterway (and for a distance of 40 kilometres out into the North Sea), a navigable channel has been dredged to a depth of 23 metres. This allows the largest oil tankers and bulk carriers (up to 350 000 tonnes) to enter Europoort. General cargoes are transported mainly in standard-sized metal boxes (containers). In 1994, Rotterdam handled more than 6.3 million containers. The advantages of containers are considerable (Table 11.6).

Between 1955 and 1975, the whole of the south bank of the New Waterway, from Rotterdam to the North Sea, developed into a port and industrial zone. This area, which includes Europoort, has five oil refineries, six oil terminals, three international pipelines for oil and petrochemical products, and numerous chemical works. Huge areas of flat land also provide storage space for oil, coal, iron ore and containers.

Table 11.6 Advantages of container transport

Cargoes can be loaded and unloaded faster.	Ships spend less time in port and more time at sea earning money. The average container ship spends only 12 per cent of its time in port.
Cargoes can be transferred between different types of transport.	Containers are a standard size. They can be loaded easily on to barges, trains and trucks.
Fewer port workers are needed.	Container handling is highly mechanised.
Cargoes are more secure.	There are few losses of cargo due to spillage, breakage or theft.
Packaging costs are reduced.	Because goods are stored inside metal containers less packaging is needed. Containers are also re-usable.

11.8 Services in the UK

FACTFILE

- *Services rather than manufacturing industry drive the UK economy.*
- *In 1999, 18.3 million people in the UK (77 per cent of the workforce) were employed in service industries.*
- *51 per cent of the top 1000 firms in the UK are in the service sector.*
- *4.4 million people work in producer services, which serve other economic activities, commerce and business.*
- *London is the dominant centre for producer services. Other important producer service cities, such as Edinburgh, Birmingham and Leeds, lag well behind the capital.*
- *The service sector will continue to expand in future, while agriculture and manufacturing will continue to decline.*

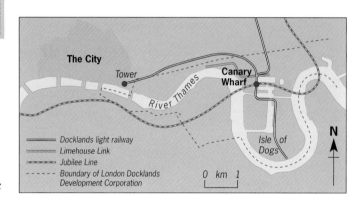

Fig. 11.25 City of London.

Changing location of offices in London

The City and West End of London account for one in seven office jobs in the UK. The City is dominated by producer services, especially financial services in the Stock Exchange and the Bank of England (Fig. 11.25). Along with New York and Tokyo, London is one of the three great financial centres in the world.

The City of London covers little more than three square kilometres. 250 000 people work in this small area in banking, insurance, shipping, commodity dealing and so on. Half of all the world's trading in stocks and shares takes place through the London Stock Exchange, and every day hundreds of millions of pounds pass through the metal, petroleum and commodity markets.

Fig. 11.26 Location of Canary Wharf.

The movement out of the City

In spite of these advantages, the City's position is under threat. Many companies are choosing to move out. The attraction is Docklands, just four kilometres to the east. Here, office rents are half those in the City and there is plenty of space for new offices, which can provide the big dealing floors needed for modern trading.

Canary Wharf

Canary Wharf is part of the London Docklands Urban Development Corporation (Fig. 11.26). Created in 1981, this UDC had the task of regenerating London's run-down port area. Between 1966 and 1981, closure of London's docks had led to 18 000 job losses and massive dereliction.

With its 244-metre office tower, Canary Wharf is the centre piece of Docklands. Several banks as well as insurers, advertising agencies and newspapers have successfully moved to Canary Wharf. Canary Wharf's early

Fig. 11.27 Canary Wharf's tower

Fig. 11.28 Large superstore in Eastbourne.

Fig. 11.29 (below) Regional shopping centres in Britain.

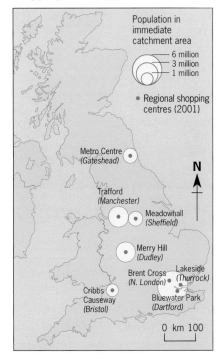

EXERCISES

11 Study Figure 11.29. Describe and explain the distribution of regional shopping centres in Britain.
12a What are the advantages and disadvantages of regional shopping centres?
b* Current policy in the UK does not allow the development of new regional shopping centres. State and explain your attitude towards regional shopping centres.

development was hampered by poor communications. Today, access to the City is provided by the Docklands Light Railway and the Jubilee underground line.

11.9 Changing location of retailing

Since the 1970s, there has been a rapid shift of retailing from the centre to the suburbs of British cities. In 1980, out-of-centre shops and shopping centres accounted for only 5 per cent of sales in the UK. Today, this figure had risen to nearly 20 per cent.

Retail parks

The first shops to locate in the suburbs were large food superstores (Fig. 11.28). Soon they were followed by DIY, furniture, carpet and electrical goods stores. In the suburbs, they occupied large 'sheds' on purpose-built retail parks. Typically, these parks had four or five units and extensive car parking for shoppers.

Regional shopping centres

From the mid-1980s, huge **regional shopping centres** like MetroCentre and Meadowhall began to appear (Fig. 11.31). They were enclosed shopping malls, usually built on two levels, with about 200 shops. Most of the shops were familiar high street names (e.g. Marks & Spencer, Boots, Debenhams, etc.) selling comparison goods, such as clothes and shoes. The new centres also provided cafes, restaurants and cinemas, features such as fountains and glass lifts, and parking for up to 10 000 cars.

Since the opening of MetroCentre in 1984, regional shopping centres have been a huge commercial success in the UK. Meadowhall on the outskirts of Sheffield is one of the largest and most successful. Opened in 1990 and built on derelict land in the Don Valley, it has 280 shops (mainly selling comparison goods). Meadowhall serves a large area, which includes much of South Yorkshire and the East Midlands. Its location alongside the M1 means that more than 9 million are within an hour's drive of the centre.

Table 11.7 Reasons for the movement of retailing out-of-centre

- The decentralisation of urban populations – many shops have followed their customers to the suburbs.
- The growth of private car ownership which makes out-of-centre locations accessible.
- Extensive low-cost sites, free of congestion at out-of-centre locations. Modern retail units selling food and bulky comparison goods require extensive areas of land and on-site parking for car-borne shoppers.
- The growth of one-stop shopping trips, and weekly food shopping trips, based on private car transport.

The impact of regional shopping centres

Regional shopping centres are controversial. They compete head on with retailing in town centres. Smaller town centres, with little investment in modern shopping facilities, suffer most. Dudley's trade fell by 70 per cent following the opening of the Merry Hill Centre in 1986. Gateshead was similarly hard hit by the MetroCentre in the 1980s.

The spiral of decline begins when anchor tenants, such as department stores (e.g. Debenhams) and variety stores (e.g. Marks & Spencer) relocate to nearby regional centres. These stores are the main attractions for shoppers. If they move out, the volume of shoppers declines and smaller shops close. Competition from regional shopping centres forces further closures. As a result, vacant shop units, cheap discounters and charity shops begin to dominate town centres.

Meadowhall and Sheffield City Centre

Sheffield city centre is the largest retail centre in South Yorkshire. It has a wide range of comparison shops, businesses, public buildings and leisure facilities. However, its size has not protected it from competition from the Meadowhall shopping centre. Meadowhall was responsible for the significant decline of retailing in Sheffield's city centre in the 1990s.

Planners in Sheffield have introduced policies to halt this decline and safeguard Sheffield city centre as the hub of retailing in South Yorkshire. These policies include:

◆ promoting major retail developments (especially non-food retailing) in the city centre;
◆ controlling non-food retailing developments outside the city centre;
◆ restricting the future expansion of Meadowhall.

Fig. 11.30 (above left) Nottingham shopping street in decline.

Fig. 11.31 (above right) Meadowhall shopping centre.

EXERCISES

13a What evidence in Figure 11.32 suggests that the centre has become run down?
b* Describe and give a possible explanation for the distribution of low-quality shopping areas and shop closures in the city centre.
c* Imagine that you are the manager of Bradford town centre. Your brief is to regenerate the central shopping area, which in recent years has become run-down. Study Figure 11.32 and write a report to the City Council describing the current situation and suggesting a plan to revive the central shopping area. Give a presentation to your class based on your report.

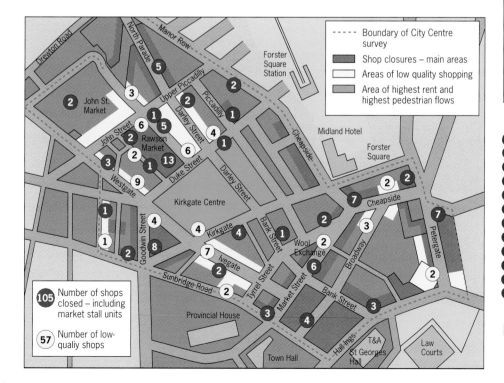

Fig. 11.32 Bradford city centre.

REMEMBER
The key to regenerating the central areas of cities is to encourage people to live in these areas. This is beginning to happen in cities such as Birmingham, Manchester and Leeds.

The planning policies for Sheffield have another advantage. Strengthening retailing in the centre should maximise use of the existing public transport system (i.e. buses, trams) which focuses on the CBD. This should help to reduce the use of private cars, and cut traffic congestion and pollution in Sheffield.

11.10 Summary: Industrial change

KEY SKILLS OPPORTUNITIES
C1.2: Ex. 1, 2b, 3, 4, 5, 8a, 8c, 9, 10, 13a; C1/2.3: Ex. 5, 7, 8b, 13b; C2.1: Ex. 13c; C2.2: Ex. 6a; N1/2.2: Ex. 2a; IT1.2: Ex. 6b

Key ideas	Generalisations and detail
Industrial activity is increasingly organised on a global scale.	• Rapid industrial development is occurring in parts of the economically developing world, such as the Asian Pacific Rim. TNCs are investing in production worldwide. A global market offers TNCs higher output and lower costs. Global operations also allow TNCs to overcome trade restrictions.
South Korea is a newly industrialising country.	• South Korea has few natural resources for industry. However, it has undergone rapid industrialisation since 1970. Its development has been based on a few very large companies (*chaebols*) e.g. Samsung. In the 1990s, these companies started to invest heavily overseas.
Old industrial regions have been hit hard by de-industrialisation.	• During the 1970s and early 1980s, basic industries such as steel, shipbuilding and coal mining declined steeply in regions like Central Scotland, South Wales and North-east England. The result was high rates of unemployment and widespread dereliction.
Re-industrialisation has transformed many old industrial regions.	• Since the mid-1980s, there has been massive investment by foreign companies in several old industrial regions in the UK. This investment, encouraged by government grants, has made Central Scotland, South Wales and the North-east leading centres of the electronics industry in the EU.
Regions that have attracted large-scale foreign investment are most vulnerable to global economic change.	• The financial crisis in East Asia (1997–98) and overcapacity in industries such as semi-conductors and motor vehicles, have led to the closure of factories operated by foreign TNCs e.g. Siemens on Tyneside, and Fujitsu in Aycliffe.
Areas in the UK worst affected by de-industrialisation have been given special status.	• The government has created Urban Development Corporations (UDCs) and Enterprise Zones (EZs) in inner-city and riverside locations. By improving the environment and offering tax breaks, they aim to attract manufacturing and services to run-down industrial areas.
There has been an urban-rural shift of manufacturing industry in MEDCs.	• Since 1970, manufacturing has declined in conurbations and large cities. New factories have preferred to locate in small towns and rural areas. Lack of space and obsolete factory buildings in large urban areas largely explain this change. Some remote rural areas such as Mid-Wales and the Highlands and Islands of Scotland, have benefited from this urban-rural shift. The growth of industry in these areas has been helped by special government agencies and grants.
Port functions and industries have undergone major locational change.	• Revolutions in cargo handling – bulk carriers for oil, coal, ore, grain etc., and containers for manufactured goods – have been responsible for a rapid downstream shift in port activities since 1960. Bulk cargoes and containers are transported in very large ships which need deep water. These cargoes also require large areas of land for storage. Most of the available deep water and space is near river mouths e.g. Europoort near Rotterdam.
In MEDCs, retailing has grown in the suburbs at the expense of the CBD.	• Food superstores, retail parks and regional shopping centres have appeared in the suburbs of many British cities since 1980. Retailers have located in the suburbs to be nearer the better-off consumers, to obtain the space needed for large stores and parking, and to benefit from less congestion and lower land prices.
The growth of suburban retailing threatens town/city centres.	• Shopping centres in the suburbs compete with retailing in the town/city centre. Smaller town centres, such as Dudley, have suffered many shop closures. Well known high street retailers have been replaced by second-hand shops and discount stores in the town centre.
Many office activities have moved out-of-centre in British cities.	• Offices have moved out-of-centre to purpose-built office parks in the suburbs. High rents and lack of space for new building have forced many financial services in the City of London to relocate in London's Docklands (e.g. in Canary Wharf).

Glossary

This glossary contains definitions of technical words, which appear in the book in bold, in the context in which they are used. They are given in alphabetical order.

added value Increase in the value of goods or raw materials through the process of manufacturing.

agribusiness Large-scale, capital-intensive farming based on scientific and business principles.

air mass A large body of air with uniform temperature and humidity characteristics.

anticline A simple upfold of rocks caused by compression in the Earth's crust.

anticyclone An area of high pressure. It brings quiet, dry weather, with variable amounts of sunshine and cloud.

aquifer A layer of rock that can hold a lot of water.

aspect The direction in which a slope faces, which often affects the amount of solar radiation it receives.

batholith A very large intrusion of igneous rock within the Earth's crust.

bedding plane The boundary separating one layer of sedimentary rock from another.

biodiversity The number and variety of plant and animal species found in an ecosystem.

biomass The total mass of plant and animal life occurring in a given area.

blockfield A large area of angular boulders that have been broken up by frost action.

brownfield site A site for housing, industry or commerce that has previously been developed and built on.

carrying capacity The maximum number of livestock that can be supported in an area without causing lasting damage to the environment.

central business district The central area of a town or city, which has high land values and is used mostly for business and commercial functions.

central place A settlement providing goods and services for its resident population and for people living in the surrounding area.

comparison goods Goods that people buy infrequently after a careful comparison of prices and values (e.g. washing machines). They usually have a high threshold and range.

conservative margin A boundary between two plates that are moving sideways past each other. Crust is neither formed nor destroyed.

constructive margin A boundary between two plates that are moving apart (diverging), and where new oceanic crust (basalt) is forming.

continental drift The theory that the continents have moved position on the Earth's surface. The driving force is sea-floor spreading.

continentality The effect of large continental land masses on climate i.e. large mean annual temperature range, summer precipitation maximum.

convectional precipitation Precipitation that occurs when warm air rises in thermals or convection currents. Most thunderstorms are formed in this way

convenience goods Goods that people buy frequently and that are relatively cheap (e.g. food). They usually have a low threshold and low range.

core The centre-most part of the Earth's interior, comprising a solid inner core and a liquid outer core.

cottage industries Small-scale home-based industries.

counter-urbanisation People moving away from large urban areas to live in smaller, often rural, settlements.

crust The Earth's rocky, outer layer, comprising the continents and ocean basins.

deindustrialisation The decline and closure of traditional industries in MEDCs (e.g. steel, shipbuilding, coal mining), which leads to high unemployment and dereliction.

delta Where a river enters the sea or a lake and deposits its load of sediment. The main river channel splits up into many smaller channels, or distributaries.

depopulation An absolute decrease in the population of a place.

depression Middle-latitude storm. It is a low-pressure area, which brings cloud, rain and strong winds.

destructive margin A boundary between two plates that are moving towards each other (converging). One plate plunges below the other and is destroyed in the mantle.

dew-point The temperature at which water vapour condenses to form water droplets.

dispersed settlement pattern A rural settlement dominated by isolated farms.

dyke A small igneous intrusion that cuts vertically through layers of older rock.

economies of scale Cost savings to businesses made by production on a large scale.

ecosystem A community of plants and animals that interact with each other and their physical environment.

enterprise The type of farming undertaken by the farmer (e.g. cereal growing, dairying).

environmental degradation The adverse effect of farming and population growth on the environment. It includes soil erosion, salination, deforestation, desertification etc.

epicentre The point on the surface of the Earth that lies immediately above the origin of an earthquake.

erosion Wearing away and transport of surface of rocks by chemical, physical or biological processes including human overuse.

escarpment A tilted block with a short steep (scarp) slope and a long gentle (dip) slope.

eutrophication The addition of excess nutrients to lakes and streams, particularly nitrogen and phosphorous. This causes the rapid growth of plants, which in turn reduce the oxygen supply in the water.

exfoliation A form of weathering where the surface of a rock peels away in layers.

external economies Cost savings for a firm derived from locating close to suppliers, markets and large urban areas.

extrusive igneous rocks Volcanic rocks, such as basalt, which cool rapidly at the surface.

faulting The fracturing and movement of rocks caused either by compression or tension in the Earth's crust.

folded rocks Rocks bent by compression of the Earth's crust.

food chain/food web A series of organisms through which food energy moves before it is completely expended.

food system The chain of activities concerned with producing, processing and selling food.

footloose industry An industry that has few constraints on its choice of location.

fossil fuel Energy resource (e.g. oil, coal and natural gas) formed by the decomposition of plants and animals that lived in the geological past.

front A boundary between cold and warm air.

gentrification The movement of middle/high-income groups into low-status inner-city areas, and the subsequent upgrading of the houses.

geothermal energy The use of hot rocks in the Earth's crust to make steam and generate electricity.

geyser A jet of groundwater heated by hot rocks and forced to the surface by steam pressure.

global shift The changing location of industry at a global scale – in particular the growing importance of the Pacific Rim and the economically developing world (outside Africa).

globalisation The worldwide location of production by trans-national corporations in order to serve a global market and reduce costs.

green belt An area of countryside around a large city in which development is restricted to prevent the growth of urban areas.

green wedge An area of agricultural or parkland preserved between spokes of urban development spreading out from a city.

greenfield site Site for industry and commerce previously used only by rural activities (e.g. agriculture).

hierarchy A ranking of settlements in a region according to some measure of their importance (e.g. number of services, population etc.).

hinterland The area behind a seaport, which supplies the bulk of the exports and to which the bulk of the imports are distributed.

igneous rock A rock formed from the cooling of magma (e.g. granite).

industrial inertia The survival of an industry in an area even though the initial locational advantages, such as local raw materials, have disappeared.

industrial revolution The development of large-scale factory production, originally based on coal and steam power. In the UK, it first occurred between 1760 and 1830.

initial advantage The reasons why an industry first located in a particular place (e.g. the availability of raw materials).

intrusive igneous rocks Igneous rocks, such as granite, which cooled slowly at depth within the crust.

isobar Line on a weather chart joining areas of equal air pressure.

just-in-time A system of production where manufacturers supply components to an assembler just a few hours before they are needed on the production line.

karst Limestone scenery.

lahar A high-speed mud flow, where volcanic ash mixes with water, often from snow or ice melted by the heat of the eruption.

lapse rate The rate at which temperature decreases with height in the lower atmosphere.

lithosphere The term for the Earth's crust and the upper part of the mantle.

mantle That part of the Earth's interior that is wrapped around the core.

metamorphic rock A rock that, owing to great heat and/or pressure, has been changed from its original state (e.g. slate).

mid-ocean ridge Steep undersea mountain range found where molten rock wells up from the mantle onto the ocean floor.

migration The movement of people from one place to another to live permanently.

monoculture The continuous cultivation of a single crop.

newly industrialising country Country that has undergone rapid and successful industrialisation since 1970 (e.g. South Korea).

nodality The characteristic of a settlement site that is well connected to other places by transport routes.

nucleated settlement pattern A rural settlement pattern dominated by villages where the houses cluster together.

nucleus (land use) An isolated area of distinctive urban land use.

ocean trench A narrow, deep depression on the ocean floor, formed by subduction.

order The position of a settlement within a settlement hierarchy (e.g. a hamlet – low order; a city – high order). Also applied to the services found in settlements (e.g. convenience – low order; comparison – high order).

organic farming Farming that uses no artificial fertilisers or pesticides.

orographic precipitation Precipitation caused by moist air being forced to rise over hills. Also known as relief precipitation.

plate tectonics The theory that the crust of the Earth is divided into a number of separate, rigid plates, which are moving all the time. Plate tectonics provides an explanation for such things as earthquakes, volcanoes, fold mountains, rift valleys and continental drift.

podsol The typical soil of coniferous forests: acidic and lacking humus and plant nutrients.

polyculture The cultivation of a wide range of crops.

post-industrial economy An economy where most of the employment is in service industries – the situation in MEDCs.

precipitation The deposition of moisture, usually from clouds. It includes rain, sleet, snow, frost and dew.

primary producer Green plant, which uses the sun's energy through photosynthesis to create new tissue, which is then used by other members of the ecosystem.

primary sector Economic activities producing raw materials (e.g. mining, quarrying, forestry, agriculture, water supply).

primate city The largest city in a country; more than twice as big as the second city.

quaternary sector Service industries for commerce and industry (e.g. banking, research) and for individual consumers (e.g. education, healthcare).

rain shadow An area on the leeward side of an upland, which receives significantly less precipitation than the windward side.

rain-fed agriculture Agriculture that relies solely on direct precipitation.

range The maximum distance people will travel to purchase a particular item or service.

regional shopping centre Very large, enclosed shopping centre, mainly selling comparison goods, located out-of-centre with a large parking area (e.g. Merry Hill, Meadowhall).

relief The variation in altitude and slopes in an area.

retail park Planned shopping centre comprising large retail sheds selling electrical equipment, DIY goods, furniture, etc. with a large parking area.

rift valley A valley formed by the sinking of land between two parallel fault lines.

rotation The changing cycle of crops grown on farms. Designed to maintain soil fertility and reduce the risk of crop disease.

rural settlement pattern The distribution of settlement in a rural area including the proportion of nucleated and dispersed forms.

rural-urban migration The movement of people from the countryside to live in towns and cities.

science park Purpose-built edge-of-town site of high-tech firms, whose activities range from manufacturing to research.

secondary sector Manufacturing industries (e.g. car making, semi-conductors, iron-and-steel).

sector (land use) A wedge of distinctive urban land use radiating out from the city centre, often along roads or valleys.

sedimentary rock A rock formed from sediments derived from other rocks (e.g. sandstone) or from the shells and skeletons of organisms (e.g. limestone).

segregation The geographical separation of different income, social and ethnic groups in cities.

sill A small igneous intrusion that cuts horizontally through layers of older rock.

strata Layers of sedimentary rock.

subduction zone A plate margin where one plate descends into the mantle and is destroyed.

subsistence farming When a farmer grows food primarily to feed the family.

sustainability An economic activity that does not use resources faster than natural processes can replenish them.

syncline A simple downfold of rocks caused by compression in the Earth's crust.

temperature inversion An increase in temperature with height in the atmosphere (opposite of lapse rate).

tertiary sector Service industries (e.g. transport, communications, gas and electricity).

threshold The minimum number of people or expenditure needed to support a shop or service in a settlement.

topological map A map that consists of a series of lines representing routes, and nodes representing places (e.g. stations). It does not show actual distances or real position.

transit-port A port where a large percentage of imported cargoes are shipped on to other international destinations.

trans-national corporation Very large firm (e.g. IBM and General Motors) that owns businesses in many countries.

transplant Assembly plant set up by foreign-based trans-national corporation (e.g. Japanese car manufacturing in the EU).

tropical cyclone (hurricane, typhoon) A powerful tropical storm associated with violent winds and torrential rain.

urban renewal The clearance of sub-standard housing in inner-city areas and its replacement with new, often high-rise, housing.

urban sprawl The unplanned expansion of urban areas into the countryside.

urban-rural shift The growing relative importance of small towns and rural areas as centres of industry.

urbanisation An increase in the proportion of the population living in urban areas.

water table The level to which water saturates a porous or permeable rock or soil.

weathering The chemical or physical breakdown of rocks by the action of rain, frost, ice and wind.

wet-point site The location of a settlement that gives access to a water supply (e.g. river, spring, well).

zone (land use) Area of distinctive land use around the city centre.

Index

Published by Collins Educational
An imprint of HarperCollinsPublishers Ltd
77–85 Fulham Palace Road
Hammersmith
London W6 8JB

www. CollinsEducational.com
On-line Support for Schools and Colleges

© HarperCollinsPublishers Ltd 2001
First edition published 1996
Second edition published 2001

ISBN 0 00 711648 9

Michael Raw and Sue Shaw assert the moral right to be identified as the authors of the first edition upon which this edition is based. Michael Raw asserts the moral right to be identified as the author of the new material in this second edition.

British Library Cataloguing in Publication Data
A catalogue record for this book is available from the British Library.

Edited by Louise Pritchard at Bookwork
Design by Kim Bale at Visual Image
Cover design by Jerry Fowler
Map artwork by Jerry Fowler
Picture research by Caroline Thompson
Production by Kathryn Botterill
Printed and bound by Printing Express, Hong Kong

Acknowledgements

Every effort has been made to contact the holders of copyright material, but if any have been inadvertently overlooked, the publishers will be pleased to make the necessary arrangements at the first opportunity.

Photographs
The publishers would like to thank the following for permission to reproduce photographs:

Aerofilms Ltd, Fig. 9.21; Aerophoto Eelde, Fig. 11.24; Airfotos Ltd, Figs 2.20, 5.1, 5.11, 5.17, 11.17; Alba Centre, Livingston, Fig. 10.31; Associated Press/AP Photo, Figs 1.1, 1.21, 3.43; J Allan Cash Ltd, Figs 6.22, 7.7, 10.5; ECC International Europe, Fig. 2.42; Environmental Picture Library/A Dorst, Fig. 4.29; Ford Motor Company Ltd, Fig. 10.25; Leslie Garland Picture Library, Figs 11.14, 11.15, 11.16; Tony Waltham/Geophotos, Figs 1.2, 1.3, 1.5, 1.9, 1.22, 1.24, 1.27, 1.28, 1.29, 1.34, 2.6, 2.13, 2.28(inset), 2.33, 4.3, 4.4, 4.7, 4.24, 6.9, 7.8, 7.17, 8.9, 8.10, 9.16, 9.35, 11.30; GettyOne Stone, Figs 2.37, 3.5, 3.10, 3.17, 4.18, 4.23, 8.7, 10.2, 10.4, 10.6, 11.5, 11.27; Robert Harding Picture Library/A Woolfit, Fig. 8.32; Holt Studios International/N Cattlin, Fig. 8.31; Hulton Getty Picture Collection, Fig. 11.9; Intermediate Technology/S LíEpine Exless, Fig. 10.33, N Cooper, Fig. 10.34; A K Jobbings, Fig. 2.16; Andrew Lambert, Fig. 2.3, 2.4; London Aerial Photo Library, Figs 2.32, 7.15, 10.21, 10.28, 10.30, 11.31; North News Press Agency, Fig. 11.8; Panos Pictures/B Klass, Fig. 3.39, T Bolstad, Fig. 4.9, P Tweedie, Fig. 4.14, R Cousins, Fig. 4.20, J Hartley, Fig. 4.28, R Giling, Fig. 8.14; Mr R K Pilsbury, Figs 3.1, 3.2, 3.3, 3.4, 3.6, 3.25, 3.30, 3.31, 3.32; Robert Prosser, Fig. 7.3; Michael Raw, Figs 2.1, 2.9, 2.10, 2.11, 2.22, 2.26, 3.12, 4.31, 5.5, 5.23, 5.24, 5.27, 6.12, 6.18, 6.20, 7.26, 7.27, 9.37; J Sainsbury plc, Fig. 11.28; Science Photo Library, Figs 1.15, 3.36, 4.15, 6.1; Self Help, Figs 9.2, 9.7, 9.8, 9.10, 9.11; Sue Shaw, Figs 2.12, 2.14, 5.19, 5.20, 6.19, 6.21, 8.21, 8.24, 8.26, 9.32; HYPERLINK "http://www.shoutpictures.com" www.shoutpictures.com, Fig. 10.3; SNH Slide Library, Fig. 4.34; South American Pictures, Fig. 6.26; Still Pictures/M Edwards, Figs 4.21, 6.24, 7.33, 8.6, 8.15, 9.9, 10.1, P Harrison, Fig. 7.28, 9.15; Stock Market Photo Agency, Fig. 2.41; Gillian Sturgess, Figs 5.3, 9.22; J Tams plc, Fig. 10.13; C&S Thompson, Figs 9.29, 9.34; University of Dundee, Fig. 3.35; The Trustees of the Wedgwood Museum, Barlaston, Staffordshire, Fig. 10.12; David Woodfall, Figs 9.19, 9.23, 9.25, 9.26, 9.27, 9.28, 9.30.

Cover photographs: Samantha Davey, (top & top centre), Ford (Reproduced with their Permission), (centre), G R Roberts, (bottom centre), GettyOne Stone, (bottom).

Maps
Maps reproduced from Ordnance Survey mapping with the permission of The Controller of Her Majesty's Stationery Office, © Crown copyright, Licence Number 100018599.
Extracts from: Grampian and Cairngorms 1992 1:50 000 (Fig. 2.19); Berwick upon Tweed 1991 1:50 000 (Fig. 5.8); Dorchester & Weymouth 1993 1:50 000 (Fig. 5.10); Leicester & Coventry 1994 1:50 000 (Fig. 6.14).